D1242864

MEN,
MACHINES AND HISTORY

MEN, MACHINES AND HISTORY

THE STORY OF TOOLS AND MACHINES
IN RELATION TO SOCIAL PROGRESS

BY

S. LILLEY

INTERNATIONAL PUBLISHERS
NEW YORK

Revised and enlarged edition
Copyright © by Samuel Lilley, 1965

First United States edition by
INTERNATIONAL PUBLISHERS CO., INC., 1966

Library of Congress Catalog Card Number: 66-21951
Printed in the United States of America

CONTENTS

PART THREE

OUR TIME

LIST OF ILLUSTRATIONS

FIGURES IN TEXT

PLATES (following p. 336)

PREFACE TO THE SECOND EDITION

WHEN I wrote the first edition of this book, one of my main difficulties was the lack of published material about its subject matter. Facts had to be scraped together from many and diverse sources. My difficulty is now the reverse. In the intervening years a great deal of research has been done and many thousands of pages have been written on the history of technology. Time has therefore been my main enemy. To have attempted to digest all this new material would have postponed to the dim future the publication of a revised edition. I have had to read selectively, and can only hope that my selections have been judicious. Certainly they have compelled me to make extensive changes in the text.

In expanding the book to cover developments since 1945, I should not have found it possible to give any adequate treatment, were it not for the happy discovery that a major part of the required information could be acquired by the process of scanning the pages of the *New Scientist* from its beginnings in 1956 onwards. I freely confess that I have only looked elsewhere for material on those not very numerous occasions when the *New Scientist* failed me, or to confirm some doubtful point. This will explain the many references to that journal in Part Three. The bulk of Part Three was completed at the end of September 1964, but some revisions take account of major developments in the following three months and a few later footnotes have been added.

It is with regret that I have decided to omit the discussion of the problem of measuring technological progress, which bulked large in the concluding chapter of the first edition. I have done so, partly to keep down the length and therefore the cost of the book, but largely because the task of revising this material in the light of later researches by others would have been prohibitively heavy, while the extension of my 'relative invention rate' index to the post-war period would have presented formidable difficulties. I still believe that the study of the history of technology can benefit from the use of quantitative methods, and it remains my hope that my early essay in this direction will not be forgotten.

For help on many points I offer my thanks to: the London representatives of the American and Soviet Governments; the editors and staff of *Soviet News* and of the American journal, *Science Horizons*; representatives of various industrial firms, who will, I hope, be content with this general acknowledgement; the Librarian of the Society for Cultural Relations with the U.S.S.R.; Professor T. Kilburn of the University of Manchester; Mr. J. May of the University of Nottingham; Mr. A. L. Morton and Mr. M. Cornforth. If I have failed to acknowledge other help, I crave forgiveness. And last, but far from least, this task could not have been undertaken without the constant support and encouragement of my wife, to say nothing of her practical help in reading typescript and proofs.

Nottingham, July 1965 S. L.

PREFACE TO THE FIRST EDITION

I HAVE aimed to write this book in such a way that it can be read by young people in their last years at school and at Universities, Technical Colleges, Continuation Schools, etc. But, as I felt that the subject is of interest to people who in the course of time have become more knowledgeable, I have not hesitated to include here and there a sentence or a paragraph specially for their benefit.

Since my aim was to consider the history of tools and machines in relation to all aspects of life, I have necessarily included many references to social conditions at various epochs. I was able to make these brief, because this book is part of a series, other volumes of which will fill in the background at greater length and correct any distortions that may arise from my brevity.

I have chosen to interpret the word 'machine' somewhat widely. In particular, I include in its scope the many electronic devices (radio, sound films, photo-electric cells in the control of machinery, etc.) which have been so prominent in this century—for I feel that, though these are not 'mechanical' in the strict sense of the word, their development does represent the modern form of that trend towards greater control over nature which was earlier expressed in strictly mechanical form.

The work had to be done almost entirely in spare time while carrying on a war job, and though a final revision was made during the first year of peace, there was not time for as full an investigation of sources as might be desired. These circumstances, coupled with the breadth of the field, compelled me to rely to a considerable extent on secondary sources. However, I have cross-checked my information wherever possible, and though some factual errors may remain, these are not likely to be ones of major importance. Responsibility on matters of interpretation is, of course, entirely my own.

My thanks and acknowledgements are due to the following,

who helped in various ways, from giving advice on particular topics to reading and commenting on the typescript: Mr. C. E. Allen, editor of *Machinery*; Mr. E. Bramhill, of the Shorter Process Company Ltd.; Messrs. Buck and Hickman Ltd.; Mr. P. V. Daley; Mr. C. Davies; Mr. W. E. Dick, editor of *Discovery*; Mr. R. E. Doré, of the British Oxygen Company; Mr. R. H. Heindel, Director of the American Library in London; Mr. A. F. P. Parker-Rhodes; the late Mr. John Wilton; the Secretary of the Institution of British Agricultural Engineers and, last but not least, the editors of the series.

Cambridge, August 1946 S. L.

PART ONE

THE ANCIENT AND MEDIEVAL WORLDS

CHAPTER I

THE BEGINNINGS
(TILL 3000 B.C.)

THE earliest men we know of made and used tools. In fact, man as we know him probably could not have survived without tools—he is too weak and puny a creature to fight nature with only his hands and his teeth. The first men were of a species very different from our own. Perhaps they could have managed to live without tools. But only with the aid of the tools that these more primitive species learned to use was it possible for the man of today to evolve, losing much in bodily strength and speed, but more than compensating for this loss by developing a brain and hands and eyes that enabled him to call to his aid his many tools and machines that made him master of the world.

For the earliest tool-using men we have no space here. We begin with men of the late Palaeolithic Age (Old Stone Age), men now of our own species, living by hunting and food-gathering. Already at this stage men had acquired a vast variety of tools. They had axes, knives, saws, spokeshaves, and scrapers of chipped stone, mallets, awls and piercing tools, needles of ivory, spears and harpoons. They even had tools for making tools. They used two very important machines: the bow and the spear-thrower. The former is the first machine which stores energy; the bowman puts his energy gradually into the bow as he draws it, storing it up ready to be released in concentrated form at the moment of shooting. And the spear-thrower is an application of the lever as an extension of a man's arm, giving the spear a greater range.

In the process of adapting themselves to changes in the climate, the transitional Mesolithic (Middle Stone) Age societies advanced yet further, developing in particular a fine range of carpenter's tools, including the adze, gouge and chisel. They added the carpenter's first machine—the bow-drill, in which the drill is rapidly rotated by means of a string wrapped round it, attached at each end to a sort of bow which is moved back and forth.[1] With these improved tools they constructed the important transport devices of the sledge and the dugout canoe with its paddles. They greatly developed fishing tackle and domesticated the dog to help their hunting.

The Coming of Agriculture

But it is with the introduction of agriculture (including stock-breeding) that this history must really begin. Agriculture was not, of course, a single invention, but the result of a host of separate advances. So far as present knowledge goes, economies based on agriculture first appeared in Jericho and Jarmo[2] in the eighth millenium B.C. and thence spread gradually throughout the Middle East.

The significance of this step can hardly be exaggerated. Formerly man gathered the food that nature unaided provided. Now he learned to make nature provide what he wanted. All his previous advances seem insignificant beside this great leap forward. The development of agriculture and the techniques that grew with it constitute the first great Technological Revolution in human history.

For agricultural purposes, men had to invent special tools : the wooden hoe to till the ground, the sickle of wood or bone set with flint to reap the corn (Figure 1), the flail to thresh it, the quern to grind it.[3] But a full change from hunting and food-gathering to agriculture as the basis of life could not take place without a whole series of auxiliary changes. The wooden hoe and sickle required tools to shape them; sometimes plots had to be cleared

[1] The bow-drill may actually be palaeolithic in origin, but the evidence is not clear.

[2] In modern Jordan and north-east Iraq, respectively. But the finds at these sites leave the possibility that the real beginning was at some other centre from which it diffused to these. Progress of research is so rapid that no firm pronouncement can be made at present.

[3] A primitive form of sickle, the straight reaping knife, appeared a little before the development of agriculture, for cutting down edible grasses not sown by man. Similarly the hoe has an ancestor in the digging-stick of mesolithic times; while pestles and mortars, which had been used for other purposes by palaeolithic man, were used as well as the quern for early corn-grinding.

before sowing. For these and other purposes men developed further the carpenter's tools that had appeared in the Mesolithic Age. In particular they made wide use of techniques of grinding and polishing stone implements, which may occasionally have been employed earlier. For this reason, the period is known as the Neolithic (New Stone) Age. Cereals required storage and new ways of cooking. The game caught by the hunter can be roasted on a spit before an open fire, but cereals need slow, gentle cooking in some sort of vessel. The agriculturalists (though not the very first of them) solved this problem with pottery.

The skins of hunted animals provided the few clothes of palaeolithic man. The agriculturalist had to find a substitute and he found it in textiles. But to master textiles he required two new

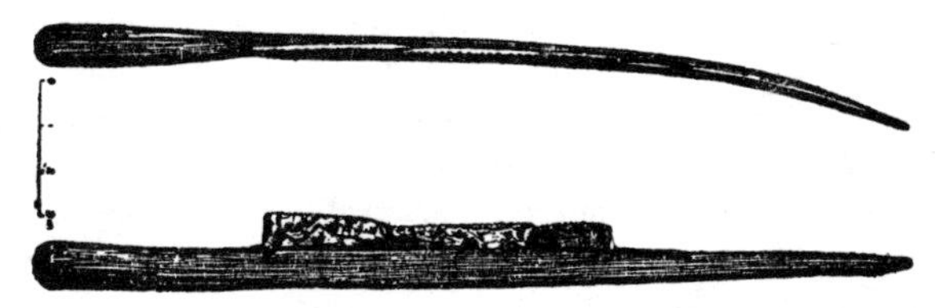

Fig. 1. Flint sickle from Fayum in Egypt.

machines: a spinning machine and a loom. The early spinning machine was very simple[4]—a distaff or forked stick to hold the unspun fibres; and a short stick with a hook or notch at one end, to which the loosely twisted fibres were attached, and with a fly-wheel of stone or pottery at the other end to ensure the continuous rotation that spins the fibres into a firm thread. The spindle is given a twist and hangs spinning in the air while the operator feeds fibres from the distaff on to the end of the thread, where they are twisted into yet more thread. It is a simple mechanism by modern standards, yet a tremendous complication compared to any previous machine. And no fundamental improvement took place in the process of spinning till the Middle Ages.

The loom, even in its simplest form of two beams, bound to

[4] Much less sophisticated methods of spinning—including the mere rolling of the fibres between the hands or between hand and thigh—were also widely used. But the distaff and free spindle, as described, was the one pointing towards the future.

pegs in the ground, between which the warp is stretched while the weaver's fingers push the weft alternately over and under the warp threads, is a complicated piece of apparatus. From this stage it was gradually developed by the addition of the shuttle, heddles, shed-rods and other devices.[5]

Thus almost from the beginning of the New Stone Age, man had vastly increased the number of tools and machines that he used. There is some hint of a temporary pause at the technical level which has just been described. But a very rapid advance was to follow soon. The change in man's way of life was propitious to invention. He had more security than ever before. The periods of leisure that intersperse agricultural activity gave time for invention. The comparatively permanent settlement that agriculture (at least in its more advanced stages) made possible allowed him to construct, accumulate and use equipment that the hunter would usually see only as an encumbrance. And lastly, man had acquired the habit of controlling nature for his own benefit, a habit which would encourage the search for further improvements.

Conditions were particularly favourable in Mesopotamia and the valleys of the Nile and the Indus, where the periodically flooding rivers, soon to be controlled by irrigation, watered the crops and spread each year a new layer of mud which prevented the exhaustion of the soil. In these countries, villages grew into prosperous towns, and here too we find a great spate of invention in the couple of millennia before 3000 B.C. In this period man learned to smelt and use metals, to harness animals; he invented the plough and the wheeled cart and the sailing ship. These, and many other inventions, laid the basis for great social changes which we shall mention later.

The Beginnings of Metallurgy

Copper and iron sometimes occur naturally as metals, and men at an early stage learned to make some use of them. But they used them as a superior sort of 'stone'—a 'stone' which was much less brittle than those commonly used for tools, and which could be hammered into shape instead of requiring chipping or grinding

[5] Textile machinery is difficult to describe and its early history is often obscure. We shall therefore deal with it only in the most general terms till medieval times.

like the common stones. The great step forward came when men made two key discoveries. First, that heating certain types of stone with charcoal produced copper—the process of smelting. Second, that copper could be melted in a suitable furnace, run into a mould where it would solidify to reproduce the shape of the mould—the process of casting. These discoveries were probably made in or near Mesopotamia about 4000 B.C. Smelting was an important step, because the supplies of natural metals in the world are so tiny that their use could have no important effect on men's lives. And without casting, the most valuable properties of copper would be left unused.

Though specialised 'factories' existed here and there, stone tools could in general be made by the man who used them, as and when required. Not so with metal; it needed a highly organised system of production. Quarrying (and later, underground mining) required a host of techniques for dealing with hard rocks, such as cracking them by lighting fires against them and throwing water on the hot surface, or splitting them by inserting wooden wedges in cracks and then soaking them in water so that they expand and prise the rocks apart.

Then the ore must be smelted. That required furnaces capable of giving temperatures so high as to need some sort of blast. The best way to produce the blast would be by bellows, but these were not discovered till about 3000 B.C., so that the earlier workers had to use blowpipes.

Then the smith had to turn the crude lump of copper into useful tools or weapons. The first process was casting, which like smelting requires a high-temperature furnace, as well as crucibles in which to melt the metal. There must be moulds of sand, clay or stone to run it into, and means of shaping these moulds as required. For anything but the simplest product the mould must be made in two or more pieces which can fit together to receive the molten metal. After casting, the tool must be finished in various ways, by hammering, smoothing with files, grinding to a sharp edge on a stone, and so on.

So it will be seen that the use of copper required many auxiliary inventions to make it practicable, and many specialised craftsmen to do the work—specialists who would not be producing food but must be fed by the community.

How men discovered the smelting of metal we do not know. It has been suggested that perhaps somebody accidentally dropped some malachite (a copper-bearing mineral commonly used to paint the eyes, partly as a cosmetic, partly as a protection against certain fly-borne infections) into a charcoal brazier, and observed a few beads of copper running out at the bottom. Or more likely a potter may have accidentally smelted in his kiln one of the coloured copper ores used in glazing. Perhaps the discovery was made many times, and many times forgotten as useless. For we must remember that the usefulness of an invention depends on the structure of society. The use of copper, as we have seen, requires specialist miners and smiths, who will devote their whole time to that work and therefore must be fed, clothed and housed from a surplus produced by other members of the community. Until the technical level was high enough to provide this surplus, it would be impossible to keep these specialists, and therefore impossible to use metals. Thus, even if the smelting of copper was discovered accidentally in some early neolithic society, it would have been brushed aside as useless and soon forgotten. But eventually, with the gradual advance of the neolithic economy, the time arrived when the community could afford to keep specialists who produced no food—and then any further accidental discovery of copper smelting would soon be developed as a useful asset.

The miners and smiths were not by any means the only specialists required to make metals socially usable. Copper ore was not found in the lands occupied by the advanced neolithic farmers, who could support the smiths and use their products. The ore or the copper had to be transported over long distances. This required traders and transport workers. Early neolithic communities had been more or less self-supporting, trade being confined to a few luxuries, ornaments and charms. But as the societies became capable of producing a surplus over their immediate needs, they tended more and more to exchange this surplus for products obtainable only from a distance, the most important of which were copper and its ores. At the same time the villages tended to grow into towns containing craftsmen like smiths and carpenters, and later entirely unproductive classes like priests, kings, nobles. All these had to be supported by food and other basic necessities carried in from the surrounding countryside. Thus a flourishing metallurgy required parallel improvements both in agriculture and in transport.

Plough, Cart and Harness

In agriculture (apart from improvements in irrigation, which are outside our field) the greatest innovation was the plough, a tremendous advance on the hoe which had earlier been used to till the ground. And with the plough is associated another major invention—the harnessing of animals, in the first place of oxen. Here for the first time men had found a way of using some non-human source of power to relieve them of hard physical labour.

The food supplies had to be carried to the towns. For this and other transport purposes the agricultural peoples greatly extended the use of the sledge which they had inherited from their mesolithic ancestors. And then they took the key step of inventing the wheeled cart, which is essentially a sledge mounted on wheels and attached to the pole of an oxen-drawn plough. Wheeled vehicles were in use in Sumeria as early as 3500 B.C., in North Syria perhaps earlier. By 3000 B.C. they were in general use in Mesopotamia, Elam and Syria; they reached the Indus by 2500 B.C. But in Egypt they were unknown till very much later.

Ships and the Beginnings of the Age of Power

The harnessing of animals, first to the plough and then to the cart, was the first instance of men using some force other than human muscles to do their work for them. At about the same time they also first learned to use an inorganic force—the wind, to drive sailing ships (Plate I). Sailing ships were in use in Egypt soon after 3500 B.C., and by 3000 B.C. they were freely navigating the eastern Mediterranean, and probably also the Arabian Sea. Today the comparative comfort and safety in which we can live is based largely on our use of non-animal power—wind, water, coal and oil. Here in the East, before the dawn of civilisation, we see the first step being taken towards our modern age of power.

It would take too much space to describe all the inventions of this fruitful period. Here we shall mention only one more, the potter's wheel (probably invented between 3500 and 3000 B.C. in or just north of Mesopotamia), which not only made possible the production of much better pottery at the cost of much less labour, but also made pottery the first mechanised production industry, the first step on the way to the mass production factory of today.

Finally, let us note how closely these inventions were interconnected. Metals, for example, could not have been used without improvements in transport to carry the ore or metal from mine to user, nor without the agricultural improvements that gave sufficient yields to allow the supporting of specialists withdrawn from primary production. And conversely the wheeled cart, the plough, the sailing ship, or the potter's wheel, requiring, as they do, quite advanced carpentry, probably could not have been used on any extensive scale without metal tools to make them.

CHAPTER 2

THE FIRST CIVILISATIONS (3000 TO 1100 B.C.)

ALONG with the progress in the field of tools and machines that we described in the last chapter, there occurred equally important advances in other techniques. For example, in the river valleys of Mesopotamia, Egypt and the Indus, systems of controlled irrigation were evolved, which enormously increased the productivity of the land. In all spheres of activity men were able to produce much more than before, because they had better tools and better methods. The savage hunter, or the early neolithic farmer, could make ends meet in good seasons—and in bad, part of the tribe died from under-nourishment. Now it was possible to produce an assured sufficiency for all, and beyond that a small surplus, available to increase the comfort and luxury of life. But social progress did not take place along the simple lines of a continually improving standard of living for the whole population; the technical developments themselves decreed a different form of evolution, one that involved a complete change in the structure of society.

Social Change

The tools and machines we have described could only be made at the cost of a considerable amount of labour. Only the few men or families who had been more than usually successful with their crops could spare the time to make them, or alternatively barter a part of their surplus crop with a specialist in exchange for an advanced tool. But once acquired, the new tool gave its possessor a great advantage. With a plough his crops would be yet better, and he would in future have a further surplus available to barter for yet more specialised tools. This was especially true of copper. It provided more serviceable tools than stone; it could be cast into forms which could not be produced from stone; copper tools lasted much longer than stone tools; when the edge was dulled, it could more easily be resharpened. But more than that, if copper is superior to stone for tools, it is much more so for weapons. If a chisel breaks, it means only a delay to make a new one. If a dagger breaks in battle, it means death or captivity. So the owner of copper weapons had a tremendous advantage in warfare. Again, copper is a much more costly commodity than stone. In the period we are speaking of, only a few could possess it. For centuries the tools of the peasant remained of stone and wood.[1]

There resulted a tendency towards the accumulation of wealth in the hands of the few. He who was already moderately well-to-do could obtain copper implements or other advanced tools. Using these, he (or his family, or later his slaves or serfs) could work more efficiently than others and gather yet more wealth, which gave him a further advantage over his neighbours—and so on, in snowball fashion. Or, if he wished to gain wealth by force of arms, or to make others work for him, his advantages with copper weapons were even greater.

The hunters and food-gatherers of the Old Stone Age had lived in an equalitarian society of the type called 'primitive communism'.[2] Their wealth was the property of the whole tribe and the welfare of every member was the responsibility of all. Some might accumulate more personal possessions (ornaments or charms, for example) than others, but differences in wealth were usually small. Every member was expected to contribute his full share of work; there was no mechanism by which one man could live by taking the products of another's labour. 'Political' organisation was correspondingly simple and equalitarian, decisions being taken by an assembly of the whole tribe, though naturally the voices of the elders carried more weight. The chief

[1] This is especially true of Egypt; in Mesopotamia sickles were sometimes made of bronze after 2500 B.C.

[2] We have no direct knowledge of the structure and workings of any society before about 3000 B.C. The descriptions that follow are based on reconstructions from the evidence of houses, tools, weapons, luxury goods, etc., left behind by these peoples, and on the structures of apparently similar societies existing in modern times in backward parts. They are, however, much over-simplified and schematised, and give only an abstract picture of the rich variety of social forms that have existed.

(where there was one) was a man with responsibilities of leadership added to his normal tasks, but he was not a privileged ruler.

It is easy to see that at this technical level no other form of society was possible. Hunters and food-gatherers, by working their hardest, can only produce enough food and other requirements to survive. There is no surplus left over that would allow one man to live by the work of another. The tribe must present an unbroken front in the hard struggle against nature; internal rivalries mean failure in the struggle, and death.

For the same reasons war was rare or non-existent before the coming of agriculture. For while they are fighting, men cannot hunt for food; and if they stop hunting, in these lowly conditions of life, they perish.

The social effects of the transition from hunting to agriculture are so profound that anthropologists have adopted special names for the types of society involved, and we shall use them throughout this book. *Savagery* is the society and way of living of people before the agricultural stage, who exist by hunting and gathering food. *Barbarism* is the state of agricultural peoples who have not yet reached the level of civilisation. Neither word, as we use it, has any pejorative sense—indeed, we shall see that 'barbarian' often amounts to a word of praise.

The change-over from hunting to agriculture, that is from savagery to barbarism, weakened the basis of primitive communism; for the family, tilling its separate fields, was capable of becoming a self-sufficient unit, and therefore the tribe as a whole became less important. The early agricultural societies remained essentially equalitarian, in that land was communally owned and the fields were commonly redistributed from year to year among the different families. Nevertheless, it now became possible for one family by greater skill or greater luck to prosper more than another. At first these differences of wealth would not be great, nor would they have any strong tendency to grow. But with the introduction of copper and the other inventions described towards the end of the previous chapter, the situation (as we have seen) became such that any person who had accumulated a small surplus had an advantage in accumulating more. Differences in wealth between members of the community increased apace. And, more important, differences in power also arose. In the hunting community, we have noticed, it was pointless to gain power over another, since the subject could produce only enough for his own necessities. But the farmer can normally produce a surplus. And so, when agriculture is established, it pays to dominate others, by force or persuasion, and to live as a privileged ruler on the products of their labour. Political power has entered the picture.

Development from this point seems to have followed two principal paths. In the one, men used the advantage given them by copper weapons to force others to pay tribute or rent for their land or to become serfs. Having dominated local communities in this way, they built up armies from their subjects and went on to conquer surrounding districts—till great kingdoms were brought into being. It was chiefly in this way that the Pharaohs became rulers of Egypt. The other path is through the formation of a ruling class of priests. The priest—at first not a full-time specialist, but a respected member of the tribe adding priestly duties to normal work—had great influence because of his role in propitiating evil spirits, securing favourable weather and the like. He was thus in a good position to command the surplus when it arose—a tribute to the gods, which nevertheless had to be stored in the temple granary. And in Mesopotamia it was corporations of priests in their temples that emerged as a ruling class before the war lords.

The Bronze Age Civilisations

These descriptions give only a very abstract picture of how the great social revolution took place, and the reality of the process must have been much more complicated. But certainly by 3000 B.C., or a century or so earlier, a decisive change had taken place in the structure of society. The simple barbarian communities of more or less equal farmers had been replaced by states in which the vast majority of the inhabitants lived at subsistence level, often as slaves or serfs, while all the surplus product of their labours was used to provide a luxurious existence for a small class of kings, nobles and priests, as well as supporting the civil services and armies which formed the mechanism for extracting from the masses the products of their work. Class-divisions had become the basis of social structure.

From the point of view of the oppressed peasant, serf or slave, this change would seem an unqualified catastrophe. But from the point of view of the human race as a whole, and especially from the point of view of people living today on the verge of another transformation of equal magnitude, it was a necessary step forward. Though factors arising from the new social structure sometimes held back advance for centuries, nevertheless the technical developments that had to come, in order to carry forward the progress described in the last chapter, would have been impossible without the form of organisation that class-divisions produced. This arose, for example, from the mere costliness of producing copper tools. If the surplus above subsistence level that neolithic society produced had remained equally divided among all the members of the village, then only rarely would a family have sufficient surplus to barter with a smith for even one tool. But the increasing concentration of wealth in the hands of a few at the expense of the many enabled these few to exchange their surplus food (or other necessities) for the smith's tools, and thus provided the basis for the existence of the smith (or the miner, or any other specialised craftsman). Irrigation cannot be effectively carried out by individuals, or even by village groups. Only the large-scale organisation of the new class-divided states could arrange the efficient irrigation systems that provided the wealth and prosperity of the civilisations in Egypt, Mesopotamia and the Indus. The building of cities, the making of roads and harbours, and many other construction works that were essential for further progress depended similarly on this concentration of wealth and of the power to command. And many of the technical advances that we shall describe in the rest of this book required the organisation of large labour forces, withdrawn from the direct production of necessities; and consequently they were only possible because a few individuals possessed sufficient wealth (or, what it really amounts to, sufficient power to make others work for them) to be able to support these large numbers of specialists.

Thus the many technical advances of the millennia before 3000 B.C. not only caused the social changes, but probably also depended on the gradual increase of class-divisions to provide the concentrations of wealth necessary for their use. And the full establishment of the great class-divided states in Egypt, Mesopotamia and the Indus valley shortly before 3000 B.C. was followed by several centuries of a great flowering of the various techniques. This was not such a period of radical innovation as that which we described in Chapter 1; rather it was one in which men built on these innovations, refining the skill with which they were used and increasing enormously the scale on which they were applied.

But there were several important inventions. About 3000 B.C., or within a century or so after, several important developments in metal-working took place in and around Mesopotamia. Tweezers were enlarged into tongs (not hinged, however, but depending on the spring of the metal) with which the smith could efficiently handle the smaller pieces of hot metal. But large objects and crucibles containing metal had to be lifted between two stones or between green twigs. The introduction of bellows improved metallurgical processes. The extremely ingenious *cire perdue* process of casting was developed. In this a wax model of the shape required is made. This is then coated with clay and placed in a furnace, where the wax melts and runs away, while the clay is baked hard to form a mould. Molten metal is then run into the mould and, after cooling, the clay is broken away. Most important of all metallurgical advances of this period was the controlled production of bronze (a copper-tin alloy, sometimes previously produced by accident from ores containing both metals), which was a radical improvement on copper. It gave harder and more durable tools, and it made possible really fine casting, which is impossible with unalloyed copper. None of these new techniques spread to Egypt till over a thousand years later.

Refinement and Organisation

Already the craftsmen of Egypt and Mesopotamia produced a wide variety of articles of high quality. The coppersmith of about 3000 B.C. made axes, adzes, chisels, gouges, drills, knives, saws, nails, clamps, needles, razors, tweezers, and so on. The carpenter made boats, chariots, furniture, harps and lyres; by about 2800 B.C. he was using plywood of six layers. The objects of great beauty found in the tombs of the period demonstrate the degree of refinement which these workers could attain in catering for the luxury—in death, as in life—of their rulers.

The ability of the new states to organise labour on a large scale produced its most beneficial effects in the great irrigation works, sources of unprecedented prosperity. But irrigation is outside the scope of this book, and so we illustrate the results of large-scale organisation from their other supreme (if less useful) example—the Pyramids of Egypt. The Great Pyramid of Cheops was built of about 2,300,000 blocks of stone, totalling some 5,750,000 tons in weight. The blocks average 2½ tons, but range up to 15 tons (while for other purposes the Egyptians quarried, handled and transported blocks up to 200 tons or so). These had to be dragged, with no more equipment than sledges, rollers, sleepers, ropes and levers, from the quarries to the Nile, where they were carried on barges, and thence raised 100 feet to the level of the site. According to a tradition reported by Herodotus, 100,000 men were engaged three months each year for twenty years in moving them to the site. At the site itself a permanent labour force estimated at 4,000 was at work, besides an unknown number in the quarries.

Only soft rocks could be cut with bronze tools. Hard rocks were pounded with balls of dolerite (a hard resilient stone). The craftsman could do this in such a way as to detach a block as required from the mass in the quarry—a task of no mean skill, since either too hard or too soft a blow will fail. Metal wedges or wooden wedges expanded by wetting them were also used to detach blocks. These were adaptations of the techniques of the copper miners. Shaping was done first by pounding with dolerite balls or pointed hammers and picks, and at the fine stage with saws and tubular drills, probably bow-driven, using an abrasive.

To raise the stones to their final positions great ramps of earth and brick were built against the rising sides of the pyramid, reaching eventually its full height of 481 feet. Up these the blocks were dragged on sledges and manhandled into position by means of ropes and levers, with a thin layer of mortar as lubricant. The only surveying methods available were sightings of the stars, measuring rods, perhaps the plumb-line, and water for levelling. The method of levelling—presumably developed from experience in levelling irrigation channels—was to run a watercourse round the work, banking it up with mud, and to measure down from it at many points to the level required. Yet with these primitive means, the greatest and least of the 756-foot sides differ only by 7·9 inches; the greatest deviation from a right angle at a corner is about a twentieth of a degree; and the maximum error in the level of the base is half an inch. And so accurately could the stone mason work, even with his pitiful equipment, that the average thickness of the joints between the few remaining facing blocks is a mere fiftieth of an inch.

As a contribution to the progress of mankind, the pyramids are of negligible value, but the techniques evolved for building them to such size and accuracy must have had a profound effect on all subsequent building and civil engineering. Our first reaction is amazement that such magnificent results should be achieved with such meagre technical equipment. Yet meagre as the equipment seems to us, it was the final product of a great advance in the mason's technique, and not for many centuries was it improved upon. The increased scale of application showed itself in other fields. Ships, for example, reached 115 feet in length by 2500 B.C.; by about 2000 they carried crews of up to 120 men.

Stagnation

Yet before 2500 B.C., what can be termed the first technological revolution of human history had come to an end. It was a revolution that began with the invention of agriculture and the techniques that came with it, continued through that great period of invention in the couple of millennia before 3000 B.C., and then, with advances in skill and scale rather than fundamental innovations, till about 2500 B.C. But after that date stagnation set in, and for many centuries only slight progress took place. Not only did fundamental advances cease for a long period, but even in many techniques where the basic ideas had been evolved earlier, but remained imperfect, and where it seems obvious to us that a little extra effort could have produced great improvements, no further progress took place till the Middle Ages.

The ancient harness, for example, had been developed for use with oxen. Its main element was the yoke resting on the backs of the necks of a pair of oxen, and the shape of the ox's neck made this a quite efficient harness. It was not, however, efficient as a harness for the onager (a type of ass) or more especially for the horse. Yet, when these were introduced,[3] it was applied to them with only minor modifications. As the horse's neck is not correctly

[3] The onager early in the third millenium, the horse about 2000 B.C.

shaped to take the yoke, a band or collar was attached to the yoke at the back of the horse's neck and passed round its throat (Figure 2). Compared with a modern harness, in which the collar rests on the shoulder blades, this was a very inefficient arrangement. When the horse pulled, the pressure of the band choked it, and forced it to throw its head back into a position ineffective for exerting its strength (or even to rear on its hind legs). Further, animals were not shod (leather sandals were probably used to protect injured feet). The result was that two-thirds, at least, of the power of the horse was lost. Again, no really effective harness for one horse or for more than two was evolved. Not till the Middle Ages did a sensible harness come into use. Till then horse traction was suitable only for the lighter loads, and heavy loads were pulled by human labour, at the cost of unnecessary suffering (Figure 3).

And so also with other techniques. Until the Middle Ages, the spindle described in Chapter 1 remained in use without radical improvement; the steering mechanism of ships, which was very imperfect (Plate I), remained unaltered. After the cart and the potter's wheel, no new applications of rotary motion were made for more than two thousand years. Until the Iron Age the smith's main hammer (and in Egypt his only one) was a ball of stone held in the hand. After the Great Pyramid, techniques of building in stone remained static (or even declined) until the time of the Greeks. And in general, after the flowering of techniques in the few centuries around 3000 B.C., no major inventions and few minor ones were made until the advent of iron entirely changed conditions.

The Negative Side of Class-divisions

The examples given will make it clear that this stagnation of technique was not caused by a lack of problems to be solved, or lack of obvious deficiencies to be rectified. Some of the problems may have been too difficult at that particular stage of progress—we do not expect men familiar with no more complicated means of transport than carts and sailing ships to create an aeroplane—but improvements to the harness, or the development of specialised hammers for particular purposes, were steps by no means beyond the capabilities of men's minds at that time. Some deeper explanation must be found. The most probable explana-

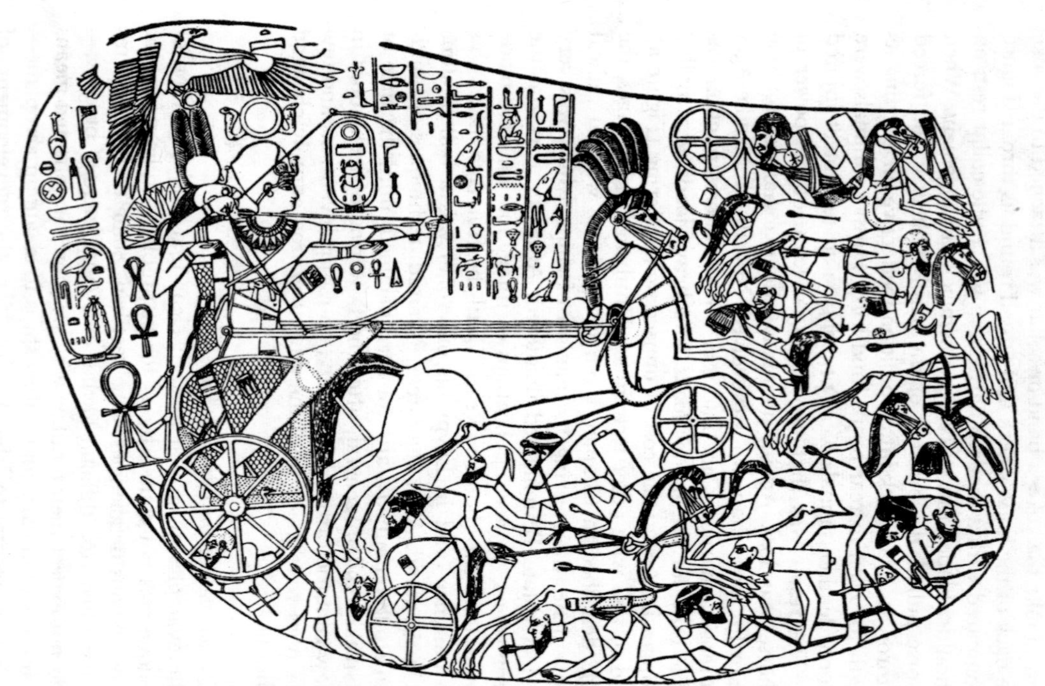

Fig. 2. The ancient harness for horses. Note how the band round the horse's throat forces its head back into a position which reduces its pulling power.

tion lies in the nature of the social system which dominated the advanced part of the world in this period of stagnation. We have already remarked that the appearance of class-divided society was necessary for the development of man's technical equipment beyond a certain stage. We also hinted that this social structure did not ensure uninterrupted progress, but at times retarded technical advance for long periods. It is now time to see how this came about.

The societies of the period we are discussing, when the social changes were complete and the class-divisions fixed and hardened, were divided, broadly speaking, into two classes. The great mass of the people, belonging to the oppressed classes of peasants, slaves and serfs, did all the productive work of the community, but received in return only the bare necessities of life. The small ruling class of priests, nobles and kings did no productive work, but lived luxuriously on the products of the work of others.

The technical conditions of the times ensured that the gulf between these two classes was very great. For copper is a rather rare metal and expensive to produce; tin, the other component of bronze, is even more so. Both could be easily monopolised by a small group of powerful men. But bronze at the current level of technology was the chief basis of economic, and especially military, power; so that power and wealth were very highly concentrated in the hands of the few. The dependence of these states on irrigation, the control of which was again easy to monopolise, accentuated this tendency. Thus such a society contained very few members of independent middle classes (a few merchants in Mesopotamia, almost none in Egypt). The division between the small autocratic group of rulers and the great mass of the working people was almost absolute.

Consider, then, the relations of the two classes to the process of invention and improvement. The labouring people were familiar with the techniques already in existence, and they had the practical experience from which it would have been possible to learn how they could be improved. But they had no incentive to make improvements, since any resulting increase of production would be taken from them and used merely to increase the well-being of their masters. Nor, worked to the utmost night and day, did they have the leisure required for invention. The ruling class, on

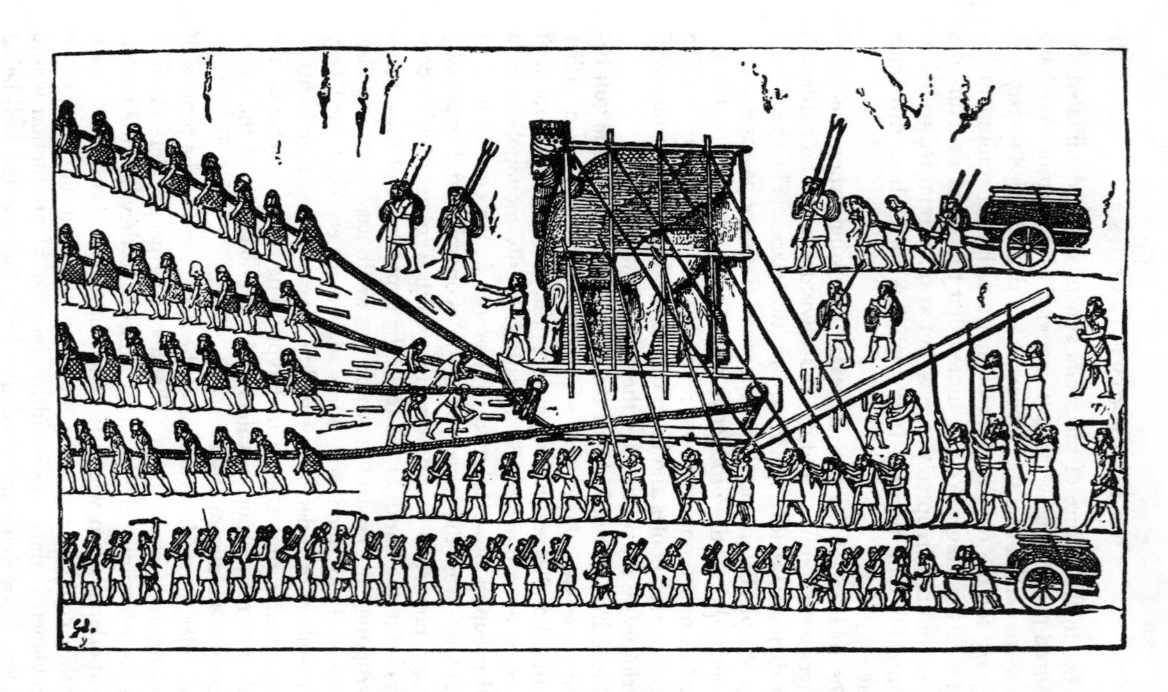

Fig. 3. Land transport in the late Bronze Age. Assyrians hauling a giant statue on a sledge—an example of the capacity of the Bronze Age civilisations for organising large labour forces. Note also the wheeled carts for lighter loads.

the other hand, saw the world only from the point of view of consumers. Ignorant of the actual methods of production, they could not usually be aware of technical deficiencies, nor had they the practical knowledge to effect improvements. They *were* familiar with the art of exploitation, of government, of extracting the last available grain of corn from the peasant, and in these arts they produced many improvements. But they were incapable of advancing the technical methods of society. Thus, with one class possessing the requisite knowledge and experience, but lacking incentive and leisure, and the other class lacking the knowledge and experience, there was no means by which technical progress could be achieved.

Evidence that it was the form of society that caused this cessation of invention comes in a variety of ways. In Egypt, where the separation of the classes was virtually absolute, the stagnation was almost complete. In Mesopotamia, where a small class of more independent merchants had a footing, and in various peripheral regions where the new social structure was less firmly and rigidly established, some modest progress continued to be made. The wheeled cart, for example had spread over Mesopotamia, Elam and Syria by 3000 B.C., that is by about the date at which the new social structure reached a stabilised form. But it had not by then reached Egypt. The Egyptians certainly knew of the wheel, for they used it on mobile scaling ladders in siege warfare about 2500 B.C. And though Nile transport made vehicles less important there than elsewhere, there were plenty of tasks in which carts would have eased labour and raised productivity. Yet they were not used in Egypt till about 1600 B.C., and even then only as a result of invasion by peoples from lands where they were already common. We are thus forced to the conclusion that the wheel was not adopted in Egypt because it failed to reach there before the structure of society became so unfavourable to innovation as to prevent its introduction. In the same way, bronze (as opposed to unalloyed copper), bellows and tongs were not employed in Egypt till about 1600 B.C., though they had been in use over a thousand years earlier in Mesopotamia. Finally, we shall see that the fundamental invention that was to start mankind once again on the road of progress was not made within the Bronze Age civilisations, despite their advantages of wealth and experience, but by barbarians on the fringe. Thus the evidence is very strong that the cause of the cessation of progress lay in the extreme class divisions of the Bronze Age states.

Yet even in this period of stagnation, progress did not entirely cease. The spoked wheel, a considerable advance on the earlier solid wooden wheel, appeared just after 2000 B.C. (Figures 2 and 3). By 1600 B.C. the Cretans were using rapiers. About 1500, metal workers learned that they could control the composition of bronze better by smelting copper and tin separately and then alloying the metals, instead of smelting a mixture of the ores, as formerly. From about this time unexplained causes (perhaps the opening up of European ore deposits or the development of techniques for using the more plentiful sulphidic ores) made bronze considerably cheaper. In Egypt its use had formerly been confined to ornaments, weapons and the tools of the finer crafts; now occasional metal hoe blades and ploughshares appeared. In barbarian Europe bronze came to be used for heavy and rough work—from about 1300 B.C. copper miners in the Austrian Alps had sledge hammers and gads with bronze tips.

But more important than this comparatively small progress was the diffusion of Bronze Age techniques over large parts of Europe and Asia, which went on continually after 3000 B.C., and made it possible for the further advances that we shall be discussing to take place on a far wider basis than ever before.

CHAPTER 3

IRON, THE DEMOCRATIC METAL (1100 B.C. TO A.D. 500)

BECAUSE of its rarity and costliness, bronze had not very greatly extended man's control over nature. It never provided any important proportion of the tools for agriculture, which thus remained at a level not very much above that of the later neolithic period (though it is probable that bronze *indirectly* raised the agricultural level by providing better tools for making ploughs, carts, and so on). While agriculture remained at this level, there could be no general increase in living standards, and surplus agricultural production must remain so small that only a tiny number of workers could be spared to specialise in other crafts. Thus, apart from weapons, bronze provided mainly tools with which a small number of craftsmen produced luxuries for a small wealthy class. Production in general remained basically neolithic. Even the great irrigation works of Egypt and Mesopotamia were for the most part carried out with stone and wooden equipment.[1]

Iron opens New Opportunities

It was through learning to use iron as well as bronze that men broke through these limitations. However, the technology of iron working is very complex and difficult. In a primitive furnace the temperatures are not high enough to melt the metal. It appears as tiny solid beads dispersed in the slag. This mixture has to be repeatedly reheated and hammered till the iron particles coalesce and the slag is driven out. Even the wrought-iron obtained in this way is too soft to be useful for tool-making. It must now be

[1] The Mayas of Yucatan (Central America) independently reached a civilisation in many ways like that of the eastern Bronze Age, but without the use of metals. This shows that metal is not essential to some sort of low-level civilisation.

repeatedly heated in contact with charcoal and hammered, to produce on the surface a casing of steel which will take a sharp edge. It is now a useful metal, but its properties can be greatly improved (and varied at the discretion of the smith) by heat treatments to harden and temper it.

Once this complex technology was mastered, iron offered many advantages. First, it is for most purposes a superior metal to bronze. Second, its ores are far more widely distributed over the Earth's surface, so that many more people could obtain it for tools and weapons without having to organise elaborate transport and exchange. And finally, iron is much cheaper to produce than bronze.

Iron had quite often been produced during the Bronze Age, but only as a semi-precious metal for ornaments and the like. It was quite useless for economic purposes. The process of producing a hard steel surface, as described above, seems to have been mastered by 1400 B.C. by barbarian tribesmen in the Armenian mountains. These were vassals of the Hittite kings, who succeeded in retaining for a time a virtual monopoly of the process. But two hundred years later, on the breakup of the Hittite Empire, knowledge of iron-working began to spread, and it is from about 1100 B.C. that iron tools and weapons began to be used widely, in Palestine, Syria, Asia Minor and Greece, spreading thence to other countries.

The cheapness and wide distribution of iron had profound effects on man's way of life. At last metal tools became generally available to the farmer and enormously increased the productivity of agriculture. Before 1000 B.C. iron hoe-blades, ploughshares, sickles and knives were in use in Palestine. From about 700 B.C. iron axes permitted the clearing of forests and allowed a great expansion of agriculture in Europe. Soon Greek and Roman farmers were using a wide variety of iron implements, including shovels and spades, forks, pickaxes, mattocks, scythes and bill-hooks. Shears for shearing sheep (which had previously been plucked) were invented about 500 B.C.—and were also applied to barbering and cloth-cutting. The greatly increased productivity of agriculture yielded a surplus which could support a large number of specialised craftsmen. The products of the craftsman became generally available instead of being the monopoly of the wealthy. In particular the craftsman provided for the farmer those same tools with which the latter increased the productivity of his work. And thus, for the first time, there arose a balanced relationship between industry and agriculture, instead of the former one-sided relationship by which agriculture provided the food for the craftsman, but the craftsman's product went mainly to a select few.

Iron also provided the craftsman with a variety of tools—and better tools at that. By 500 B.C. carpenters had frame-saws and cross-cut saws, as well as a greater variety, in iron, of tools they had formerly possessed in bronze or stone. The auger was probably added to this equipment about 400 B.C., and the plane before 50 B.C. Smiths, by 500 B.C., had hinged tongs, bits, rymers, chisels and improved bellows. They had several kinds of specialised hammers, in sharp contrast with the limited range available to their Bronze Age predecessors (Plate II). The new and better tools increased the productivity of the crafts and therefore tended to enhance their economic status. In all directions, iron was tending to break down the barriers between classes which had put a stop to progress in the Bronze Age. And so it is not surprising that we find a new wave of fundamental inventions arising.

New Advances in Rotary Motion

The pulley, for example, appears to have been invented in the early Iron Age. The pulley seems an obviously useful invention and a simple step for peoples acquainted with the wheel. Yet there is fairly strong evidence that, for example, the Bronze Age Egyptians did not have it for the obvious use of hoisting sails, and it was certainly not employed in their great building operations. The first definite evidence of its existence is in an Assyrian relief of the eighth century B.C. (Figure 4). Perhaps this is yet another example of how the social structure of the earlier civilisations retarded technical progress; or perhaps it merely indicates that, simple though it is, the pulley could not be made cheaply enough for practical use until iron became available both for materials and tools. Be that as it may, the pulley soon revolutionised the building industry. It provided a far better way of hauling stones into position than the Bronze Age method of pulling them up an earthen ramp, and then dropping them into position. It was developed into a rudimentary crane, which was used

Fig. 4. The earliest known representation of a pulley.

by the Greeks by 450 B.C. Capstans were also in use by that time, while by the beginning of our era sheerlegs with block-and-tackle appeared.

The lathe, first and most fundamental of machine tools, appears also to have been a product of the new inventive wave of the early Iron Age.[2] It may have been in use as early as 1200 B.C., probably by 1000, certainly by 800.

The possibility of using metal parts in machines and the use of iron tools for working in stone and wood created new potentialities for the making of various types of machine, and thus for new inventions. Most notable is the mechanisation of corn-grinding. The Bronze Age method was to pound the grain in a mortar or rub it on a slightly hollowed stone (the 'saddle quern') with a roller-like stone held in the hand and pushed to and fro. Every household did its own grinding. About 600 B.C. (or perhaps rather earlier) there appeared the rotary quern, in which the corn is ground between two circular stones, the upper revolving on an iron pivot projecting from the centre of the lower. Even in its simple form, turned by hand, the rotary quern saved much labour, besides giving a better flour. A century or two later the further step had been taken of increasing the size of the quern, now installed in a commercial bakery, and working it by a donkey attached to a shaft projecting from the upper stone and walking round and round (Figure 5). A similar machine was applied (perhaps rather earlier) to the grinding of ore, for instance in the Athenian silver mines at Laurion; and another, more complicated, animal-driven machine was used for crushing olives to release their oil. These were the first extensions of the use of non-human power to do man's work since the harnessing of animals to ploughs and carts before 3000 B.C. They opened up great possibilities for the easing of human toil. But, as we shall see, the opportunity was not fully grasped until the Middle Ages.

The general availability of iron tools also made possible the cutting of tunnels and building of aqueducts to bring water to towns and made many other such amenities available. It allowed

[2] Some authors claim the lathe for the Bronze Age on the grounds that certain pieces of fine woodwork could only have been produced on this machine, but R. S. Woodbury in his *History of the Lathe to 1850* (Cleveland, Ohio, 1961) makes it clear that these are merely the results of very expert carving

considerable advances in the sphere of transportation (though there were no fundamental inventions here), by providing the means for building more, larger and better ships and wagons, and for road-making on an increased scale (for which purpose iron picks were in use by 850 B.C.).

Fig. 5. A Roman horse-driven quern. In fact asses were more commonly used than horses.

Towards Athenian Democracy

In all these ways the use of iron brought about radical changes in the life of mankind. The total capacity to produce both necessities and luxuries greatly increased. The Bronze Age condemned the vast majority to live at a subsistence level, a very few being supported in luxury on the tiny surplus that the many produced. In the Iron Age a much larger proportion of the people could have a comfortable standard of living, and correspondingly the class of really wealthy could also grow considerably. The craftsman and trader could now work for a general market, in which even the peasants could afford their goods, instead of being condemned, as in the Bronze Age, to remain dependent on the nobles and temples. At first they produced to order, but to orders coming from a much wider section of the community than before. Later, it even became possible to produce their goods for sale on a general market, not knowing who the eventual purchaser would be—as the factory worker of today does not know who will ultimately use his products. With improvements in transport the market for which they produced could be a very distant one, though these potentialities could only be fully realised in countries like Greece, well situated for marine transport. Even by 650 B.C.

Greek exports were traded all over the eastern Mediterranean and the Black Sea. The development of coinage about this time, freeing merchants from the restrictions of barter, greatly facilitated the extension of commerce. Now some states became more and more dependent on trade, till eventually, around 450 B.C., Athens was incapable of providing herself with the basic necessity of corn and depended on importing it in exchange for exports of her specialised agriculture (olives, olive oil and wines)[3] and her mining and manufacturing industries (pottery, arms, etc.).

Within such an economy, then, far more people enjoyed economic independence than in the Bronze Age. Bronze, as we have seen, had implied the centralisation of economic power, and therefore also of political power, in the hands of an aristocratic few. Iron, with its consequence of good tools and weapons for a much greater number, and with the large classes of craftsmen and traders, independent of the patronage of noble families, led to a greater economic equality and a decentralisation of economic power. Inevitably, this must produce political changes of a corresponding nature. The first few centuries of the Iron Age show a gradual democratisation of society (not without bitter resistance from the aristocrats) till by 450 B.C., concurrently with its transformation into a state depending entirely on trade, Athens had a constitution in which there were virtually no *legal* differences between the rights of *citizens*. The word 'citizens' is italicised here because this democracy was limited by the exclusion of women, slaves and foreigners from citizenship; and the word 'legal' is emphasised as a reminder that here, as in any society based on private ownership, wealth implied power.

Athens led the world in this change to a more democratic form of society, largely because she also led the world in making

[3] The working up of this agricultural produce had a big influence on the development of machinery in classical times. An olive-crushing machine has already been mentioned. Again, in earlier societies which produced wine chiefly for immediate household use, the pressing of grapes had been done by such crude means as compressing them in a bag by twisting the ends. But for their extensive wine and olive trades, the Greeks developed special presses. The beam press appeared in Crete in the period 1800–1500 B.C., became common in Greece after 1000 and continued to receive many improvements down to the begining of our era. The more advanced screw press appeared in the second or first century B.C. The invention of the screw itself is traditionally ascribed to Archytas of Tarentum, about 400 B.C.

use of the new industrial possibilities opened up by iron tools. Besides contributing her share to the technical advances that we have mentioned earlier in the chapter, she was the first state to live by producing specialised goods for export. In order to be able to do this she also made fundamental innovations in the organisation of industrial production. At first production, even for the export market, was carried on by a host of independent craftsmen. But production for the market can be made more efficient by the concentration of several workmen within a factory, each specialising in one aspect of the job and all together mass-producing the articles to be sold. A pottery factory, from the sixth century B.C. on, would often have separate specialists for throwing (i.e., shaping the vessel on the wheel), painting, and baking in the furnace. And, as Athenian industry grew, the size of the factories grew too. At the end of the fifth century B.C. we hear of a bedstead workshop employing twenty slaves, an arms factory with thirty-two, a shield factory with 120. Perhaps twelve to fifteen slaves constituted a largish factory, but in mining the numbers ran up to 1,000, and perhaps more.

Slavery and Warfare

The workers in these later factories were slaves. This was another new development, industrial slavery on a huge scale, largely replacing the former free craftsmen. It provided the labour for the great expansion of the export industry mentioned above, but at the same time it introduced new factors which were soon to put an end to Athenian progressiveness. Slave labour, while triumphant Athenian armies and successful pirates made it generally and cheaply available, was a convenient solution to all problems of heavy labour. It was usually simpler and cheaper to put slaves on to heavy work (even if it wore them out in a few years) than to design and construct a machine to do it. Thus, after about 450 B.C. the growth of slavery very greatly inhibited the spread of the animal-driven machines that we described above. At the same time, since manual work, and even the management and the supervision of it, was the lot of these slaves, it came to be despised by citizens.[4] And so the type of contradiction that we

[4] Wage labourers often shared the work with slaves, but it was the existence of slave labour that determined the status of manual work.

described near the end of Chapter 2 was revived in a new form. The slave, with no education, no leisure and no hope of reward, was not in a position to invent better productive methods; the citizen despised manual labour, and even despised the process of invention as being connected therewith.

A second factor which greatly inhibited technical advance in this period was the division of the Mediterranean world between a large number of tiny city states, almost continuously at war with one another. On the one hand this division greatly restricted the markets available for manufactured goods; on the other it diverted to warfare the energies of many men (perhaps some geniuses) who might otherwise have contributed something to human progress.

The Alexandrian Expansion

The Greek world, especially Athens, had made enormous advances by 450 B.C. But now, as a result of these contradictions, the creative impetus waned, and after 400 B.C. industry went into decline. The contradictions were partially solved when Alexander the Great made his series of conquests which forcibly united the Greek world and then expanded it into a vast empire embracing Egypt, most of hither Asia, and even parts of India. On Alexander's death this empire disintegrated, not however into city states, but into three or four empires of considerable size. And a new economic and cultural unity held all this territory together. Many of the restrictions arising from the former divisions were removed. Commerce expanded fivefold in a few years. Formerly Greek trade was more or less confined to the Mediterranean (and mostly to its eastern parts); now it reached from the Danube in the north to Ethiopia in the south, from India and even China in the east to the Atlantic coasts. Ships increased in speed and size. Great harbours were built and canals dug, for example between the Mediterranean and the Red Sea. Lighthouses were built, beginning with the famous one at Alexandria. This city, capital of the empire of the Ptolemys, centred on Egypt, became the commercial centre of the world.

Industry expanded along with commerce. Division of labour was carried much further—till, for example, the stonemason did not sharpen his own tools, and the quarryman who cut the stone did not sweep away the sand. Industrial slavery decreased, though only for a time, and the factories were run either by free wage-labour, or the temporarily conscripted labour of men who otherwise were free (a method adapted from the Bronze Age). Such conditions once more encouraged mechanical inventiveness, and the three centuries after 330 B.C. produced a crop of inventions greater than in any comparable period between 3000 B.C. and the later Middle Ages.

Educated Inventors

For the first time we begin to find fairly comprehensive written descriptions of some mechanical matters to supplement the archaeological evidence and occasional literary references on which our story of previous periods is based. The educated classes, who could leave a record of their work, were at last beginning to take some interest in mechanical matters. In theory the upper classes still despised everything connected with the crafts, but in practice, apparently, industry now held such an important place in the general economy that a few of them applied their theoretical training to industrial matters. Some crafts or professions had become respectable, too : for example, surveying. The division between the worker and the man of the leisured classes who had time and education at his disposal, which had frustrated advance in the Bronze Age, and again after 450 B.C. in Greece, was less clear than before. It did, however, remain and it tended to grow again; so that gradually the interest of the educated in mechanical matters was diverted from the invention or improvement of useful machines to the construction of ingenious mechanical toys. And, in point of fact, the most important inventions of the period were still the work of unknown craftsmen.

Among those of the educated classes who tackled serious mechanical problems, the most outstanding was Archimedes (287 to 212 B.C.), one of the greatest mathematicians of all times. By developing the theory of the lever he virtually initiated the science of theoretical mechanics (though but little use was made of it in antiquity and it did not prove of much practical value till its study was once more taken up at the end of the Middle Ages). He is usually regarded as the inventor of the compound pulley and may also have invented the screw pump which bears his name, and which at any rate came into use about that time for irrigation. And he invented and constructed various military devices for the defence of Syracuse, with such success (according to the tradition) that the attacking Romans fled in fear when any strange apparatus appeared on the walls of the town.

The chief military machine of Greek and Roman times was a sort of artillery using, not explosives, but the elastic power of twisted ropes. Devices on these lines were probably invented early in the fourth century B.C., and when fully developed were capable of throwing a sixty-pound stone 200 yards. Archimedes is said to have greatly improved these machines. Other attempts to improve this 'artillery' were made by Ctesibius (who lived about 100 B.C.)[5] and Philo of Byzantium (about 180 B.C.),[5] the latter in particular suggesting the use of the power of bronze springs or compressed air instead of twisted ropes. None of these attempts was successful; those of Philo certainly could not have been carried out with the technical equipment of the times. Ctesibius is also generally considered to have invented the force-pump. This was used by the Greeks and Romans, though apparently not very widely, for water supply, in fire-engines and for driving hydraulic organs (which may have been invented by Ctesibius himself).

Hero, a later Alexandrian writer who probably died about A.D. 70[5] left treatises which described a large number of mechanical devices then in use. He was probably a surveyor and it is therefore interesting that two of the most useful of them were a sort of theodolite and an instrument for measuring distances by counting mechanically the rotation of a wheel, as a cyclometer does today. The latter contains a train of gearing—the first literary record of gearing in existence.[6] He also described pumps, a syringe, a fire engine, and gadgets for automatically adjusting the wick and oil level of lamps. But by far the greater part of the devices he described amount to no more than mechanical conjuring tricks. They include, for example, a slot machine for delivering holy water, puppet theatres worked by falling weights, a device whereby a fire lit on an altar causes the temple gates to open (these had

[5] These dates are very uncertain.

[6] The invention of gearing as such is sometimes attributed to Archimedes, and in any case cannot (on present evidence) have been made earlier than 500 B.C.

their 'use' for overawing the superstitious masses as a part of technique of government), and things like 'an automaton, the head of which continues attached to the body after a knife has entered the neck at one side, passed completely through and out of the other; which animal will drink immediately after the operation'. This illustrates well enough what happened when the first impetus of the expanding industry after the Alexandrian conquests had petered out and increasing class distinctions had once more cut the theoretician adrift from the practical problems of the craftsman.

Two of Hero's devices are worth special note. One is apparently (though there is some doubt about the meaning of a vital word in his description) a windmill arranged to drive the bellows of an organ by means of a trip-hammer action (Figure 6). The other is a primitive reaction turbine, whose mode of action can be seen from Figure 7. The significant point is that here we have two devices capable of being developed into effective prime movers.[7] But to Hero they were merely toys. The turbine merely turns; it does not turn anything. The windmill drives the organ merely as an exhibition of ingenuity. True, the turbine could not, at the current technical level, have been made into an effective machine, but the windmill probably could. Yet we have no evidence that any attempt was made to apply it to lighten toil. While the apparently inexhaustible supply of slaves gave an easy solution to the problem of power, upper class inventors saw little reason to apply themselves to the task of harnessing natural forces.

New Prime Movers

While much ingenuity was thus being wasted in constructing elaborate toys, unknown craftsmen were making inventions of far more lasting importance; and among these were important steps towards the production of really useful power-driven machinery. The water-raising wheel—a vertical wheel fitted with pots which lift the water and pour it into a trough for irrigation purposes—may have come into use about 600 B.C. It was originally driven by human power through treadmill or windlass. Sometime after

[7] A prime mover is an apparatus (water-wheel, steam-engine, petrol-engine, etc.) which converts some natural source of energy into mechanical power capable of driving machinery.

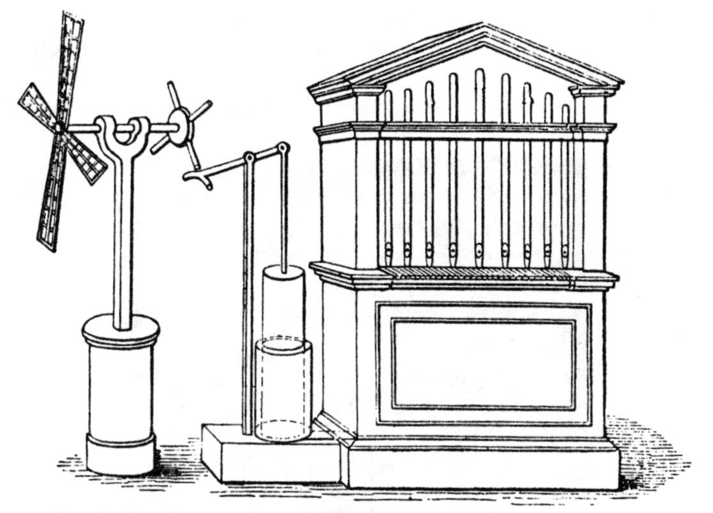

Fig. 6. A reconstruction of Hero's windmill driving a hydraulic organ. It is not certain that this reconstruction is substantially correct.

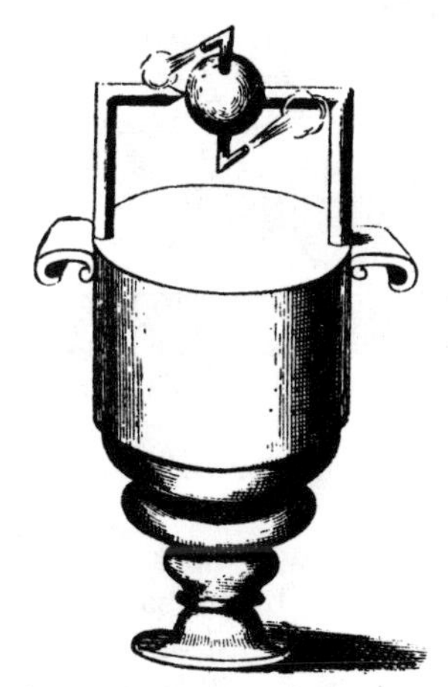

Fig. 7. A reconstruction of Hero's primitive steam turbine. The reaction of the steam issuing from the nozzles causes the sphere to rotate.

200 B.C. it was adapted to be worked by an ox (Plate III). The animal walked round a vertical shaft, as in the rotary quern described earlier, and this was geared to the horizontal shaft of the wheel. This represents another important extension of the use

Fig. 8. Reconstruction of Vitruvius' water-mill.

of animal power and is also probably the first use of gearing to transmit power.

Far more revolutionary was the invention of the water-wheel, which was probably made by barbarian people in a mountain region somewhere north and east of the Roman Empire early in the first century B.C. Men, it will be remembered, had first harnessed the power of inorganic nature by their use of sailing ships before 3000 B.C. The water-wheel was the first further use of such power and also the first application of inorganic power to stationary machinery. For centuries its use was confined to flour-milling, but it was eventually to provide the chief power source on which the early stages of modern civilisation were based. One of the earliest references is in a poem by Antipater of Thessalonica (about 85 B.C.):

> Cease from grinding, Oh you toilers. Women, slumber still,
> even if the crowing rooster calls the morning star.
> For Demeter has appointed Nymphs to turn your mill
> and upon the water-wheel alighting here they are.
>
> See how quick they twirl the axle whose revolving rays
> spin the heavy rollers quarried overseas.
> So again we savour the delights of ancient days,
> taught to eat the fruits of Mother Earth in ease.[8]

In its primitive form the wheel revolved horizontally on a vertical shaft, being driven by a fast-moving stream guided by a chute. But the Roman engineer, Vitruvius, late in the first century B.C. described an improved form (which *may* have been invented by him or some other Roman engineer) in which the wheel is vertical and the power is transmitted to the grindstone by gearing, as in Figure 8—the form, in fact, that is familiar today. Note that the gearing is simply that of the ox-powered water-raising wheel, used in reverse.

The Role of the Romans

This invention came at the time when the Romans were acquiring their domination over the whole western and near-eastern world. The Roman economy, more even than the Greek, was based on slave labour. While the Empire expanded, the supply of captured slaves was apparently inexhaustible. Slavery was a more convenient way than machinery of dealing with heavy power problems. The wealthy Roman invested his capital in slaves, not machines. Furthermore, slavery together with other faults in the economy led to large-scale unemployment, and labour-saving machinery came to be frowned on as tending to

[8] Translated by Sir W. Marris in *The Oxford Book of Greek Verse in Translation.*

aggravate this problem. Thus during the period of Roman expansion there was little development of the use of the water-mill. Even the driving of querns by animal power considerably decreased, slaves doing the work instead. (This is probably connected with the inefficiency of the ancient harness, referred to in Chapter 2. So little of the potential power of the animal was actually effective that it was but a poor competitor of the slave.) Thus slavery, as always in the ancient economy, prevented the full application of non-human power.

The other contradictions and antagonisms that had retarded technical progress at various times in the Greek world applied with redoubled force to the Roman Empire. Slavery depressed the conditions of the free craftsmen. Manual and mechanical matters were despised by the educated as fit only for slaves. Apparently the Greeks had carried technology about as far as could be done in an economy based on slave labour. The Romans, living with the same basic social organisation, could do no more therefore than exploit, sometimes in new contexts and on a larger scale, the techniques they had learnt from the Greeks. For example, to drain their mines in Spain and Portugal they used large and elaborate machinery based on the water-raising wheel (page 36) and the screw of Archimedes (page 34), but drove them by slaves in treadmills instead of by animal or water power.

As individuals the Romans did not lack inventiveness. Several attempts were made, for example, to improve the inefficient horse-harness, but none was pushed to completion or generally adopted.[9] It was not lack of ability, but frustration arising from social conditions, that held back progress. Perhaps the only important invention that the Romans gave the world was that of concrete—and its applications in building and in military and civil engineering. But the role of the Empire in spreading knowledge of existing techniques was very important for the future of Europe.

When Roman power began to decline, when successful armies no longer brought in victims as slaves, a serious labour shortage

[9] Presumably in the earlier periods of stagnation there were also inventive individuals whose work was not followed up. But the literary and archaeological record before Roman times is too scanty to tell us about them.

began to appear. This led an unknown author about A.D. 370 to propose various labour-saving devices, including a warship to be driven by paddle-wheels powered by oxen (on the same lines as the water-raising wheel). These ideas did not get beyond the manuscript, but at least some notable development began to take place in power machinery. The fourth and fifth centuries saw a considerable spread of water-mills in various parts of the Empire. In the mid-fourth century they appear near Rome and before the end of the century in Rome itself. Thus, haltingly, began the trend, not to be fully expressed till the Middle Ages brought new social conditions, towards the widespread use of water-power to lighten toil. But in Roman times it was applied only to corn-milling.[10] It was to be the role of the Middle Ages to generalise the use of the water-wheel and apply it to a whole series of new tasks.

[10] There is a reference in a fourth century poem to a water-driven saw-mill for cutting marble. But there is reason to think that this may be a later insertion. It is difficult to believe that any inventor could achieve success in the difficult technique of marble cutting as the first application of the water-wheel beyond corn-milling.

CHAPTER 4

THE MIDDLE AGES
(500 TO 1450)

THE decay and final collapse of the Roman Empire meant that for a time some of the higher peaks of civilisation were lost. Art, literature and the more formal and theoretical aspects of science were forgotten (except in small areas where they were preserved in a petrified condition until a later age found a use for them). Many historians of culture have been concerned only or mainly with these particular aspects of civilisation and have therefore seen the Middle Ages as the 'Dark Ages' in which 'civilisation' had perished, in which little progress was made till, in a rather magical 'Renaissance', men rediscovered the arts and sciences of Greece and Rome and thereupon began a return to 'civilisation'.

Progress Renewed

But is must be remembered that art, literature and theoretical science in the ancient world were the prerogative of a few rich and leisured men. They were not true indexes of the level of civilisation. If we look beyond them to consider the way in which mankind in general lived, we find a different picture of the Middle Ages as an era of renewed advance after the long period of comparative stagnation. The level of civilisation is to be measured, not only by its peaks of intellectual culture, but also by the standard of living of its *whole people*. And the latter in turn depends on improvements in the means by which men wrest their living from nature—on technical invention and its application. We have seen how the progress of technology came virtually to a standstill about 2500 B.C. It was renewed in the Iron Age, but even the material discussed in the previous chapter does not represent a very high rate of progress, when it is spread over more than a millenium and a half. And we have seen how the classical world failed to make adequate use of the more advanced techniques which it had at its disposal—particularly of labour-saving machinery like the water-wheel. The Middle Ages began by applying widely those techniques which had previously been restricted by the availability of slave labour and, after a few centuries, went on to produce a series of inventions which laid the foundations of the modern world. As a result, the standard of living of the ordinary man rose very notably, and it has been said that the serf of the tenth century (when the renewed advance had hardly started) was already better off than the proletarian of Rome's most prosperous days.

The reasons for this renewal of technical progress are not yet fully understood. They must be sought partly in the social changes within the Roman world brought about by the decline of Roman power, and partly in the blood-transfusion of the barbarian penetration, and eventual overthrow, of the Empire.

Outside the Empire, free from the inhibitions described in the previous chapter, barbarian tribes had been inventing and developing new techniques—just like those other barbarians on the fringe of civilisation who long before had developed the use of iron. They invented the scythe, which the Romans adopted from them, and a very much improved plough, which the Romans knew of, but made little use of. Even barbarians living under Roman domination continued to show progressive tendencies. For example, the inhabitants of Gaul developed a very crude ox-driven reaping machine in the first century A.D., and invented the hinged flail for threshing, probably in the fourth century.[1] And the invading barbarians who eventually overran the Empire brought with them a more equalitarian society that had certainly moved a long way from primitive communism (page 12), but one that nevertheless was far from having developed the severe and rigid class divisions of the Roman state.

At the same time Roman society was itself gradually changing, and in particular slavery—whose adverse effects we have had so often to notice—was on the decline. Slavery did not suddenly

[1] Hitherto threshing had been done by driving cattle over the stalks, dragging over them sledges fitted with stones in the bottom or beating them with straight sticks.

and abruptly disappear; it progressively diminished in scale throughout the last few centuries of the Roman Empire and the first few of the Middle Ages. In fact the slave supply could only be maintained while Rome was a strong and expanding military power. As her power declined, the supply dwindled and that, until a new basis of production was found, could only mean a return to a more primitive life.

Later Roman society tended to return to a form of organisation that had commonly existed before the great slave states emerged—a system of local self-sufficient units, based on their own agricultural production, doing their own simple manufactures on the spot with little trade except in a few essentials like iron and salt. And from the blend of this with the more nearly classless society of the barbarian invaders, there emerged the manorial system of the Middle Ages—a system which greatly reduced the severity of class divisions. Instead of ranging from a 'divine' Emperor to a 'sub-human' slave, the strata ranged only from a serf who, while bound to the soil he worked, had very definite rights to a certain proportion of the products of his own labour, to a lord of the manor who was sufficiently closely in touch with his serfs to have some real knowledge of the processes of production.

In these conditions manual labour climbed to a new level of dignity and respect. And the new humanitarian ethic of Christianity (which itself began as a revolt against the inhumanity of Roman rule) helped this trend, which was expressed very clearly in those monastic orders where monks undertook manual labour as well as scholarship and so created the first *continuous* tradition of literate and educated men interesting themselves in technological matters. Outside the monasteries, the craftsman was at first only a specialised serf, but that is one step better than a specialised slave. And later, when towns won their independence from the lords, and guilds developed into strong organisations for protecting the conditions of craft workers, the master craftsman became quite an important element in society. In these conditions the ingenious artisan had both the opportunity to invent and improve, and the incentive of knowing that he—and not just his masters—could benefit from his exertions. Such changes encouraged inventiveness.

Gathering Inventions from the Whole World.

In some ways the most interesting novelty of medieval society was its ability to adopt and develop technologies that had been invented elsewhere. Most previous peoples had strongly tended to resist the introduction of ideas from outside—Egyptian technology stayed at a Bronze Age level till that country was conquered by the Greeks (and see another similar example on page 23). The Romans, as we have just noted, failed to make use of techniques invented on the fringes of, or even within, their Empire. But the European Middle Ages collected innovations from all over the world, especially from China, and built them into a new unity which formed the basis of our modern civilisation.

Throughout most of the period covered by this chapter, Western Europe was *not* the most advanced part of the world—far from it. Byzantium preserved more of the refinements of ancient civilisation, which were only re-absorbed by the West in the later Middle Ages. Islam, from its rise to power in the seventh and eighth centuries, was for several hundred years in advance of the West. And almost to the end of this period the most progressive country, technologically, was China.[2] Yet all these regions eventually declined, and it was medieval Europe, collecting ideas and inventions from all the others, adding some of its own, developing them all and welding them together into an entirely new machine-based civilisation, which ushered in the modern world. This willingness—even eagerness—to learn from others may be a result of the continuous shake-up of European society by wave upon wave of barbarian invasion from the third to the tenth centuries: Europeans were forced to develop the habit of changing their ways.

[2] Because the aim of this book is largely to help towards an understanding of the development of European civilisation, which eventually became world civilisation, it cannot do justice to these other areas, particularly to China. In any case the study of Chinese technology and its relations to that of Europe is still, despite the herculean efforts of Dr. Joseph Needham, in a very early stage. We know in a great many cases that a certain invention appeared in China well ahead of Europe. We cannot, in most cases, decide whether the Europeans made their invention independently or derived it from China, or—as an intermediate possibility—heard travellers' tales of a Chinese technique and re-invented it for themselves.

The Rational Use of Power

The supply of slaves having failed, the early Middle Ages was faced with a severe shortage of labour. For tasks of heavy labour the answer of antiquity had been simple—many slaves. The Middle Ages had to find another answer and this answer had to be the development and application of sources of power other than human muscles.

First the water-wheel, whose use had been inhibited till late in Roman times by the easy availability of slave labour, was applied on a greatly increased scale. In the sixth and seventh centuries almost every charter mentions a water-mill. In England in 1086 there were 5,624 water-mills south of the Trent and Severn. That is about one to every fifty households, certainly enough to make a profound difference to people's way of living. A new variant, the tide-mill, appeared in the Adriatic in 1044, and between 1066 and 1086 at Dover.

At first the wheel was used (as in Roman times) only to grind corn. But soon it came to be applied to a great diversity of industrial processes, beginning with fulling. This is the process of beating woollen cloth in water to shrink it and so increase its density and durability. Formerly it was carried out with the hands or feet or with clubs, but from the eleventh century (perhaps the later tenth) water-power was applied to the process, using trip-hammers raised by cams on the shaft of a water-wheel (Figure 9). Such fulling mills became common in the thirteenth century. Water-driven forge hammers and forge-bellows working on the same principle were developed in the eleventh and twelfth centuries,[3] pulping mills for paper-making in the thirteenth and stamping mills for crushing ore by the fourteenth. Water power was also applied, through this or other mechanisms, to the crushing of woad, tan-bark and other materials from the eleventh century onwards. Towards the end of the eleventh century it came to be used for water-lifting and irrigation, in the thirteenth century for saw-mills and grinding cutlery, in the fourteenth for wire-drawing (Plate IV), grinding pigments and driving lathes. In three

[3] Both these applications of water-power had been anticipated in China early in the first century, very shortly after the arrival of the water-wheel there. But there is no evidence on what relation (if any) the European development bears to the Chinese.

Fig. 9. An advanced form of the water-driven fulling mill, from the sixteenth century.

or four hundred years the water-wheel had developed from a specialised device for milling corn into a generalised prime mover useful in many branches of industry and ready to relieve human effort wherever the need and opportunity arose.

In the late twelfth century the appearance of windmills made another source of power available to Europe. There had been windmills in Islam since the seventh century, but these were of a quite different type, consisting of a set of vertical sails fixed round the rim of a horizontal wheel on a vertical axle, which drove the stone directly. The European version, on the other hand, was similar to that of today, with its sails fanning out from a horizontal axle, from which the drive was transmitted through a pair of gears. It was essentially the Vitruvian water-mill (Figure 8) turned upside down and with the sails substituted for the water-wheel. Thus it is very unlikely that this was a mere copy of the Eastern mill. But it may well have been the response of men already familiar with water-wheels to the news (perhaps brought home by Crusaders) that the Saracens were harnessing the power of the wind.

The European windmill is first mentioned in a document of about 1180 from Normandy. Before the end of the century it had been recorded in places ranging from Yorkshire to the Levant. The windmill was not so easily adaptable as the water-wheel to purposes other than corn-milling, but from about 1400 onwards its application to water-lifting became the key to the drainage of the Netherlands, and it was from time to time applied to drive many sorts of machinery—a Bohemian mine hoist of the fifteenth century, for example.

The earliest European windmills were of the post-mill type, in which the whole mechanism revolved to face the wind (Plate VI). This severely restricted the size of the mill. The tower or turret windmill (Plate VII) has the machinery housed in a fixed tower, with a rotating turret at the top to carry the sails and the transmission gearing. It can give two or three times as much power. It seems to have first appeared in the later fourteenth century,[4] but was not widely used till the sixteenth, when its potentialities were fully developed by the engineers of the

[4] One document might possibly be interpreted to push this date back to 1295.

Netherlands, who by that time were using windmills for many industrial purposes.

The Harness

Besides wind and water, the only other source of power available before the steam-engine was that of animals. It will be recalled that the harness at the stage it had reached before 3000 B.C. was adequate for oxen, but such as to waste most of the power of a horse or ass (Figure 2). The history of the development of the modern harness is very obscure. In China an important improvement appeared by the second century B.C. at the latest—the 'breast-strap' or 'postillion' harness. In this the band hangs lower on the horse's breast, and about its middle is attached a horizontal strap that transmits the pull—thus relieving the pressure on the animal's throat which had made the ancient harness so ineffective. Shafts were also used instead of the yoke and pole of Figure 2. A few attempts along similar lines had been made in the Roman Empire, but the improvement was not generally adopted there. Finally, this method of harnessing appeared in Europe by the ninth century and soon became firmly established. These facts (and a few other details about its occurrence in other places) suggest that the breast-strap improvement may have been made quite early by the peoples of the Central Asian steppes; that it diffused thence to China, where it was fully adopted, and to Rome, where it was tried but discarded by the technologically less flexible society; and that it reached Europe again by a quite separate transmission in the Middle Ages.

The fully modern harness, based on the padded collar, traces and shafts, may have a similar history of diffusion from a Central Asian source, for it appeared in China between the third and seventh centuries A.D., while in Europe there are suggestions of it from the ninth century on and it is fully developed and widely used by the twelfth century. The harnessing of several horses in file had also been tried occasionally in Roman times, but did not become common till the Middle Ages. Horse-shoes, which may again be the invention of steppe nomads,[5] appeared

[5] The ancients, down to Roman times, sometimes fixed temporary shoes to horses' feet for work on hard or slippery ground or to protect injured hooves. But they did not know the nailed horse-shoe.

in Europe in the ninth century and were widely used by the twelfth.

In this way it at last became possible to make full use of the tractive power of animals. As a result the cost of overland transport was reduced by a factor of about three between Roman times and the thirteenth century. And much more than transport was involved. The horse and ass, more efficient than the ox, could now be used in agriculture. Alfred the Great mentions horses ploughing in Norway in the later ninth century, and the Bayeux Tapestry (about 1080) shows both horse and ass at work in the fields. Animal power was also used widely for driving machinery, on lines which had been opened by inventions of Greek and Roman times, but little developed because of the inefficient harness and the availability of slave labour.

These three sources of power, at last rationally used, made a tremendous difference to the world. Before their arrival a high level of civilisation could only be provided for a few, on the basis of huge numbers of slaves, used not as workers, but as sources of power, as engines. But a horse driving a machine with the now efficient harness was the equivalent of ten slaves, while a good water-wheel or windmill gave the work of up to 100 slaves. Athens had had about one slave to every two freemen. England's cornmills alone in 1086 already represented one slave to every four or five of the population and that was before the use of water-power had been anything like fully developed. These new sources of power, therefore, provided the basis for the development of a high level of civilisation without slavery, and as they were developed slavery died out.

Other Advances in Transport

The devising of an efficient harness was by no means the only major improvement in transport machinery in medieval times. From the fourth millennium B.C. to the later Middle Ages the steering mechanism of ships had remained basically unchanged. It was, in fact, little more than an oar, such as was used in propulsion, somewhat specialised for steering (Plate I). In the larger ships it was lashed to the stern and fitted with a lever, not unlike a tiller, to give more purchase. All this was little more than an extension of the method of steering a canoe by a paddle held by a man sitting in the stern. It was not an effective method. Little purchase could be brought to bear on it and it was too easily deflected by the battering of the waves. For the small coasting ships of 3000 B.C. these disadvantages mattered little, but as ships grew in size the inadequacy of the steering mechanism became more and more serious and in fact limited the size to which ships could be built. Attempts were made to overcome the difficulty by fitting several steering oars, but these were never really effective. Also, with such a poor steering mechanism ships could not sail close against the wind and were always at the mercy of a lee shore. With sailing so inefficient, galley slaves had to be used for many purposes, and so the poor steering mechanism was another factor in maintaining slavery.[6] In eighth-century China and thirteenth-century Europe[7] there appeared the modern type of rudder, hinged firmly to the sternpost, itself an extension of the keel and therefore an integral part of the ship. It was well under water, free from the effects of waves, and so its size could be greatly increased, permitting a corresponding increase in the size of ships and also allowing them to sail closer to the wind. The greater control which it gave permitted rapid improvements in rigging (which had been slowly developing since the fall of Rome), culminating in the full-rigged ship of the fifteenth century. Between the thirteenth and fifteenth centuries shipping made more progress than in the previous four millennia. From the first sailing ships to the end of the ancient world navigation merely developed from sailing on rivers to crossing the Mediterranean and coasting round continents (with the one very special exception of crossing the Indian Ocean by running before the reliable monsoon winds). But in 1492, only two or three centuries after the European appearance of the modern rudder, the Atlantic was crossed.

The compass, that other great medieval contribution to navigation, is again first found in China. Knowledge of the properties of magnetic needles had been growing gradually there since the first century B.C., being 'applied' in geomancy and the like. The

[6] Galley slaves remained in war vessels till the development of artillery revolutionised naval tactics in the sixteenth century. While ramming and boarding were the chief methods of attack manœuvrability made the galley superior, but crowded with oarsmen it could not carry enough guns.

[7] Perhaps rather earlier in Byzantium.

compass was used for navigation in China in the eleventh, or at the latest the early twelfth century. The European compass, which appeared late in the twelfth century, is so different in design that it can hardly have been copied direct from China, but it may well have been inspired by news (coming, perhaps, through Islam) of what the Chinese had done.

The canal lock and its gates meant a great improvement in inland transport. Starting from single gates to allow boats to be dragged through sluices, the true pound lock with a gate at each end was developed, apparently independently, in the fourteenth-century Netherlands and fifteenth-century Italy. In China, single gates were used before the Christian era, and locks with two gates appeared in the ninth or tenth century. But the Chinese made singularly little use of this device, and the European invention arises so obviously from local problems that it was probably an independent development. A minor, yet significant, invention affecting local transport 'on the job' was the wheelbarrow, which appeared in China early in our era and in Europe by the thirteenth century at the latest.

Naturally these tremendous changes in transportation had very great social effects. One of them, not obvious at first sight, was to make possible the wider application of water, wind, and animal power that we discussed above. For power-driven machinery can only be used if there is sufficient work to do to make it economical; and that usually implies bringing the work over considerable distances to the machine. The improved transport facilities of the Middle Ages made it possible to carry the corn to a central water-mill or the tree trunks to a central saw-mill. With its inferior transport the ancient world had to be content with more localised industry on too small a scale to use much power-driven machinery. Thus the development of power machinery, the improvement of transport and (as we have seen) the abolition of slavery were all closely interlinked.

Again the new transport facilities paved the way for what is often called 'the commercial revolution', the era of great commercial expansion which began in the later Middle Ages. Within a few centuries the countries of Europe were no longer self-sufficient, but imported raw materials and products (luxuries at first, later necessities) from all over the world. And this was an important factor in the growth of industry and with it of more and more powerful machinery that we shall describe in later chapters. Furthermore, water, wind and animal power remained the basis of all heavy mechanical developments till the eighteenth century, and transport till then was entirely based on the horse with its improved harness and on the improved sailing ship. So the medieval inventions that we have been discussing gave the real start to our modern mechanised world.

Agriculture and Textiles

Changes in the plough contributed to a revolution in agriculture, which greatly increased food supplies. The version developed in pre-historic times (page 9) was a swing plough; that is, it had no wheels, but was held at the correct height and angle by the ploughman. It ploughed an irregular furrow and the ploughman had to use an excessive amount of energy even to do this. It was ineffectively designed, so that it merely scratched the ground, instead of cutting the sod and turning it over, as does a modern plough. This inefficient form, improved only by the addition of an iron ploughshare, remained in use in the Mediterranean countries till the Middle Ages. It was not hopelessly inadequate for light soils, but for the heavy soils in much of northern and western Europe it was useless.

Before 100 B.C. (perhaps as early as 400) barbarians living somewhere between Denmark and Bavaria invented a much more adequate heavy plough, which turned the sod over instead of merely scratching the surface. This new type of plough began to spread widely in Europe from the sixth century. In its fully developed form it had a coulter to make a vertical cut, a ploughshare to cut under the sod, a mouldboard to turn it over, and wheels which enabled a more even furrow to be ploughed and lightened the work of the ploughman by relieving him of the task of keeping the plough at the proper level. It is not clear when these various devices were added. Wheels were known in Roman times, but not widely adopted till the eleventh century; and the mouldboard may not have been developed till that time. Successive refinements brought the plough to an essentially modern form by the thirteenth century. Apart from turning over the soil more efficiently, this plough could be used to create a 'ridge and furrow' effect, which improved drainage and so allowed the working of the rich soils in 'bottom lands'.

Clothing is second only to food as a necessity of life; so it is natural that in this era of progress textile machinery should also undergo fundamental change. To the end of classical times, the loom had remained a light structure of a few rods bound or pegged together or pushed into the earth, and with a minimum of mechanical aids for the weaver. The Middle Ages developed it into a strong box-like frame with roller devices that allowed long pieces of cloth to be woven continuously, a suspended reed to ensure close and regular beating of the cloth, a shedding mechanism worked by treadles, and many other devices. This was a complex machine, beside which the ancient loom looks rather like a toy for children to play weaving with. In Europe it appears as a near perfect instrument in the thirteenth century, but it may well have been derived from developments taking place in the Near East since early in the Christian era.

Medieval Europe also received from China an important new kind of loom, the draw-loom, which allowed the weaving of complex patterns through an arrangement for selecting the set of warp threads to be raised or lowered at each passage of the shuttle. This type of loom was used in China by the second century B.C., reached the Near East by the third century A.D., and in the Middle Ages spread to Europe.

The spindle at the beginning of the Middle Ages had not advanced beyond that of the earliest spinners. Now basic changes took place, leading to the invention of the spinning machine. The technically simpler processes of doubling and reeling silk were mechanised at Bologna in 1272 (perhaps on the basis of Chinese machines of the late eleventh century), and fourteenth-century water-driven versions of this machinery were so efficient that two or three operators could do work previously requiring several hundred. It was the fact that silk starts as a continuous filament that made possible this rapid development to factory-scale production. Linen, cotton and wool, which have to be spun in the true sense to join short fibres into a continuous thread, could not progress so fast. But parallel developments transformed the simple spindle into the spinning wheel which was to be found in every cottage until a couple of centuries ago and which still figures largely in our museums. In this a large wheel is turned by hand (and later by treadle, see page 60) and a band from this to a small wheel attached to the spindle causes the latter to rotate quickly (Figure 10). At first the wheel was apparently used merely for the process of quilling, that is winding on to a bobbin or quill a thread that had already been spun on a primitive spindle. But by 1280 at the latest the wheel was used for the spinning itself and in the fourteenth century such spinning

Fig. 10. A fourteenth-century quilling wheel. The thread is being wound on to the bobbin from a primitive spindle hanging from the spinster's left hand. By that date, this type of wheel was also in use for spinning, but the quilling and spinning had to be done alternately.

wheels spread widely. We have already mentioned another important advance in textiles—the application of water-power to fulling.

The Mechanical Clock

The most complex machines produced by the Middle Ages were mechanical clocks. Water-clocks, measuring time by the amount of water dripping out of a vessel through a small hole, had been in use from the Bronze Age. They were improved in Greek times by the addition of various regulating devices and mechanical connections to show the time by means of a pointer on a scale. And, possibly in Greek or Roman times, certainly among the Arabs from the sixth century on, there were added elaborate devices to work puppet shows at each hour. But the water-clock was never a reliable time-keeper.

The mechanical clock, driven by a falling weight, depends for its time-keeping on an escapement—a mechanism which regularly interrupts the motion of the clockwork. The origins of this device are even more obscure than those of most medieval inventions. The Chinese from early in our era had clocks (or astronomical working models) in which the drive was provided by a water-wheel mechanism. One of these, which was built between 1088 and 1092, involved a sort of escapement device which checked the motion of the wheel until each successive scoop in its turn was full, and then allowed it to move one step forward; and there is fairly good evidence that arrangements of this type date back to the year 725. But this was not a true escapement, since the motion was governed mainly by the flow of water. It was very different from the foliot balance and verge escapement that controlled the European clocks of the fourteenth century (Plate V). And, though the possibility cannot be firmly excluded, there is no evidence that the Chinese development influenced the European.

In Europe, Villard de Honnecourt described about 1250 a crude escapement device used to keep a model angel always pointing towards the Sun, but this again bears little resemblance to the verge escapement. There may have been mechanical clocks in the thirteenth century, but the use of a single word for both kinds prevents us from making a clear distinction between mechanical and water-driven clocks. And the earliest certain date that can be given for the appearance of mechanical clocks, with verge escapements, is a few years before or after 1340. From then on they quickly became common, and were soon a matter for civic pride. Spring-driven clocks had arrived by 1450, and before the end of the century portable versions—rather too large to be classed as watches today—were in use.

Clock-making, even though the early clocks were large and crude, demanded a much higher standard of accurate workmanship than any previous machine. And it has been said that modern engineering is the child of a marriage between the clock-maker's skill in fine workmanship and the techniques of heavy engineering that were used by the millwrights and builders of other power-driven machinery.

Paper and Printing

One of the latest and most revolutionary developments of medieval times was that of printing. China had printing several centuries before Europe, but it is not clear how much the Europeans learned from that country and how much they developed printing independently. Europe certainly owes to China one of the fundamental materials for printing—namely paper, the only material with suitable properties that could be produced cheaply enough. It appeared in China about A.D. 100, and until the end of the seventh century it was confined to the Chinese Empire. Thereafter it appeared in Samarkand, on the route from China to the then flourishing empire of the Arabs, in 751. We can next trace its spread through the countries dominated by Islam, through Baghdad (793), Egypt (900), Morocco (1100), till about 1150 it reached Spain, the main point of contact of the Arab and European civilisations. Thence it spread to Southern France by 1189, Italy in the thirteenth century, Germany in the fourteenth and so on.

Three main stages may be distinguished in the invention of printing. First came printing from wooden blocks, so that a separate block had to be cut for every page. The next stage was printing from movable characters (of wood or other material), so that by having several hundred copies of each character the printer could combine them in a frame to set up the type for each page in turn; but each of the several hundred copies of each character had to be cut separately. Finally came the use of movable metal type, all copies of each character being mass-produced by casting from a single mould.

In China wood-block printing appeared in the sixth century. Movable earthenware type was used about 1045, and movable wooden characters about 1314. Finally, cast metal type appeared in Korea in 1392 and a book was printed by this technique in 1409. But the enormous number of different characters required for the Chinese script prevented any widespread use of cast type. Printing reached Persia in 1294, but does not seem to have spread further for another century.

The techniques used in Europe were distinctly different from those of China. Hence, despite a considerable time-lag, it seems fairly certain that the invention was not simply imported to

Europe from China. But it is rather likely that, with more frequent trading contacts between the two civilisations, news of Chinese printing reached Europe and stimulated some individuals to see if they could produce a similar process.

Block-printing for paper currency, playing cards and religious pictures appeared in Europe in the late fourteenth century and became fairly common in the early fifteenth (and this must surely be connected with reports—or even samples—of similar applications in China and Mongolia, reaching Europe through commercial contacts). Block-printed books perhaps appeared about 1450. The transition to movable metal type seems to have followed quickly (the intermediate stage being omitted in Europe). There are traces of experiments in Avignon in 1444 and in Haarlem perhaps rather earlier. But the credit for solving the many technical problems involved in making a success of the process is usually (though not unanimously) given to Gutenberg in Mainz, who may have been working on the idea from 1436 on, and whose first printed books were produced within a year or two on either side of 1450. By 1500 printing was established in twelve European countries and about 40,000 editions of books had been published (Plate VIII).

Printing has had as profound effects on human life as the inventions in power machinery and transport that we discussed above. The reader can think out those effects for himself by pausing to consider the role of printing in the modern world or its influence on the history by which the modern world developed from that of the fifteenth century. But let us note here that it played an important part in breaking down one of the major contradictions that had hitherto prevented the best application of human ingenuity to technical invention—the separation between the practical craftsman and the man with education. We have seen how changes in social structure reduced this separation by lessening class distinction and making practical affairs more important and more 'respectable'. Printing also helped by bringing books, which had hitherto been valuable treasures because of the costly process of hand copying, within the range of wider classes of people. Within a century or two the ambitious craftsman had the means to study in books the accumulated experience of others and to apply it to his own problems. This was a revolution comparable to that brought about by the introduction of iron. Iron democratised physical tools; printing did the same for the tools of thought. This was an important factor in the increasing rate of invention that came in the following centuries.

Crank and Treadle

The machinery we have been describing is very much more complicated than that of the ancient world. It depended on a growing understanding of the ways of interconnecting mechanical elements so that one type of motion produces another. Particularly important in this respect are methods of converting rotary into reciprocating motion and vice versa. For the former conversion, the chief device is the cam, which had been known to Greek engineers like Hero, but used in Antiquity only for what we have called 'mechanical conjuring tricks' (page 35). It was left to the Middle Ages to put this device to useful work, in machines like those mentioned on page 46.

The main mechanism for the reverse transformation of reciprocating motion into rotation is the crank, which appears to have been totally unknown to the Ancients. Even the idea, which seems so simple to us, of driving a rotary quern by hand-cranking a vertical handle inserted near the edge of the upper stone is one that does not seem to have occurred to them. Their large querns were driven by slaves or animals walking round; their smaller ones by means of handles projecting sideways (so that a to-and-fro partial rotation was probably used). The vertical handle allowing continuous rotation by crank motion did not appear till the Middle Ages.[8] Perhaps it was one of those inventions brought in by the barbarians. Even then the idea seems to have been a difficult one to grasp and generalise, for no further application of the crank is known till about 850, when it was used to work grindstones. Its next application was to the hurdy-gurdy, possibly in the tenth century, certainly by the twelfth. It was used to wind up the springs of crossbows in the fourteenth or early fifteenth century. By then other applications were becoming common, for example a cranked reel for winding skeins of yarn and—extremely important despite its apparent simplicity—the carpenter's brace. In all the uses so far mentioned the crank is driven directly by

[8] Or just possibly very late Roman times.

hand. But about 1430 we find the first known case of a crank and connecting rod,[9] used to drive a flour mill.

The treadle, meanwhile, had been undergoing its independent evolution—in looms (page 54), for driving lathes (by a mechanism that will shortly be described) and in the 'oliver' or treadle-operated hammer of the smithy, which appeared in the fourteenth century. And now (about 1430) treadle, connecting rod and crank were combined to give the form of drive which is familiar to those of us whose sewing machines have not yet been electrified. The first application was again to flour-milling. Here at last had appeared one of the really vital mechanisms of modern machinery. But even now it was slow to be adopted—perhaps because of mechanical difficulties of making good bearings. It was applied to grindstones by 1480, but not to the spinning wheel or lathe till well into the sixteenth century.

The Lathe

The primary kit of carpenter's tools with which these many new machines were produced was, on the whole, not greatly advanced since ancient times, but some significant advances were made. The brace and bit replaced the bow-drill which had been in use since the mesolithic period. And the lathe was completely transformed.

The ancient lathe (so far as we know it) was a flimsy affair, consisting of a few rods lightly joined together and pegged to the ground. The drive was applied by a cord wrapped round the work and pulled back and forth by an assistant. The tool was held in the hand without guidance or support. The Middle Ages transformed the lathe bed and stocks into rigid and substantial structures. From about 1250 at the latest, the cord driving the work was attached to a treadle below and a flexible pole acting as a spring above, so that the turner could himself drive it by foot and still have both hands free for manipulating his tools. Water-power was also applied to driving lathes from the middle of the fourteenth century on. And the drive by means of cranked

[9] A few quite complicated applications of crank and connecting rod, or their equivalent, had been made in China in the first few centuries A.D., but the idea was not developed further there. And there is no evidence of whether Europe derived this device from China or not.

wheel and cord appeared, perhaps in 1411, certainly later in the century. First steps towards the slide-rest were made about 1480.

Changes in Metallurgy—Cast Iron

Though the machines we have mentioned were constructed largely of wood, they did require metals for certain bearing parts and cutting edges. A much greater demand for metals came from medieval warfare, with its complex armour and its crude cannon added to earlier types of armaments. Thus in metal working we find the beginnings of methods that in the next century or two were to revolutionise the industry. For example, the draw-plate for making iron wire (which had previously been forged) was invented in the tenth century, and water-power was applied to the process by 1351 (Plate IV). We have seen (page 46) that several other iron-working processes also became water-powered. It was, in fact, the application of water-power to produce blast that made possible in the late Middle Ages the production of *cast* iron. Previously the furnace was not hot enough to melt the metal, so that only wrought iron (with or without a steel surface) could be produced (page 25). As medieval furnaces grew in size, the more powerful blast enabled molten metal to be obtained—at first by accident, later intentionally and in controlled conditions.

Cast iron first appeared in the thirteenth century, but technical problems, only slowly overcome, delayed its general use till the fifteenth.[10] The technique of casting in sand probably developed in the fourteenth or fifteenth century. Cast iron has a different composition and therefore different properties from wrought iron (in particular it is more brittle) and therefore could not be used in all the places where wrought iron had previously prevailed. Nevertheless by producing cheaper iron, eminently suitable for some purposes, it contributed greatly to the industrial changes of the succeeding centuries. Indeed, with the appearance of cast iron man now had all the basic materials that were to serve till the middle of the nineteenth century.

[10] As so often, China has precedence over Europe in the matter of iron-casting, which was used there from the fourth century B.C. onwards. But the technique used—one of re-melting wrought iron in crucibles in the presence of carbon—is so different that it can hardly have contributed in any way to the western development (which in any case arose from mere increase in the scale of furnaces and the efficiency of the blast).

Looking Towards the Future

Thus the Middle Ages changed the face of industry. The Power Age had begun and, though it was still a long road to the general application of power that we know today, yet already water, wind and animal power were doing many things for which previously only human muscles were available. Machines entered into many phases of life. They had become familiar objects. What is more, they had been successful—obviously so—in solving many problems of living. Men began to have a new faith. The spirit of the times was expressed, as early as the mid-thirteenth century, by the English monk and scientist, Roger Bacon:

'I will tell first, therefore, of the wonderful works of Art and Nature, in order to assign to them afterwards their causes and means; in these there is nothing of a magical nature. Hence it may be seen that all magic power is inferior to these achievements and unworthy of them. . . . For first machines of navigation can be constructed, without rowers, as great ships for river or ocean, which are borne under the guidance of one man at a greater speed than if they were full of men. Also a chariot can be constructed that will move with incalculable speed without any draught animal. . . . Also flying machines may be constructed so that a man may sit in the midst of the machine turning a certain instrument, by means of which wings artificially constructed would beat the air after the manner of a bird flying. Also a machine of small size may be made for raising and lowering weights of almost infinite amount—a machine of the utmost utility. . . . Machines may also be made for going in sea or river down to the bed without bodily danger. . . . And there are countless other things that can be constructed, such as bridges over rivers without pillars or any such supports. . . .'

The possibilities Bacon speaks of were not to be realized for many centuries,[11] yet these were well-founded speculations—founded on the observation that machines had in fact succeeded in giving men many of their desires, where hopes misplaced in magic had been dashed. They epitomised the new faith, by which man was in the next seven centuries to make more progress to-

[11] Some of them were not so very distant. A successful submarine was built in 1624, though of course it was not till modern times that submarines could be anything other than curiosities.

wards a fuller life than in the whole of his previous history. While Bacon wrote of great things far ahead, other men were tackling the practical immediate problems in terms of the new faith—a faith based on experience—that these problems *could* be solved by mechanical inventions.[12]

[12] Magical beliefs, of course, lingered for centuries, but we are concerned here to emphasise the new positive and progressive trend.

CHAPTER 5

TOWARDS THE MODERN WORLD (1450 TO 1660)

THE outlook expressed by Roger Bacon found yet fuller manifestation in the period we are now to deal with. In these years the use of machines already known was greatly extended and many new types of machinery were invented. But more significantly it was a period of first attempts on many mechanical problems, some of which were not to be successfully solved for centuries. From the conscious strivings of this period, unsuccessful though they were at the time, arose many of the successes of later years. Thus, as we shall see below, it was in these two centuries that men began to appreciate the enormous potential power of steam and to seek for some way of harnessing it for driving machinery; they did not succeed, but building on their experience, others at last produced practical steam-engines. And if the reader will watch carefully in subsequent chapters, he will see that many machines which reached success only in the nineteenth century were first attempted in the period we are now discussing.

The striving to improve old machines and invent new ones became far more conscious than ever before. Men who were interested in scientific and technical progress began to form societies, the first being the *Academia Secretorum Naturæ* (Academy of the Secrets of Nature) founded at Naples in 1560. These societies had, of course, many interests besides machinery, but they did devote a good deal of attention to gathering and systematising knowledge about machines, promoting their wider use and encouraging invention. This period also saw the publication of the first treatises on machinery and applied mechanics, like Agricola's work on mining and metallurgy in all its aspects, *De Re Metallica* (1556), from which several of the illustrations for this chapter are taken, or the treatises of Ramelli (1588) or Zonca

(1607). And in the latter part of the period began the development of scientific theories of mechanics, providing a general basis for the solution of the various problems concerned with machinery.

All this took place against the background of that vast expansion of trading which is called the Commercial Revolution. With growing transport and commerce, the tendency of each locality to produce its own essential requirements progressively disappeared. It became possible for a district to specialise in the production of commodities for which it was naturally best suited, obtaining its other requirements by exchanging its own products for those of other districts or other countries. This allowed the growth of concentrated, comparatively large-scale industry, which in turn permitted mechanisation on an ever greater scale.

Leonardo da Vinci

The outstanding mechanical genius of the times was Leonardo da Vinci (1452–1519). Throughout his life, alongside many other interests, he was continually inventing and improving machinery. He meticulously recorded his ideas, whether complete designs or mere tentative suggestions. He left 5,000 pages of notebooks on various scientific and technical subjects, a very great part of which was devoted to machinery. It is difficult to evaluate his influence on contemporary industrial practice. Some of the machines which we first find sketched in his notebooks may represent contemporary practice which had not previously been recorded. Others he may have introduced into Italian industry by direct contact with the manufacturers concerned. Friends and patrons, or artisans who worked for him, may have spread his ideas. His notebooks were not published till long after his death, but they were read by quite a number of people, who may well have used Leonardo's ideas and introduced them into practice without acknowledging their debt. On the other hand, the fact that an invention is sketched by Leonardo and some time later appears in practice does not prove that the idea was taken from him—for the same industrial problem that led him to work on any particular invention would cause others to do the same, and they might then arrive at the same results independently.

There is, perhaps, only one outstanding invention that we can with reasonable confidence put forward as having been made by Leonardo *and* introduced into practice as a result of his work. Canal lock-gates had previously been of the portcullis type. About 1495 Leonardo drew a sketch for a pair of mitred gates, fitted with small wickets for passing the water to fill or empty the lock—a sketch which might well be taken for a drawing of a modern lock-gate. And in 1497 locks so equipped were built on the Milan canal, of which he was engineer. In many other cases, machines or devices which he drew or described appeared in practice within fifty years of his death. This applies to some of his textile machinery, which will be mentioned below. And, choosing examples more or less at random from a long list, his wheel-lock pistol is paralleled by a wheel-lock musket that appeared in Germany about 1500; his roller bearings (which he described as 'marvels of mechanical genius') turned up in practice in the sixteenth century, though they were not generally used till the nineteenth; his use of the pendulum to drive pumps more evenly is recorded again in the treatises of Ramelli and Besson, which probably owe a lot to Leonardo; and his dredges are mentioned by Besson. On the other hand, many of his inventions did not appear in practice for a very long time. Sometimes this was because his schemes were based on entirely wrong principles—his flying-machine or his power loom, for example. Often it was because, though fundamentally sound, they would have required standards of workmanship or materials that were not available in his time—such are his centrifugal pump, hydraulic press, rifled fire-arms, breech-loading cannon. In these cases it is reasonably safe to assume that the later practical device was created independently of Leonardo.

Even when Leonardo's schemes were for the time being impracticable, they do typify the spirit of invention that permeated the age and was shared by many lesser geniuses. Typical, too—as well as prophetic of the more scientific engineering yet to come—was Leonardo's enthusiasm for studying elementary mechanisms as such, without reference to the particular applications to which they might eventually be put. He sketched many devices for converting rotation into reciprocating motion or the reverse, designed spirally cut gear-wheels and bevel gears, studied link chains, and much else of that sort. In the same way, he was more conscious than any of his predecessors of the distinction between the machine that does the job and the prime mover which powers it—many of his machines are drawn with a driving shaft or wheel to which any prime mover could be attached.

Clocks and Chronometers

As an example of how the striving and experimentation of this age prepared the way for later generations, let us consider a commercial problem that concentrated much attention on clocks. The great expansion of sea-going commerce called for more accurate methods of navigation. When ships sailed the Mediterranean or north-south along the coasts of Europe and Africa, a determination of latitude, supplemented by dead reckoning, would fix the ship's position accurately enough for most purposes. And latitude could easily be found by astronomical methods familiar to the Phoenicians, if not to earlier sailors. But when, in the fifteenth and subsequent centuries, vessels began to cross open oceans east to west, the accurate determination of longitude became very desirable. An error in estimating longitude meant at the least a delay, perhaps shipwreck on an unexpected coast. Now the determination of longitude amounts in essence to the comparison of the time (by the sun) on the ship with the time at some fixed point, such as Greenwich. To find the time on the ship needs only a simple astronomical observation, but to find for comparison the time at Greenwich is much more difficult. Two methods were possible; first, one which required astronomical prediction so accurate that even after centuries of effort it was never fully satisfactory, and which need not concern us here; and second, by carrying an accurate mechanical clock aboard ship.

As early as 1530 the mechanical clock was suggested as a possible method. But many difficulties stood in the way. The existing clocks, based on the foliot balance and verge escapement, did not keep time sufficiently accurately. The first step towards the production of an adequate clock was the introduction of the pendulum as its governing mechanism. In 1581 Galileo (Italy) discovered that a pendulum swinging in small arcs made its oscillations at constant intervals of time, irrespective of the exact length of swing. With the possibility of its navigational use in mind, he designed in 1641 a pendulum clock, and after his death this was partly built in 1649 by his son. Huygens (Holland) spent some twenty years of his life in trying (amidst many other activities) to make the pendulum clock reliable at sea, adding many important new devices to it and building several much improved clocks from 1657 onwards. But these, like the many subsequent attempts that continued till 1726, failed to overcome the difficulty of making the pendulum behave regularly under the irregular motion of the ship.

A more promising method of control was the balance-wheel and hair-spring, invented about 1658 by the Englishman, Hooke, who again had navigational uses in mind. Hooke, Huygens and others strove hard to make adequate marine clocks with his new device, but still success was elusive (though meanwhile the balance spring served usefully in pocket watches). The longitude problem was becoming more and more desperately important. Various governments and individuals offered prizes for its solution, the last and largest being the offer by the British Government in 1714 of from £10,000 to £20,000 according to the accuracy achieved. These prizes greatly encouraged further work. Major improvements were the anchor escapement which Clement introduced about 1670, and its further modification to the dead-beat escapement by Graham in 1715. Among the outstanding problems the chief was that of temperature compensation, to ensure that the clock kept the same time in all seasons and weathers. Not till the middle of the eighteenth century was this solved, independently and within a few years of one another by Harrison (England), Le Roy (France) and Berthoud (Switzerland). Harrison, who had built four increasingly successful chronometers (as these accurate clocks came to be called) by 1759, was awarded the British Government prize, but it is on Le Roy's chronometer of 1766 that actual subsequent developments were based. By 1780–90 stabilised designs had been reached and navigation entered a new era of reliability and safety.

New Advances in Textile Machinery

Let us now return to the period of this chapter and consider the further progress of textile machinery. The spinning wheel, as we left it on page 55, was such that the two processes of spinning and quilling (winding the thread on the bobbin) had to be done alternately. The addition of the flyer (Figure 11), which re-

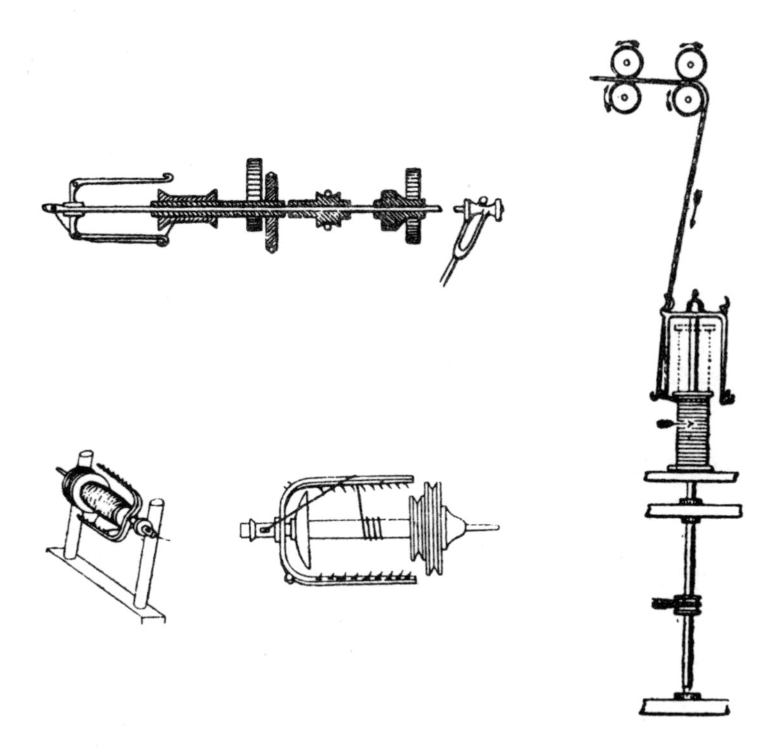

Fig. 11. Various forms of the spindle with flyer, which allowed spinning and quilling to be carried on continuously and simultaneously.
The first form, dating from the fourteenth century, is shown at the bottom, left and centre. There is no 'building' mechanism for winding the thread evenly on the bobbin; instead the spinner had to move the thread at intervals from one to another of the hooks on the flyer. Leonardo's design (top) incorporated an automatic building mechanism, but had no influence on practice. This mechanism was re-invented in the eighteenth century in the systems designed by Wyatt, Paul and Arkwright (right). The picture also shows the mechanism for 'spinning by rollers'—the right-hand rollers rotate faster than those on the left, thus drawing out the bundles of fibres before passing them to the spindle and flyer below.

volved round the spindle at a different speed, enabled the two processes to be done simultaneously. The flyer is first recorded in a picture dating from about 1480, which shows a design so good that the original invention must have been made some years earlier. Leonardo sketched an improved flyer incorporating an automatic 'building' mechanism (see caption to Figure 11), but this did not affect practice and had to be re-invented in the eighteenth century. The use of the flyer allowed the spinster to be seated (contrast the stance shown in Figure 10). And seated spinning made possible the use of a treadle-and-crank drive, which was in use by 1524 and perhaps a few decades earlier.

The ribbon loom is an adaptation of the loom to weave several ribbons simultaneously, a single movement of the weaver causing each operation to be performed on all of them. It is a fairly complex piece of machinery, as a glance at Figure 12 will show, and represents a notable inventive achievement. According to a Venetian writer of 1629 it was invented at Danzig in 1579, but the City Council, fearing unemployment among weavers, suppressed the invention and had the inventor secretly strangled. It appeared again at Leyden in 1621, and by the end of the century was in use in Holland, Germany, Switzerland, England and France.

The knitting machine (Figure 13) was invented in 1589 by the Rev. William Lee, curate of a village near Nottingham. This was a very remarkable achievement, considering the great complexity (compared with, say, weaving) of the operations the machine must perform. Though by no means completely automatic, the knitting machine, even in its earliest form, was considerably more so than any other machine of the times performing an equally complicated job. Together with the ribbon loom, it represents a significant step on the way to the machines which today perform very complex operations with no human interference except in feeding and maintenance.

Considerable progress also took place in the various auxiliary textile machines. Water-driven fulling machines were more widely used. Leonardo sketched power-driven machinery for silk reeling and twisting (perhaps owing something to the machines of 1272 at Bologna, mentioned in the previous chapter), but the machines that appear in actual use in the late sixteenth century are sub-

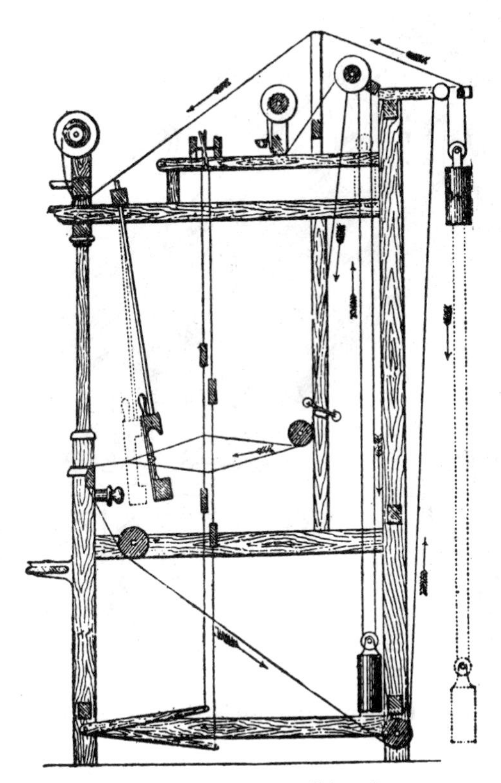

Fig. 12. An early ribbon loom.

stantially different from Leonardo's designs. Leonardo also designed a power-driven gig-mill (for raising nap on the cloth). Such machines are found in actual practice in the mid-sixteenth century (whether derived from Leonardo or not). The earliest full description of gig-mills as used in practice comes from Zonca (1607); they are better in general design than Leonardo's, but are hand-driven.

In all these ways the basis was being laid for the spectacular mechanisation of the textile industry which was to be one of the

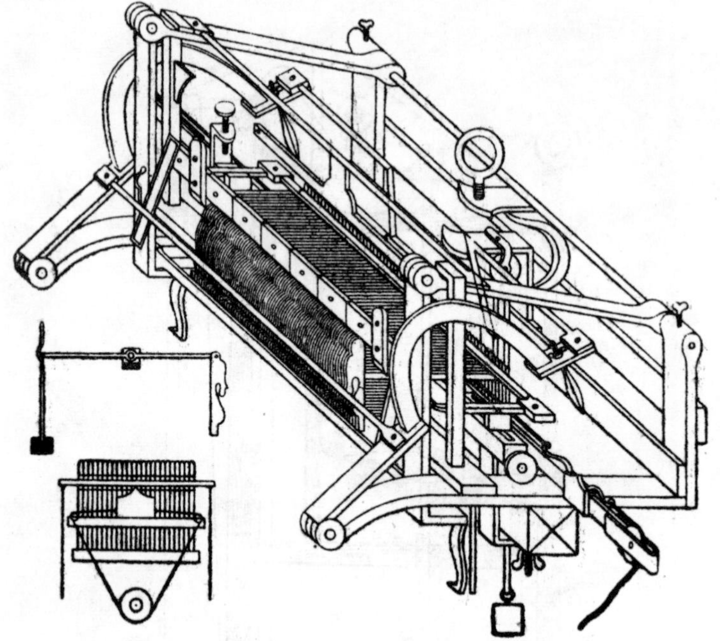

Fig. 13. An early knitting machine (stocking frame).

main elements of Britain's rise to industrial supremacy in the eighteenth century.

Heavy Engineering, Mining and Metallury

The developments of the period in heavy engineering took place mainly in mining and metallurgy. Commercial and industrial evolution had increased the demand for metals, so that these two industries expanded more rapidly than any other. To meet this expansion, especially to meet the requirements of much deeper mining, heavy power-driven machinery had to be used. The illustrations included in this chapter (mostly from Agricola's *De Re Metallica*, 1556) will give a far better idea of this machinery than any verbal description. But in considering them it should be noted that some of them do not represent new inventions, rather increases in scale of application; also that develop-

Fig. 14. A horse-whim for mine winding from Agricola's *De Re Metallica*.

ment was very uneven, so that simultaneously with these advanced machines, much cruder methods were in use.

Figure 14 shows the application of the horse-whim for winding This derives from the use of animal-power for corn-milling (fifth century B.C.), but with the improved harness of the Middle Ages, and from the gearing of the water-raising wheel (after 200 B.C.) and water-mill (first century B.C.). But the whole apparatus is so much increased in size that it represents the solution of much greater problems of engineering construction. Note the brake acting on the drum (centre). Figure 15, of a hoist driven by a water-wheel 36 feet in diameter, probably represents the most powerful machinery that could be produced with the materials of the age. It was used here for raising water, as a substitute for pumping, but it could, of course, be applied equally to the hoisting of ore. Note the two sets of buckets on the water-wheel, providing a reversing mechanism controlled by the workman, who pulls one or other lever to open the sluice which gives the required direction of rotation. For transporting the ore from the minehead crude railways, such as those shown in Figure 16, were in use in Germany by the end of the fifteenth century. After about 1500 water-power was applied to crushing ore, through water-driven stamp-mills.

The most difficult problem of mining, however, was that of pumping away the water that always threatened to drown the workings—a threat that increased rapidly with the depth of the mine. The most advanced heavy engineering of the times is concerned with mine drainage. One such machine, described by Agricola, we have already noted (Figure 15). Agricola also describes the use of force-pumps,[1] suction-pumps, chains of pots (like those used for irrigation purposes as described in Chapter 3, but with the important change from ropes and earthenware pots to iron chains and iron buckets), and the rag-and-chain pump portrayed in Figure 17. This last is a compromise, with many advantages at the current level of technique, between the force-pump and the chain of pots. The balls (made of horsehair) fill the vertical tube, whose top can be seen in the picture and whose bottom lies

[1] The force-pump had been known in Greek times (page 35), but it was only in the later Middle Ages that pumps (as opposed to devices like the chain of pots and the Archimedean screw) were applied to draining mines.

Fig. 15. A very powerful water-driven hoist from Agricola's *De Re Metallica*.

in the sump, and, as the chain moves up, they carry the water to the top. In the force-pump the bottom of the pipe has to stand the pressure of the whole column of water, and it is no easy task to make such strong pipes, but with the rag-and-chain much of this pressure is taken away from the pipe and transferred to a load on the chain. Note that the pump is worked by human power through a treadmill. Human power was still often used, sometimes through the cruder mechanism of the capstan or windlass. On the other hand Agricola describes a plant at Chemnitz consisting of three rag-and-chain pumps working in series, the lowest being 660 feet below ground; the whole plant was worked by four shifts of twenty-four horses—a quite considerable use of power. The suction pump suffers from the great disadvantage that it will only lift water through some 30 feet. Figure 18 shows a device for overcoming this difficulty by coupling in series a number of suction pumps all driven by the same water-wheel; Agricola says this was invented about 1545.

The increasing commerce and industry resulted in a notable growth of the towns. This brought with it new problems of water-supply, which resulted in the introduction of heavy pumping machinery for this purpose also. Germany led the way here, as in the mine engineering we have just discussed. Several German cities had notable water-pumping plant by 1500, though the earliest known description is for Augsburg in 1550, by which time a very complex system had grown up there. The plant was driven by water-wheels and it used the screw of Archimedes (page 34) repeated several times in series to raise the water to the tops of towers, from which it was distributed in pipes; force-pumps may also have been used. Several very ambitious schemes were attempted at Toledo from 1526 on, but without success. A windmill was used in 1542 at Gloucester to feed the town reservoir. London's first pumped supply came from a machine, driven by a tide-mill, erected in 1582 near London Bridge by a German engineer named Peter Morice. Other London schemes followed. Paris had its first water-works erected in 1608, and so on.

The Search for More Power

Besides the machinery we have just been describing and a great expansion in the use of the other power-driven machines we men-

Fig. 16. A sixteenth-century minehead railway. Note also the crude winding by winch in this case.

tioned in the last chapter, water-power was now being used in many other industries, such as paper-making, gunpowder manufacture, nail-making, sword-making and most branches of metallurgy. There was thus a constant and increasing demand for more and larger sources of power. Many and determined attempts were made to produce new prime-movers or improve old ones—yet the problem was so difficult that notable successes did not, on the whole, arrive till the period covered by our next chapter. Water-wheels increased in size, as materials and constructional methods improved, till in the early seventeenth century wheels yielding 20 h.p. were in use. Various modifications of design were tried, which began the evolution of the water-turbine (see Chapter 7). Windmills also increased in size, and many improvements were made in their mechanism. The turret mill (page 48 and Plate VII) came to be widely used, raising the power that a windmill could produce to something like 14 h.p. In the Netherlands of the sixteenth and seventeenth centuries windmills were being applied to every conceivable industrial purpose.

The demand for power was slowly but surely outrunning even these sources and men began to look for new prime movers. The possibilities of steam may have been vaguely appreciated for some centuries, but till the middle of the sixteenth century, no serious attempts were made to harness it and there was no clear conception of its nature or properties—it was not clearly distinguished from air, for example. From 1550 on, however, and increasingly in the seventeenth century, men began to investigate the properties of steam and to seek for methods of using its power. The earlier attempts were of no practical value, but they do demonstrate a conscious search for a way of harnessing steam, and it is on the experience thus gained that the successful steam-engine was eventually built. Battista della Porta showed in 1606 how water could be raised both by the pressure of steam and by condensing it in a closed vessel to create a vacuum into which the water would be 'sucked up'—methods which form the basis of the Worcester and Savery engines to be described later. Salomon de Caus described in 1615 a steam-driven fountain, which works in much the same way as when a boiling kettle with a tight-fitting lid forces water from the spout. In 1629 Branca suggested the impulse turbine shown in Figure 19. This was not

Fig. 17. A rag-and-chain pump driven by a treadmill from Agricola's *De Re Metallica*.

a practical proposal, but the picture seems to indicate that he had hopes of steam as a source of industrial power. The Marquis of Worcester in his *Century of Inventions* (written 1655, published 1663) described, in language intentionally vague for purposes of secrecy, a steam-engine for driving fountains. The engine was built before 1664. From the obscure descriptions available, it seems to have been somewhat like the Savery engine discussed in the next chapter. Though these attempts show increasing approximation to it, the workable steam-engine was not to appear for several decades, and only after social changes in England had given a new impetus to the search.

Social Repercussions

Meanwhile the technical advances that have been described in this and the previous chapter were once more affecting social structure. Throughout the Middle Ages, industry had been subservient to agriculture; correspondingly political and economic power was chiefly in the hands of the feudal lords, who maintained it through their control of the land and of the workers thereon. In industry the typical unit of production was the independent craftsman owning his own tools and workshop. The master craftsman would be helped by a few apprentices and perhaps one or two journeymen working for wages, but these were merely preparing for the not very distant date when they would themselves become masters. Where industry was concentrated on any scale, the master craftsmen were organised in Guilds, which established craft standards, ensured that apprentices were properly trained before becoming journeymen or masters, resisted the intrusion of unqualified outsiders, and generally protected the conditions of the craft. The Guilds were often politically powerful. This form of industrial organisation remained dominant in most trades till long after the end of the Middle Ages .

But before the end of the Middle Ages, a new form of industry had begun to appear, timidly as it were, and on a restricted scale; and during the period covered by this chapter it made great strides towards eventual domination of the whole economic system. The heavier machinery that we have described can only be used properly by a number of men working together. This provided the basis for the growth of the capitalist system of pro-

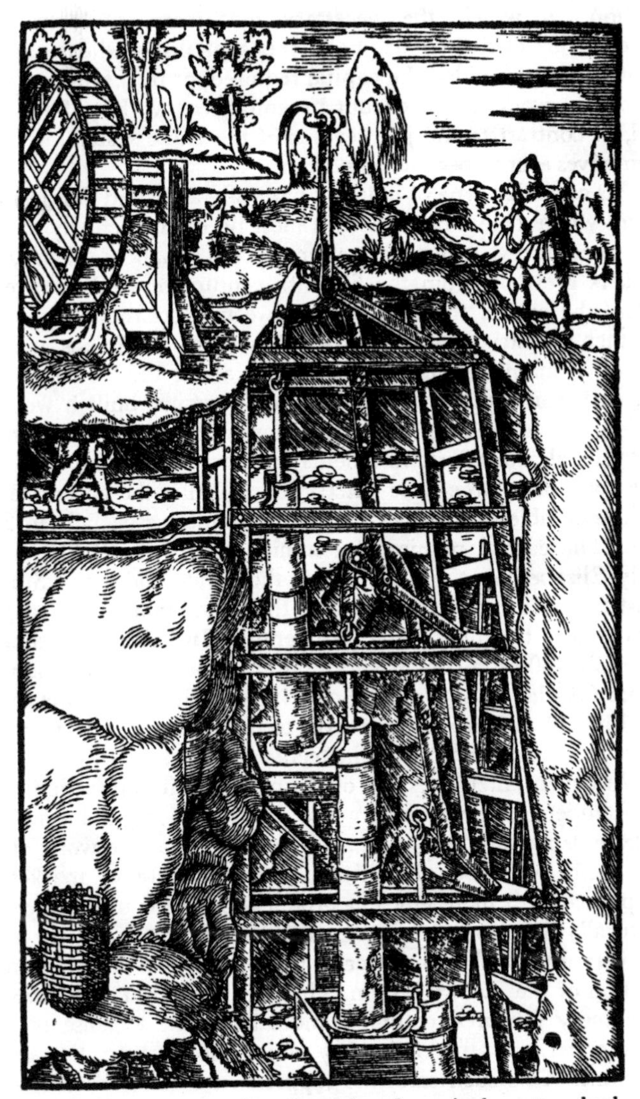

Fig. 18. Suction pumps in series, driven by a single water wheel, from Agricola's *De Re Metallica.*

duction, in which the necessary machinery, buildings and materials are owned by one man—the 'capitalist'—who, by saving or otherwise, provided the capital required, or by a group of such men. The work is carried out by employees working for wages and, in contrast to the journeymen of the Guild system, unlikely themselves ever to become employers.

This capitalist type of industry naturally appeared first in those trades where heavy machinery is most necessary—chiefly mining and metallurgy, where large enterprises financed mainly by bankers grew up from the fifteenth century onwards. But even before the end of the Middle Ages we find occasional examples in other industries—a factory of 120 weavers at Amiens in 1371, one of as many printers in Nuremberg about 1450. In the early sixteenth century the famous Jack of Newbury built a weaving factory with more than 200 looms, employing about 600 workers,[2] and several similar establishments were in existence by 1550. Before 1660 such large-scale enterprise, requiring the accumulation of considerable capital, became more common, especially in England. The capital required for mining rose from £100 or so in early Elizabethan times to several thousands under the Stuarts. Blast-furnaces involving several thousand pounds of capital appeared in the mid-seventeenth century. In 1649 two capitalists spent £6,000 on a copper-wire mill at Esher. A London brewery under Charles I had a capital of £10,000. All these, however, are but hints of the great change-over to the factory system that took place in the eighteenth and nineteenth centuries.

With such enterprises the old-fashioned guild craftsmen could not compete. They were in grave danger at least of losing their independence and becoming mere employees, at the worst of losing their livelihood altogether, when a failure of markets to keep pace with more efficient production caused unemployment. Naturally they opposed the new capitalist type of industry, using the very great political power of the Guilds to prevent the introduction of the factory system. They saw, too, that the growth of machinery favoured capitalist industry at the expense of their own crafts and therefore they sought to prevent the use of machines. One such case, the suppression of the ribbon loom at

[2] The numbers—known only from a poem—may be exaggerated; but the man and his factory were real.

Fig. 19. Branca's suggestion for an impulse turbine.

Danzig in 1579, has already been mentioned. Similarly, Cologne tailors were forbidden to use machines for pressing pinheads in 1397; the English Parliament under Guild pressure prohibited in 1552 the use of the power-driven gig-mill; in 1623–4 Charles I ordered the destruction of needle-making machines. Such opposition could never be successful in stopping technical advance—but it did hinder progress sufficiently to be an important factor in making necessary the political changes that are described in the next chapter.

PART TWO

THE CAPITALIST ERA

CHAPTER 6

THE INDUSTRIAL REVOLUTION:
THE EARLY DAYS (1660 TO 1815)

IN all that has gone before, the names of British inventors are few. Some crept in because we carried the history of chronometers well beyond the period covered by the last chapter. The others, like Lee (whose knitting machine of 1589 was the *first* English mechanical invention of note), Hooke and Worcester, occur only towards the end of the period in question. But in the present chapter British names occur almost to the exclusion of all others. This sudden change reflects a great social transformation which took place first in England.

Though England had not been conspicuous hitherto in mechanical invention, she had from the mid-sixteenth century on made outstandingly rapid strides in the industrial application and use of such inventions. Already we have noted some of the large industrial enterprises set up in England in the early seventeenth century. Similarly, between 1540 and 1600 there were introduced from abroad the first paper and gunpowder mills, cannon factories, alum and copperas factories and sugar refineries (some of these industries existed earlier on a small non-factory basis). The average annual production of coal rose from 210,000 tons in the decade 1551–60 to 2,982,000 tons in 1681–90. The number of merchant ships over 100 tons rose from 35 in 1545 to 183 in 1588 and 350 in 1629. The new English ships were technically superior, too, to those of the older mercantile countries—this was one of the principal reasons for the crushing defeat of the Spanish Armada in 1588. In their new and excellent ships, British merchant sailors traded with the whole world and provided the commercial activity which was a necessary parallel to the expansion of industry.

The Transition from Feudalism to Capitalism

Thus, in the century before 1640, England was transformed from one of the more backward to one of the most rapidly advancing commercial and industrial countries of Europe. This brought to a head contradictions, which have already been hinted at, between the existing political structure and the new forms of industry required to use advanced mechanical methods. By this time England had already moved politically beyond strict feudalism. Yet the feudal basis remained, and tended always to frustrate industrial and technical progress. Besides the types of restrictions mentioned in the last chapter, there was, for example, the growing practice of granting monopolies for the manufacture or sale of this or that article, sometimes as an encouragement to individuals to promote some backward industry, more often as rewards to court favourites (this being, in fact, an attempt to divert the profits of new industry to the benefit of the feudal upper classes). Local tolls and taxes hindered commerce, whose free growth was essential for the full use of the new industrial methods. The power of the Guilds, together with feudal law and customs in general, restricted development of the free market, in both goods and labour, which a capitalist economy required. The concentration of wealth and power in the hands of landowners made it difficult to obtain capital for new large-scale ventures.

Round these and other issues, great political struggles raged in the early seventeenth century, culminating in the Revolution, which began in 1640 and in a few years had replaced the old political structure by a new one from which most of the former restrictions were gone. Political power now passed mainly into the hands of the new class of capitalists or *bourgeoisie* (for which reason this is referred to as the *bourgeois* revolution) in alliance with the more progressive sections of the aristocracy. The description given here is greatly over-simplified. For one thing, the revolution was not completed in a few years in England (as it was later in other countries); preliminary steps had been taken in Tudor times, and its completion required further changes, first in 1688 and then in a series of reforms extending well into the nineteenth century. The capitalists who gained political power in the seventeenth century were merchants and bankers, rather than industrial manufacturers, since the latter hardly existed at that time; and so further struggles were needed in the late eighteenth and nineteenth centuries before the manufacturers obtained the share of political power which they needed to promote the full prosperity of large-scale industry.

In the new social structure, free in the main from feudal restrictions, British industry forged ahead at an unprecedented rate. Since Britain was by over a century the first country to take this step, she was without serious rival throughout that period. And with expanding industry came increasing invention to cope with the many new problems that arose. That is why for over a century the names on the roll of inventors are almost entirely British.

It will be worthwhile to consider briefly why the capitalism of the next two hundred years was technologically so much more progressive than any previous civilised society (as the reader knows it was, even before we have surveyed the details). It provided a better economic mechanism for accumulating the capital needed to use large-scale machinery, and similarly for supplying the wage-labour to work it. Through its free competitive market it could arrange for the commercial expansion that was necessary to make large-scale production economic. Free competition forced less efficient producers out of business and thus put a premium on progressive and inventive methods. And above all, capitalism radically altered that division between rulers and workers which had in the past so often held back the advance of technology. In previous class-divided society the ruling classes had had little direct relation to production.[1] They appeared in the economic picture mainly as consumers, who took a share of the product but were not to any great extent concerned with how that product was made. In sharp contrast, the capitalist, though he did not himself produce, was responsible for the control and direction of production. His prosperity depended directly on how efficiently his factory or mine was run, and so he had a strong incentive to

[1] Where the Guilds were strong, the medieval master craftsmen could be considered as virtually members of the ruling classes—at least locally—and they were, of course, directly concerned with production. This, together with the fact that the feudal lord was often less separated than his predecessors from the realities of economic life, helps to explain the technological progressiveness of the Middle Ages. But as the period drew towards a close, the craft Guilds tended to become conservative, and the torch was carried forward by budding capitalism.

interest himself in invention and improvement, an incentive that had been absent—or at least much weaker—for previous ruling groups.

A new flexibility came into economic and technological affairs. In the eighteenth century and much of the nineteenth the ordinary workman with ingenuity and ambition could rise to become an industrial magnate. The aristocrat would become a mine-owner, or the old-style master craftsman would develop his workshop into a factory. Capitalism did not abolish class divisions : it merely changed their nature. But these changes were such that for a time most of the troubles which had previously held back progress were abolished or reduced to negligible proportions.

Craftsman and Scholar: the Rise of Modern Science

Earlier societies since the beginning of civilisation had suffered from another division, which paralleled that between rulers and ruled—the division between thinker and doer. Learned men were members of the ruling classes or their privileged servants, and like them had little or no direct interest in production (we have noted a few partial exceptions, like the later Greek engineers and some medieval monastic orders). Science—or what passed for it—was therefore concerned with scholarly theories about the universe and the things that are in it, but not with the improvement, or even the understanding, of productive processes. But when capitalists, with their direct interest in production, became wealthy and influential, then scholars who depended on their friendship or patronage were also forced to interest themselves (though not, of course, exclusively) in industrial and commercial matters. From this there arose a new intercourse between craftsman and scholar, the craftsman learning that scholarly theory could help his practical endeavours, and the scholar in turn discovering that the craftsman's knowledge and practical methods could be a great aid in his learned investigations of the nature of things. Theory and practice were thus brought closer together than ever before. And what is this but science?—a method of uniting theory and practice in such a way that each benefits the other.

In fact one can show, though there is not space to do so here, that this new relationship between scholar and craftsman was one of the three or four most important causal factors in the transformation of classical and medieval learning into modern science. The trend began long before the political victory of capitalism in England. Since the fifteenth century, anywhere in Europe where the capitalist mode of production was emerging, even within a framework of feudalism, we find a tendency towards more practically minded thinkers and more theoretically informed doers—in other words, towards modern science. And the effects of this trend have already showed themselves in Chapter 5. But it was in England after the 1640 Revolution that the movement found full expression.

In a book of this size we shall not be able to do justice to the role of science in technology from the seventeenth century onwards—a role that was modest at first, but grew steadily until in our time almost every important practical advance is based on a mass of fundamental scientific research. We can drop occasional hints on this matter in what follows. But meanwhile let us look at one early example—the way in which science provided the knowledge on which the first successful steam-engines were based.

The Science behind the Steam-Engine

We have seen that by the early seventeenth century men like Porta (page 78) were experimenting with the use of steam to create a vacuum in order to raise water. They were working, however, without much theoretical understanding of what was happening. About the same time, or a little later, the attention of Galileo was drawn to a suction pump which was alleged to be faulty because it would not pump water to more than a certain height. Actually this was not a fault; the limitation is inherent in the nature of suction pumps. This fact had long been known to miners (the repetition of pumps in Figure 18 implies awareness of it). It was not, however, the miner's job to ask why, and hitherto scholars, being little interested in practical affairs, had failed to do so. But Galileo, one of the great founders of modern science, *was* interested in obtaining a theoretical understanding of practical things. He gave a wrong explanation, but his pupil Torricelli found the correct one in 1643. The water is not 'sucked up' by the vacuum created by the pump; it is forced up into the vacuum by the pressure of the atmosphere acting on the water in the sump below; and since the pressure of the atmosphere is limited, the water can be forced up to a certain height (rather over 30 feet in theory, less in practice) but no higher.

From then on there was a growing interest in the properties of the vacuum and of atmospheric pressure. In the 1650s Otto von Guericke of Magdeburg invented the air-pump for creating a vacuum at will, and with its aid demonstrated the enormous forces that atmospheric pressure could make available—in one of his experiments a vacuum in a small vessel created forces which eight horses could not overcome. Others like Pascal and Boyle pursued more refined experiments which led in the second half of the seventeenth century to a profound understanding of the nature of vacuums and atmospheric pressure, and to a quantitative appreciation of the magnitude of forces involved. And it was on this basis that Savery and Newcomen created the first practical steam-engines around the turn of the century.

The First Practical Steam-Engines

Not only did the pump provide the starting point from which the requisite knowledge was developed, but pumping problems—both for draining mines and for water supply—also gave the chief incentive for the development of the new prime mover. Coal-mines in England reached depths of 400 feet by 1700 and 600 feet by 1750—and with every increase of depth the problem of pumping became more acute. One mine operator in 1702 was using 500 horses to give power for pumping. Many improvements in pumps were made to meet this trouble, but these do not concern us so much as does the role of the pumping problem in bringing to fruition at last the attempt to make use of the power of steam.

The first engine to achieve even partial practical success was that of Savery, patented 1698, which is shown diagrammatically in Figure 20. He intended it as a solution of the mine drainage problem, as is made clear by his pamphlet of 1702, *The Miner's Friend*. It was, however, inadequate and there is no record of its use in more than one mine, though several were made to pump water for country houses.

The Worcester and Savery engines had shown an appreciation

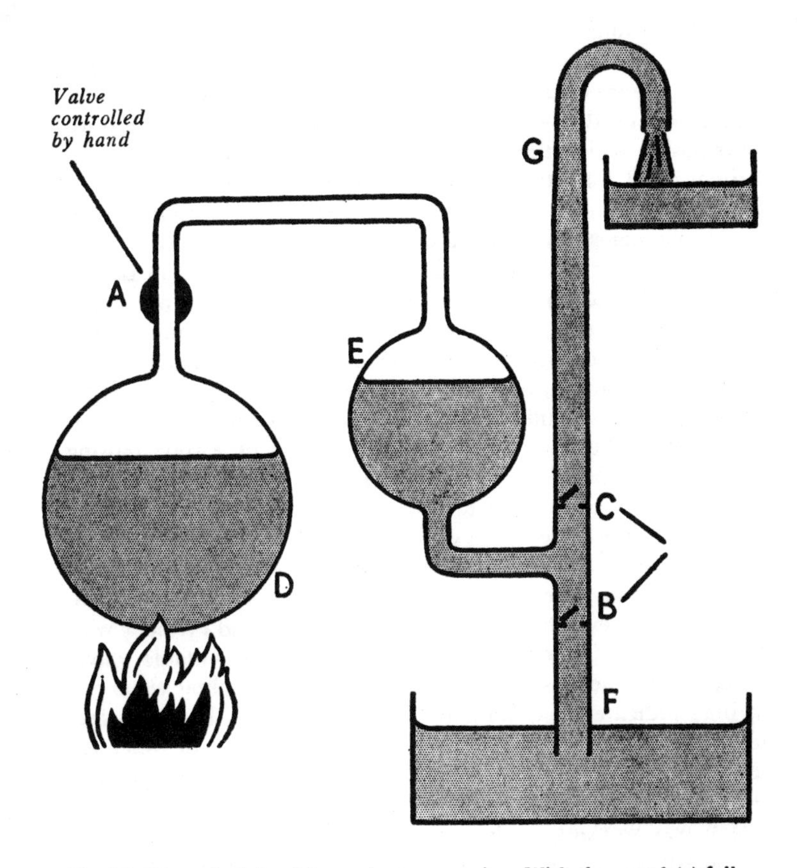

Fig. 20. The principle of Savery's steam-engine. With the vessel (E) full, the valve (A) is opened; steam from the boiler (D) drives the water out of (E); the pressure closes the clack-valve (B) and opens (C), so that the water is driven up the pipe (G). When (E) is empty, the valve (A) is closed and cold water is poured over the outside of (E); the steam condenses and creates a vacuum; atmospheric pressure now acts through (G) to close valve (C), and also acts on the surface of the water at (F), opening valve (B) and pushing water into (E); after which the first process is repeated.

of the harnessing of steam power, both through using it to create a vacuum and through using its expansive force. But before really adequate steam-engines could be produced another vital component was needed—the piston and cylinder. This was the third contribution which the pump made to the mastery of steam. As early as 1680, Christian Huygens, one of the leading scientists of his time, who has already been mentioned in connection with the chronometer, had attempted to make a piston-and-cylinder engine using the explosion of gunpowder as the source of power. The attempt was naturally unsuccessful, but it led Denys Papin (another scientist of distinction) to try to use a similar mechanism with steam. His rudimentary 'engine', produced about 1690, made use of the expansion of steam to drive a piston up in a vertical cylinder, and its condensation to create a vacuum and draw it down again, thus raising a weight by means of a rope passing over a pulley. But there was no separate boiler; the water lay in the bottom of the cylinder, and the evaporation was done by placing the fire under the cylinder and the condensation by removing it again. It was not, therefore, a practical engine.[2]

Success came when Thomas Newcomen, a Dartmouth ironmonger, discovered how to combine the piston and cylinder with the separate boiler of Savery's engine and with suitable valves to control the admission of the steam and of a cooling water-jet, on lines indicated diagrammatically in Figure 21. It is not clear how much Newcomen knew of Papin's 'engine' or of other experiments that he and others had made with pistons and cylinders and vacuums, but there is probably some connection. Newcomen was working on his invention before 1705, but the first engine whose construction we definitely know dates from 1712.

The Newcomen engine really was a success. By 1729 it was in use in Austria, Belgium, France, Germany, Hungary and Sweden. After 1720 it was widely used in the Cornish tin mines and there were more than seventy engines in Cornwall by 1778. Nine years before that a hundred engines were working in the north of England, fifty-seven being in the Newcastle (coal-mining) district. Despite their low efficiency, many Newcomen engines survived

[2] Papin was also the inventor of the pressure cooker; and in this connection he made one very important contribution to the steam-engine—namely, the safety valve (1681).

long after the invention of Watt's superior variant, though only at coal-mines, where waste low-grade fuel was available. The last was not dismantled till 1934.

The Transformation in Textiles

Meanwhile several of England's main industries were transformed in the eighteenth century from local craft or cottage work to mechanised factory production. The most startling changes took place in textiles. Early in the century the Lancashire textile industry was carried on by hundreds of weavers and spinners working in their own homes, buying raw materials from 'factors' and selling their finished products back to them. They used the equipment described in previous chapters. The first great change came with John Kay's invention of the flying shuttle in 1733. Formerly the shuttle was passed from hand to hand through the web. The flying shuttle, as its name implies, flew freely through the web, being driven from a box on one side to a box on the other by a mechanism controlled by cords which the weaver held in one hand. To use it required considerable skill, but given that, it allowed the weaving of wider cloth, left one hand free for other operations and roughly doubled the weaver's output. It was adopted only slowly; in some parts of the country it was little used even in 1820. In Lancashire, however, it had come into general use by about 1760, and it had the immediate effect of making it very difficult for the spinners to keep up with the requirements of the weavers.[3] And so in the decade after 1760 we find a series of inventions designed to improve the productivity of the cottage spinning-wheels.

But more radical changes were required in spinning, and the first of these came considerably earlier. The first steps in spinning are to arrange the fibres parallel and then draw them out till they form a loose thread of appropriate thickness, which is then twisted on the spindle. The drawing out was formerly done by hand. In 1738 Lewis Paul obtained a patent for spinning by rollers (on somewhat doubtful evidence it is said that a similar idea occurred to Wyatt in 1730 and a machine was constructed in 1733). This machine drew out the fibres by passing them between

[3] It had previously needed three to five spinners to supply yarn for one weaver. Now the disparity became greater.

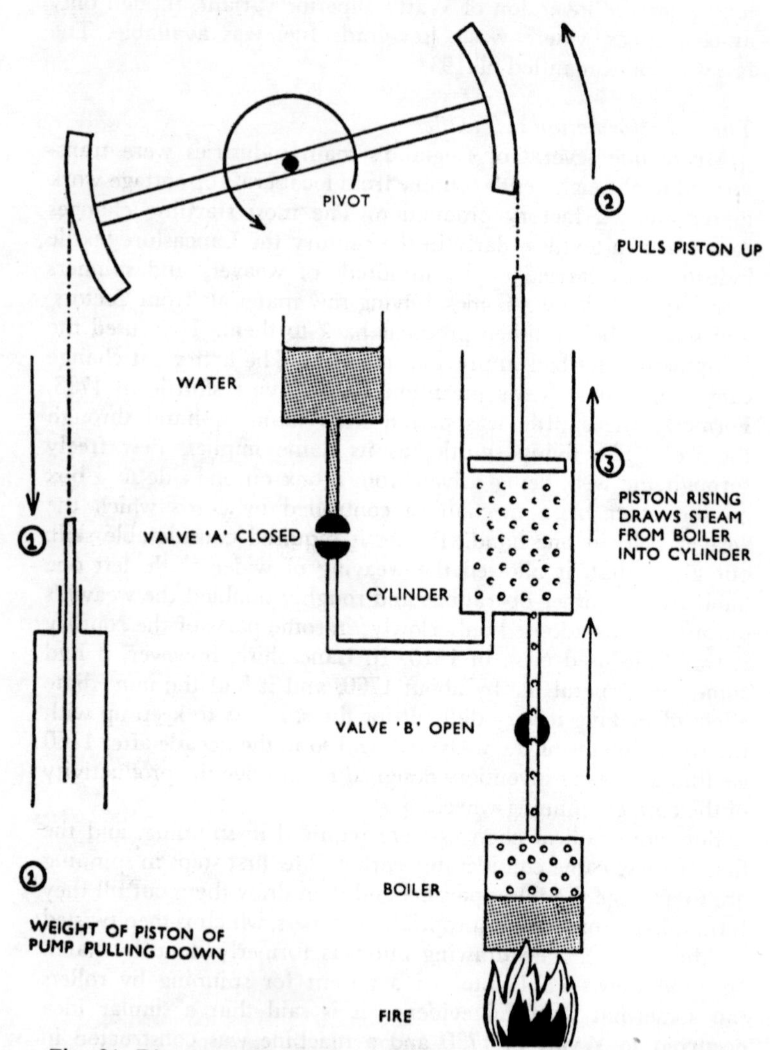

Fig. 21. Diagrammatic drawing of Newcomen's pumping engine. To understand its working, follow in each diagram the numbers in circles

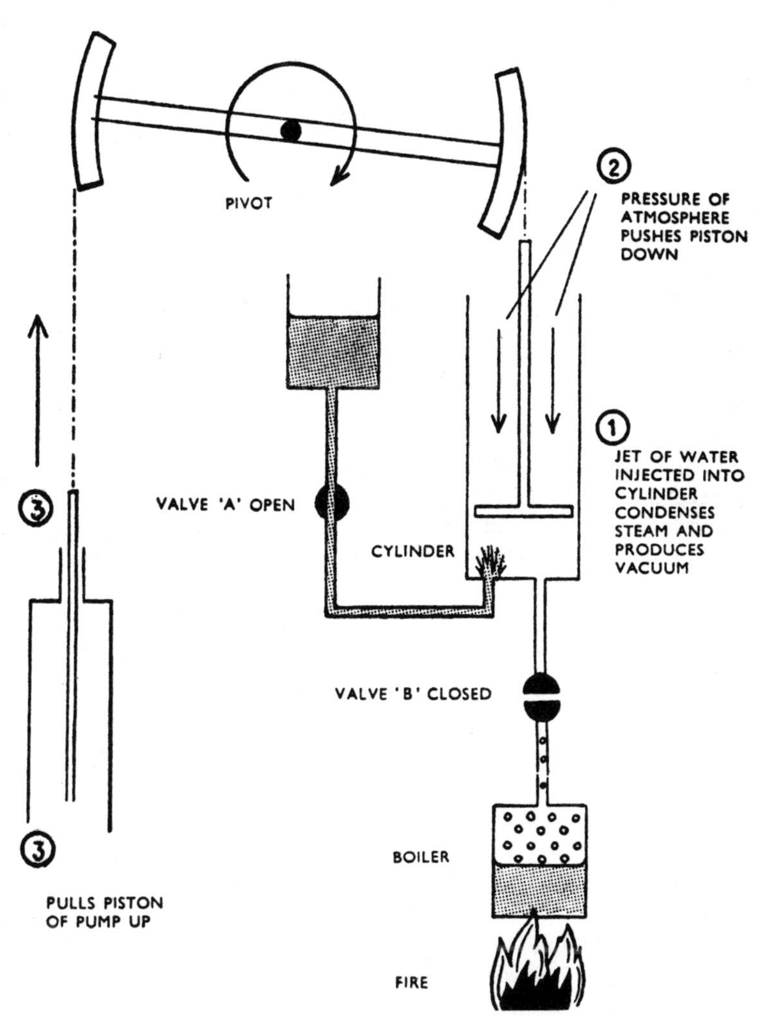

and the attached legends. Note that the work is done by the pressure of the atmosphere during the working stroke (second picture). For this reason the engine is called an atmospheric engine. Many important details (such as the arrangement for getting the condensed water out of the cylinder) are not shown.

pairs of rollers (Figure 11). In 1741 Wyatt and Paul had a spinning mill working on this principle, employing ten girls and using power from a capstan driven by two asses.

However, the most rapid advances came after the general use of the flying shuttle had greatly raised the demand for yarn. First came Hargreaves' 'spinning jenny', probably conceived about 1764 and perfected by 1768, which allowed one operator to control at first eight spindles, later eighty or more. It was without rollers or flyer, so that the processes of drawing out, twisting and winding on were performed intermittently by means of a moving carriage. It was essentially a device for enabling one spinner to do the job of many, and was not adaptable to power drive. On the other hand, Arkwright's 'water frame' or 'throstle', introduced in 1769, was specifically intended for spinning by the use of animal or water power. It used rollers and flyer (Figure 11) and, after various improvements, produced a much firmer thread than was hitherto possible. Formerly cotton thread was so imperfect that it could only be used for the weft, linen being used for the warp. Arkwright's machine made possible the production of all-cotton fabrics.

Crompton, after five years of work, had by 1779 completed his invention of a machine (Plate X) combining the best features of Hargreaves' and Arkwright's. He took Arkwright's rollers and Hargreaves' moving carriage and spindles without flyers, and with this combination it became possible to spin a much finer thread than formerly and, by various adjustments, to produce a greater variety of yarns. Because it was a cross of the two earlier machines, this was known as the spinning 'mule'. In its original form it was not suitable for power drive. Attempts to adapt it for this purpose were made from 1790 onwards. By 1800 some success had been achieved and the mule became a factory machine, though still requiring skilled operators. In 1825 there appeared a fully self-acting mule, which could be power-driven without the assistance of skilled operators, though a completely satisfactory version did not appear till 1830. Ring spinning, now the main system except for very fine soft yarns, was introduced by John Thorp of the U.S.A. in 1828, and developed into an effective method by his fellow countryman, Mason, three years later.

The greatly increased productivity of these machines soon

transformed the spinning industry, especially after the introduction of steam-power. The cottage industry gave way to the factory where hundreds of spinners worked as wage-earners for the factory owner. Factories sprang up in dozens alongside streams which provided water-power. By 1811 there were 310,500 spindles in Great Britain working on Arkwright's frames, 4,600,000 on Crompton's mules and 156,000 on Hargreaves' jennies. In 1761 the Manchester cotton industry had been so unimportant that there were no cotton workers in a procession representing the principal trades of the city; by 1774 there were 30,000 people in the industry in or near Manchester.

As the efficiency of spinning increased by leaps and bounds, it was the turn of the weavers to find they could not keep pace. Renewed attention was given to the problem of producing a power-driven loom. It will be remembered that Leonardo had designed a power-loom, though his conception was inherently impracticable. Other attempts were made in the seventeenth century, but the various mechanical elements that had to be combined to make an efficient machine were lacking. Improvements to the ribbon loom by Kay and others made it substantially automatic by 1745 and a decade or so later it incorporated most of the essentials of automatic weaving. The outstanding remaining problem was that of the control of the shuttle in wide webs, and Kay's flying shuttle of 1733 provided the basis for its solution. With these elements available renewed attempts were made. Some progress was made by Barber in 1774 and the chief steps forward were taken about 1787 by the Rev. Edmund Cartwright, whose loom (Plate IX) embodied the main principles in use for power-weaving today. His machine was used to some extent, but the power-loom was not sufficiently perfected for general use till after the improvements introduced by such men as Radcliffe (1802), Johnson (1803–5), Austin (1789 and subsequently) and Horrocks (from about 1810 onwards).

Horrocks' improvements represented the decisive advance to a machine of general practical use; his loom was put into regular manufacture after 1822. The number of power looms in England was only 2,400 in 1813 and 12,150 in 1820, but after the appearance of these improved looms it rose to 45,500 in 1829 and 85,000 in 1833. The Northrop loom, in which empty shuttles are automatically re-charged, was patented in 1894 and first sold in 1895. It doubled the number of looms that a weaver could look after.

All this refers to the ordinary loom for plain weaving. Meanwhile the draw loom (for various patterns) had elsewhere been undergoing a long evolution, culminating in the perfection about 1804 of the Jacquard loom (so called after its inventor, a Frenchman). In this the raising and lowering of the various selections of warp threads to produce complicated patterns were automatically controlled by cards punched with appropriate holes.

At the same time the auxiliary stages of textile production were being rapidly mechanised. Carding machines were invented independently by Lewis Paul and Daniel Bourn in 1748, but the most successful attack on this problem was made from 1775 on by Arkwright, who eventually had a process for carding, drawing and roving, which was all but continuous and was power-driven. The first machine for combing wool was that of Cartwright (1792), but it was only from 1832 on that combing machines became really successful. Thomas Bell invented in 1783 a machine using engraved cylinders to print cotton. In America modern types of rotary shearing engines appeared in 1792 and 1793, and other versions soon followed in England.

With the aid of these machines the British textile industry expanded several hundredfold between the middle of the eighteenth and the end of the nineteenth century. It captured the markets of the whole world, as is shown very clearly by the following table:

Year	Value of exports of cotton goods, yarn, etc.
1701	£23,253
1751	£45,986
1780	£355,000
1790	£1,662,369
1800	£5,406,501
1820	£20,509,926
1860	£52,012,430
1870	£71,416,345

after which the figure remained stable and then slowly declined. The decline was partly caused by the rise in industrial strength of other countries, which broke Britain's world monopoly; but it was also partly due to the technical backwardness of the British industry compared with its new rivals—at the end of the Second World War only 5 per cent of looms in Lancashire were automatic, against 95 per cent in the U.S.A., while over half the cotton-making machinery then used in Lancashire had been installed before 1910.

Renewed Search for Power

Though we have carried the story well beyond that point, it will be clear that by the 1770s the mechanisation of the cotton industry was such as to put a serious strain on existing sources of power. It was the same in other industries. Most of them, however, saw no such spectacular pageant of invention as in textiles; rather there was an increase in the size and capacity of machines already well known, an increasing use of power to drive them and a growth of factories in place of craft or cottage industry. Thus the eighteenth-century potteries used increasing amounts of wind- and water-power for such purposes as grinding and crushing flints, grinding enamel colours and mixing clays. With growing towns, flour mills increased in size. And so through the whole range of industry. Only in metallurgy and heavy engineering (and at the end of the century in light engineering also) was progress as spectacular as in textiles. All the aspects of industrial progress that have been mentioned, together with growing shipping, bridge building, and the continued progress of the steam-engine made heavy demands on metallurgy and engineering, calling for larger furnaces and therefore larger bellows for blast, heavier rolling mills, boring machines, and so on—all in their turn requiring more and more power to drive them.

In such an atmosphere men turned in the mid-eighteenth century to serious attempts to improve the known sources of power—water, wind, animal and the Newcomen steam-engine (which, it must be remembered, would not drive rotary machinery). All these prime-movers had been pushed as far as trial and error could push them. The intuitive approach of the skilled craftsman could carry them no further. To produce further increases in efficiency required careful comparative measurement, in controlled conditions, of all the factors involved and the power output obtained. In other words, further progress depended on the application of scientific analysis. Among those who tackled water-wheels scientifically was John Smeaton, one of the outstanding engineers of all time. In 1752–3 he built laboratory models of water-wheels and, by carefully measuring their output of power while he varied the shapes and relations of their various parts, he was able to redesign water-wheels to a greatly increased efficiency. By the end of the century, the plain water-wheel (as opposed to the turbine) reached the end of its evolution. Meanwhile, on the Continent various workers were pursuing theoretical investigations which, though producing little of practical value at the time, prepared the way for the creation of the water-turbine in the nineteenth century.

Smeaton also scientifically investigated and greatly improved windmills. In 1745 Edmund Lee added the fantail mechanism—the small auxiliary windmill at the back which automatically turns the main sails into the wind. The problem of making sails which would automatically adjust themselves to the strength of the wind was tackled with some success by Andrew Meikle in 1772 and Stephen Hooper in 1789, and finally solved by William Cubitt in 1807.

Smeaton again, around 1770, undertook a scientific investigation of the Newcomen engine and as a result of his experiments was able to tabulate the best cylinder diameter, stroke, rate of working, boiler size, water injection and coal consumption for a given power. With this data he was able to build bigger and better engines—for example, one at Chasewater with a 6-foot cylinder, 9½-foot stroke, yielding 76½ h.p. It can be said that with Smeaton's work, the Newcomen engine reached the limit of its development and further progress depended on the fundamental changes introduced by Watt.

Water-wheels had the disadvantage that the factory had to be placed by a stream. Windmills suffered from irregularity of working. The Newcomen engine was free from these disadvantages but it would drive only pumps, not rotary machinery. Hence attempts were made to adapt it for the latter purpose. Since the engine would pump water and since water-wheels would drive machinery, the most obvious method was to use the engine to pump water to supply a wheel which drove the machinery. In 1742 the firm of Darby, the ironfounders who took such a prominent part in eighteenth-century progress, installed a Newcomen engine which pumped water for ten water-wheels to drive their machinery. A similar device was in use in the Potteries in the years 1750–60. In the second half of the century this method was commonly used for winding in mine shafts; the pumping engine, required in any case for drainage, pumped water over a wheel operating the winding gear. In 1780 Pickard was granted a patent for producing rotary motion from a Newcomen engine, using the crank; the attempt produced little success, but the patent later obstructed Watt's work.

James Watt's Steam-Engine

Such was the drive to produce better sources of power. Such was the atmosphere in which James Watt was urged to do the work which transformed the crude Newcomen engine into a really efficient machine. Watt was not the father of the industrial revolution. It was not his engine that started the great drive of mechanisation. The mechanisation started first, based chiefly on water-power. But soon more power was needed than rivers and streams could supply, and so men sought to improve the steam-engine. Watt was outstandingly the most successful. He answered the problem of power and on his work industrialisation could go forward assured of adequate power sources.

Mine drainage still presented the largest single power problem, while the Newcomen engine was a basis from which to start; so it is natural that Watt's first steps were to improve the pumping engine out of all recognition. In 1763 he was called to repair a model Newcomen engine belonging to Glasgow University and noted its inefficiencies, but so difficult was the problem of eliminating them that it was not till 1765, after much thought, consultation with scientists and scientific experimenting of his own, that he saw the solution. He observed that the main source of inefficiency in the Newcomen engine arose from the condensing of the steam in the cylinder; the cylinder was cooled at every stroke and a great part of the steam was wasted in reheating it. His main improvements were therefore to keep the cylinder permanently hot by enclosing it in a steam jacket and to do the condensing in a separate condenser, kept permanently cold (see Figure 22). He built a model in 1765, but it took him till 1769 to solve the problems of full-scale working, and obtain his patent.

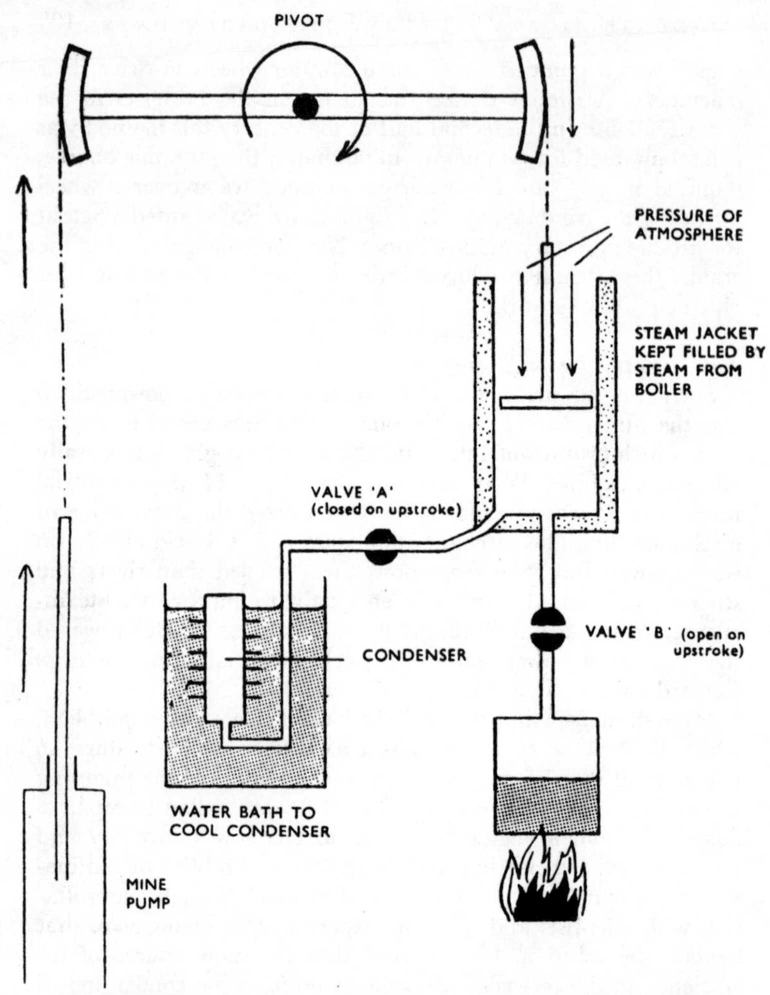

Fig. 22. Diagrammatic representation of Watt's pumping engine (working stroke). Compare with Figure 21. This is still an atmospheric engine, working on the same principle as Newcomen's, except that (a) the steam jacket keeps the cylinder constantly hot, and (b) the condensing is done in a separate condenser, kept constantly cool by cooling water and exhausted by a pump. This diagram shows only the principles of the engine, not the details as designed by Watt. For example, the condenser was actually of the injection type, the pumps for exhausting it are omitted, and Watt's working cycle was more complicated than that illustrated.

Even then, both financial and engineering difficulties slowed his progress to a snail's pace. But in 1774 he left Glasgow to join forces with Matthew Boulton of Birminghan, a man of immense stature as an industrial organiser, in a position to provide or borrow the necessary capital and able to command adequate supplies of engineering skill, both at his own factory and in those of the Black Country iron-masters. Within six months the prototype was working satisfactorily, and success was assured.

The first two engines for customers were made in 1776—one for draining a colliery at Tipton in Staffordshire; the other to drive the bellows of a blast furnace at the Broseley (Salop) ironworks of John Wilkinson, who was responsible, along with the firm of Darby, for many of the great advances in heavy engineering and metallurgy, and whose improved boring machine (page 147) had made possible the production of Watt's cylinders. In 1777 came the first order for a pumping engine for a Cornish tin mine and thereafter Cornwall was the best field for these engines. There had been more than seventy Newcomen engines at work in the county in 1778; by 1790 all but one of these had been replaced by the engines of Boulton and Watt.

By the time the pumping engines were in regular production, the demand of the textile and other industries for improved sources of power had grown fully effective and Watt, at the request of his partner, Boulton, turned his attention to the production of an engine for driving rotary machinery (Plate XII). His rotative patent was taken out in 1781 and the following year he developed the double-acting engine and expansive working. In 1788 he added the centrifugal governor (to right of cylinder in Plate XII) and in 1796 the steam-engine indicator.

Applications and Further Development of Steam Power

In 1783 a Watt rotative engine was installed in Wilkinson's works for driving a forge-hammer and another at Wedgwood's pottery (the first of several there). The first for winding at a coal-mine was at Newcastle in 1784, and by 1800 thirty Watt engines of both types were being used at collieries and twenty-two at copper mines. In 1785 it was used to drive a flour mill. In the same year came the first application to cotton-spinning and by 1800 there were eighty-four Watt engines in cotton mills, after which date steam-power became common in the industry. By 1850 cotton mills were using 71,000 h.p. of steam, against 11,000 h.p. of water-power. If the reader will glance back at the export figures already quoted, he will see that the general introduction of steam allowed an even greater expansion of the industry than did the original inventions of the sixties and seventies. Wool-spinning was more backward and was only using nine of the engines by 1800. Large-scale power weaving belongs to the nineteenth century, but by 1789 a Cartwright loom was driven by steam. In 1796 Wilkinson ordered another engine to drive a rolling-mill and by the end of the century there were twenty-eight Watt engines in foundries and forges. In 1812 came the first application to mine haulage on a dip-road, when George Stephenson altered a pumping engine for that purpose. These examples will show how great the need for power had become and how much the further progress of industry was helped by the satisfaction of that demand by Watt's engines.

The subsequent history to and beyond the rise of the modern high-speed reciprocating engine after 1870 would require a book in itself. Here we can only note the beginnings of two important developments. Watt's engines were still primarily atmospheric engines working at little above atmospheric pressure. The transition to the modern engine working at high pressure depended on improvements in iron-working and metallurgy towards the end of the eighteenth century. Murdock, a workman of Watt's, made a successful model in 1784, but the significant development of high-pressure engines begins with the work of Trevithick in England and Evans in the U.S.A. in the first decade of the nineteenth century. The compound engine was first used by Hornblower in 1781, but it had to be abandoned because it infringed Watt's patent. After the expiry of the patent in 1800, compounding was reintroduced by Woolf in 1803, but it was not till 1845 that McNaught produced a really satisfactory compound engine.

The Rise of the Steamship

In all the applications of the steam-engine mentioned above, the method of driving was obvious—the machines were previously driven by a rotary mechanism, such as a water-wheel, and it was only necessary to attach a rotative engine instead. But with one other application which reached considerable success before 1815 the method was less obvious—the application to shipping. Ships were driven by sails, oars or paddles, and none of these are in any obvious way adaptable to a steam-engine drive. It is therefore not surprising that many weird devices were tried. John Fitch of the U.S.A., for example, designed in 1785 a steamboat driven by an endless chain of floating boards—a sort of naval tank-track—and later adopted a set of paddles moving like those used in canoeing. He also suggested jet-propulsion in 1790 and the same system was proposed on numerous occasions and even tried out by Rumsey, who in 1793 succeeded in driving a jet-propelled boat on the Potomac at 4 m.p.h. These more fantastic experiments were soon eliminated (though jet-propulsion was to reach limited success for ships in our times, apart from its recent application in the air) and only two remained—the paddle-wheel and the screw.

The former was occasionally used for propulsion even before the advent of steam, being driven by human power through cranks or capstans. Naturally attempts were made from time to time to substitute the power of a Newcomen or Watt engine, but without notable success until 1788, when Miller and Symington built a paddle-boat, which on trial on Dalswinton Loch reached a speed of 5 m.p.h. Symington carried on the work and built the *Charlotte Dundas*, which in 1802 towed two 70-ton barges 19½ miles in 6 hours against a headwind so strong that no other vessel on the canal dared to move. The greatest of the pioneers, however, was Robert Fulton, an American citizen who worked in France and England, but achieved his success after returning to the U.S.A. He used a very scientific approach, making experiments on water resistance and similar topics. His *Clermont* of 1807 created a sensation by steaming 150 miles from New York to Albany in 32 hours. Thereafter steam navigation on rivers in the U.S.A. made rapid progress and was thoroughly established by 1815. The first commercial paddle-steamer service in Britain was provided by Henry Bell's *Comet* on the Clyde in 1812. But progress here was slower till about 1830, and in 1815 the country had only twenty steamers. Incidentally the first American steam-driven warship was launched in 1814; Britain did not follow suit till 1833.

Britain regained the lead as steam conquered the oceans. The first steamer to cross the Atlantic was the *Savannah* in 1819, but she was primarily a sailing vessel using steam as an auxiliary, and the same applies to several later crossings. It was commonly held that steamers were useless for long voyages, because the coal they would have to carry would reduce the payload too much. These beliefs were dispelled in 1838 when the *Sirius* crossed the Atlantic under continuous power in less than twenty days—a record which she held for a few hours [!] before the *Great Western* reduced it to fifteen days. Thereafter the position of steam was secured; large shipping companies with steam vessels came into being—the Cunard Line, for example, was established in 1840.

These vessels were of wood and paddle-driven, but about the same time the screw and iron construction were beginning to appear. The screw had been tried at various times since 1796 (and indeed had been proposed even earlier). Only towards the middle of the nineteenth century did it come into regular use and there is much doubt as to which of the many claimants should be given credit for making it a practical mechanism. The critical work is usually taken to be that of John Ericsson and Francis Pettit Smith, leading to the first really successful use of the screw on the *Archimedes* in 1838. Perhaps it would be more just to give the credit to the designers of engines working at higher speeds, for undoubtedly with the slower engines of earlier years the screw was bound to be less efficient than the paddle-wheel.

After the launching of a 70-ton iron barge by John Wilkinson in 1787, and many subsequent experiments, iron construction became common about the middle of the nineteenth century. Steel was tried in 1859, but the era of steel in ship-building may be said to begin effectively from the launching of H.M.S. *Iris* in 1877. The use of turbines and diesels as power units completed the transition to the modern ship, which binds the world into a single unit in which national divisions become more and more anachronistic.

Agriculture and Other Things

While these great industrial changes were going on, an agricultural revolution was also taking place—indeed the growing industrial population could not have been fed without great agricultural changes. The more important advances were in such things as the introduction of new crops, new methods of rotation of crops and so on, but mechanical matters also played their part. A smaller, lighter plough, introduced into England from Holland about 1730 under the name of the Rotherham plough, led to many improvements in design and construction. Robert Ransome started producing his self-sharpening shares in 1789. About the turn of the century ploughs made wholly of iron began to appear, coming into common use about 1820.

Early in the eighteenth century Jethro Tull (famous for the part he played in all aspects of the agricultural revolution) introduced his horse-hoe. The seed-drill, which opens a furrow, inserts the seed and covers it, is a great improvement on the traditional broadcast sowing. Various forms of drill had been tried in the sixteenth and seventeenth centuries, but the real development began from the one that Tull invented in 1701 and made public in 1731. Tull's drill bore little resemblance to the machines of today, but an essentially modern version was invented by Cooke in 1782, after which the drill developed rapidly.

Threshing was the only aspect of agriculture to which power, other than that of animals, was applied until near our own times. In 1636 Van Berg patented a thresher consisting of several flails operated by cranks. In 1732 Michael Menzies invented a water-driven thresher, which according to his advertisement would 'give more strokes in a day than forty men and with as much strength'. This had some success, but the first really useful thresher was that of Andrew Meikle, working on the rotating drum principle, invented in 1786. Threshers were adopted widely in the early nineteenth century and from 1802 began to be steam-driven (though for some time the water-wheel or horse-gin remained the normal source of power). A rotary chaff-cutter was invented by James Cooke in 1794 and about the same time machines were developed for slicing root crops as cattle fodder.

All the developments we have described in this chapter depended, of course, on improved methods of producing and working metals, but this subject we shall leave for a special discussion in Chapter 8. Besides, there were many minor inventions, such as Bramah's water-closet of 1798, and a most ingenious lock produced by the same inventor in 1784. This lock was so secure that, despite a substantial reward, it was not picked till 1851 (and even then took fifty-one hours' work); but it was even more significant because its fineness and intricacy played a key part in the development of more accurate machining methods.

In 1810 a London printer adapted a hand-press to be driven by steam. He was using the ideas of the German immigrant, Friedrich Koenig, who in the next year took the key step of using rollers to make the impression in a power-driven press. By 1814 an improved version began to print *The Times* at 1,100 sheets an hour—the beginning of the cheap and plentiful newspapers which are so essential on the one hand for an informed democracy, so amenable on the other to use by interested parties to mislead the public.[4]

In addition this period saw the first significant achievements in various lines that were to be fully developed in the nineteenth and twentieth centuries; the beginnings of balloon and even dirigible flight, of electrical devices, the first steps in the mechanisation of agriculture, in coal-cutting machines for the mines and the first achievements in mass-production methods.

Consequences of Industrial Change

The social effects of these industrial changes are probably better known to the reader than any previous ones. The most obvious are evil. The superior efficiency of machines drove handworkers out of employment. When they sought work again in factories, their wages were continually depressed; so much so that all the family had to work and even toddlers worked long shifts in cotton mills. Working conditions were foul. Hours were long—twelve or even sixteen a day—perhaps no longer than they had spun in their own cottages, but then they had worked freely, choosing their own periods of rest, while now they were subject

[4] Further developments may be briefly mentioned. Hoe's sheet-fed rotary press appeared in 1846; making 20,000 impressions an hour, it was used by many newspapers for a time. But the modern rotary press, printing from a continuous roll of paper, developed from the work of William Bullock (Philadelphia, 1865) and from the famous Walter presses of *The Times* (patented 1866, working in 1868). A modern rotary can print 60,000 copies an hour. Machinery for making the continuous lengths of paper which these presses require was invented by Robert of France in 1798 and developed in Britain by the firm of Fourdrinier in 1802.

to the relentless discipline of the factory which waited for no man. Housing conditions in the new towns that sprang up round the mills were as bad as working conditions. Individual houses were, perhaps, no worse than the cottages they had lived in before, but sanitary conditions that will do for a village are of no use for a crowded town, and housing methods utterly failed to cope with the new problems.

Perhaps most obvious of all was the unemployment of displaced craft workers, only slowly absorbed by the expanding factories. Such unemployment (at this period) was only temporary, but was nevertheless serious to those displaced. Machines, it seemed, were the cause of that unemployment. They did work formerly requiring many hands. Small wonder that the craftsmen at times turned against these machines. In 1663 and again in 1767 they wrecked mechanical sawmills which had been erected in London. There were riots against the ribbon loom in 1676 and stocking frames in 1710. John Kay had his home wrecked in 1753 and was forced to leave the country. In 1768 the Blackburn spinners destroyed Hargreaves' jennies. In 1776 and subsequent years systematic attacks were made on Arkwright's machines. Crompton had to go into hiding. Yet such a list, in itself, can be misleading. Cases of opposition to machinery carried to the length of sabotage are really few in relation to the number of cases in which new machinery was introduced without such a reaction. And many cases of the destruction of machinery were not so much the result of hostility to the machine itself as a method of coercing an obnoxious employer—of resisting a wage cut or the imposition of harder working conditions. The famous outbreak of the Nottingham stocking-frame knitters, from which the term Luddism is derived, was mainly of this character. Luddism in this sense was not a substitute for trade unionism but a tactical weapon adopted by it to meet the special circumstances of the eighteenth and early nineteenth centuries.

But behind all this open misery, the machinery and the factory system were also bringing immense benefits. They made available far greater quantities of all commodities. The workers, of course, did not automatically get their share of these goods—they had to learn how to fight for it—but they did get some share, and living conditions on the whole did improve, after the black period of the first few decades. The best index is perhaps population, which in England and Wales rose from 6½ millions in 1750 to over 10 millions in 1811.[5] Part of the rise was due to a rise in the birth-rate, but more to a fall in the death-rate, which was a sign of better health and a rising standard of living. These in turn came partly from the increased productivity of the machines, though it must not be forgotten that the parallel revolution in agricultural methods was equally important. In a London lying-in hospital between 1749 and 1758 one mother in every forty-two and one child in fifteen died; in the years 1799 to 1800 deaths had been reduced to one mother in 914 and one child in 115. Partly, this shows that the mothers coming in were healthier and better fed. Partly, that medical knowledge and medical service had improved—but that in turn owes something to the fact that increased industrial and agricultural productivity allowed a greater number of men to withdraw from the production of essentials and devote themselves instead to the study and practise of medicine.

Thus, in spite of their black side, the industrial changes of the seventeenth and eighteenth centuries did mean a tremendous step forward for mankind, a step towards the position in which we find ourselves today with the prospect of eliminating poverty for ever and providing for all the material essentials on which to base a full and happy life.

[5] The effect of industrial changes on the size of population is better brought out by comparing the average annual increase over various periods. Between 1483 and 1700 the average annual increase per thousand of population was 0·7; between 1700 and 1750 it was 3·3 per thousand; then as the effects of the Industrial Revolution became more marked, it rose quickly to 8·5 in 1750–1811 and 12·8 in 1811–51.

CHAPTER 7

THE INDUSTRIAL REVOLUTION: IN MATURITY (1815 TO 1918)

BRITAIN'S almost unchallenged lead in advanced industrial methods could not last indefinitely. By the end of the eighteenth century other countries had started to develop along similar lines. The French Revolution of 1789 swept away the hindrance of a feudal-absolutist state, as the English one had done in 1640, and did so more suddenly and completely. The people of the American colonies gained their independence in 1783 and the United States of America were soon on their way to industrialisation. Other countries followed in the course of the next century.

The Industrial Revolution Spreads

Freed from the restrictions that had held them in check, the industries of these countries began to grow as that of Britain had done before. Naturally their citizens turned to science and invention to provide better industrial methods. Already we have noticed how the U.S.A. took the lead in steam navigation within a few years of winning their independence. France and America figure as prominently as Britain in the present chapter and towards the end of it Germany also comes to the fore. In France in particular, the more complete and uncompromising revolution was followed at the beginning of the century by very conscious efforts to encourage inventions and raise the level of industrialisation. Government commissions were set up to encourage technical progress. New institutions for scientific and technical education were created. Napoleon, on hearing of a project by Fulton for steam navigation, wrote to his Minister of the Interior in July 1804: 'I have just read Citizen Fulton's project, which you have delayed sending much too long, for it seems capable of changing the face of the world. In any case, I request you to have the matter enquired into at once by a committee composed of members of the Academy who are authorities on European science. A great physical truth is here disclosed to me; it is for these gentlemen to see it and make it serviceable. Send me the report if possible within a week, as I am burning to hear the result.—N.'[1] Such direct interest of political leaders in invention, because it was 'capable of changing the face of the world', was a quite new phenomenon and indeed was not to be paralleled until after 1917 in the U.S.S.R. The *Société d'Encouragement pour l'Industrie Nationale* subsidised inventors, offered prizes for important inventions (their prize offered for the construction of a practical water-turbine was largely responsible for the early lead of France in that field) and compiled critical reports on inventions with respect to both their technical excellence and their economic and social effects.

In the U.S.A. the interest of political leaders in technology was nearly as great. Thomas Jefferson concerned himself with mass-production methods and also used mathematics to work out the best shape for plough mouldboards. Benjamin Franklin was at once America's first noted scientist and one of her greatest diplomats. George Washington himself experimented with the mechanical sowing of grain. In Britain the inventor was left to take care of himself, though voluntary organisations like the Royal Society of Arts did something to help; but Britain's lead at the beginning of the nineteenth century was such that she was able to maintain her place almost unchallenged until near the end of it.

The period 1815 to 1918 saw the development of steam navigation on an ocean scale (see Chapter 6), the growth of the railway, the completion of the mechanisation of textiles, the development of several prime-movers—the water-turbine, the steam-turbine, and the internal combustion engine—the appearance of the motor car and the aeroplane, the development of electric power, the telegraph, telephone and radio, much progress towards the effective mechanisation of agriculture and of coal-mining, besides many hundreds of minor advances. It was so fruitful a period that in this book we can do no more than skim over its surface—a full history of the mechanical inventions of these times would require volumes to itself.

[1] The Academy turned down the proposal.

The Growth of the Railways

Few innovations have had more far-reaching effects than the railway—that is, the steam-driven public railway, for railways as such are of much earlier origin. We have already noticed in Chapter 5 (see particularly Figure 16) that railways were used at German mineheads in the late fifteenth century. They were similarly applied in England—near Nottingham and at Broseley—in the first decade of the seventeenth century (and perhaps a little earlier). The railway provided a cheaper and more efficient mode of transport at mines than the ordinary cart running on a necessarily very imperfect road. As industry grew, the number of such railways grew too. Gradually they were improved, by covering the original wooden rails with iron plates (hence the term 'platelayer'), and eventually by the total substitution of iron for wood. By the end of the eighteenth century such railways were common at British mines and also at foundries, where transport was equally heavy. The Darby ironworks at Coalbrookdale, for example, had about 20 miles of railways. All these were horse-drawn.

The next great innovation was the driving of railways by steam. The earliest steam locomotives were not intended for use on railways, but as road carriages. Proposals for steam carriages go back to the late seventeenth century, but the first to achieve even limited practical success seems to have been that of Cugnot in 1769. It was sound in conception but defective in proportions, so that it ran at 2½ m.p.h., but stopped every 30 yards or so to get up more steam. Murdock made a highly successful model in 1784. But the real pioneer was Richard Trevithick, who worked on the problem from about 1797, produced moderately successful road carriages, and then conceived the idea of applying this new method of haulage to the railway. He probably did not envisage the public railway we know today, merely the idea of using a new and better method of haulage on the lines that connected with the mines and ironworks. In 1802 he built a locomotive at the ironworks in Coalbrookdale, and in 1804 another for the Pen-y-Darran ironworks, which pulled 10 tons of ore and seventy passengers at 5 m.p.h. These early locomotives were not very successful, but the need for a better haulage system on the railways became generally felt in the next few years and many men worked on the problem. Of these George Stephenson was outstandingly successful and it was he who established the railway system as we know it today. He built his first locomotive (for a colliery) in 1814. It pulled 30 tons at 4 m.p.h. up a gradient of 1 in 450. Thereafter by careful analysis and brilliant workmanship he rapidly improved the efficiency of his engines.

At the same time a new idea was developing—that of the public railway, though this at first meant a line on which anybody could use his own carriages in return for paying a toll. One such was opened in 1805 for carrying merchandise between Wandsworth and Croydon. It used horses for traction; the idea of steam traction was then little known and the railway was merely a method of using horses to better effect than on the roads. Transport problems in this rapidly industrialising era were becoming acute—the roads were poor, road transport costly, and though canal transport was cheap, the canals were seriously overburdened. That was the background against which a Bill was put before Parliament in 1821 for a railway between Stockton and Darlington to be worked 'with men and horses or otherwise'. There was still general doubt as to whether the steam locomotive could do the job. But Stephenson convincingly demonstrated that it could and the railway was opened in 1825 with locomotives of his manufacture, although till 1830 private horse-drawn traffic ran between the steam trains worked by the company.

Meanwhile the cotton manufacturers of Manchester had been finding that the Liverpool-Manchester canal was inadequate to carry the enormously expanded export trade that we noted in the last chapter. A Bill was put before Parliament in 1825 to sanction a railway between those towns. But it was met by organised opposition of the landowners, who objected to this spoiling of their estates, and of canal, turnpike and coaching interests, who saw only its potential effects on their own position. A campaign of vilification was started, in the Press and by special leaflets: cows, frightened by the trains, would yield no milk; smoke from the funnels would kill the birds; sparks would fire houses; boilers would burst and kill the travellers, and so on. By such tales and by much lobbying, the vested interests obtained adverse votes in the Parliamentary Committee, and the Bill had to be withdrawn. The opposition had also organised sabotage and even armed attacks on the men who were surveying the line. Then came the success of the Stockton-Darlington line and that, aided by an expenditure of £27,000 by the railway interests, got a second Bill for the railway passed in 1826.

A competition was held in 1829 to decide whose locomotives should be used. Stephenson's 'Rocket' (Plate XI) was the only one that satisfied the conditions. On the second day of the trial it pulled thirty passengers at 30 m.p.h. The line was opened in 1830 and the steam railway was established as the primary mode of inland transport for nearly a century. Yet opposition continued to hold back development and by 1838 only 490 miles had been laid in Britain. Then came the railway boom, and the mileage reached 1,900 in 1843 and 5,000 in 1848.

The railways opened up possibilities of travel to wider classes than ever before. But far more important were their effects in relation to further industrial developments. The railways became the arteries of industry. The trends that we shall discuss in subsequent pages demanded more and more centralisation of production in large units. The benefits of industrialisation depended on a transport system which could carry raw materials and finished products where they were wanted. The railway on land and the steamship at sea provided this transport.

The Water-Turbine

The water-turbine has a longer and more complicated evolution than most previous inventions. Its ancestry can be traced back to the primitive horizontal water-wheel. With the earliest rise of modern mechanical methods various improvements took place in the design of such wheels, all leading gradually in the direction of the turbine. One of the earlier modified wheels was proposed by Leonardo and in the seventeenth and eighteenth centuries many more followed, some of them being used fairly widely in practice.

But though the general idea of the turbine, in which the water would act on blades in a close-fitting casing, was simple, and though the obvious possibilities of greater efficiency than the comparatively crude water-wheel made it attractive, yet there were many difficulties to be overcome. The details of the correct shaping of blades and casing were very far from obvious, and unless these were correctly designed the turbine could not fulfil its promise. Thus ultimate progress depended very greatly on theoretical investigations, in the light of the rising science of hydrodynamics, which were made by a number of men in the second half of the eighteenth century. These led gradually towards a sound grasp of the essentials of turbine design. Indeed Euler, as a result of his theoretical work (1750–4), was able to produce a crude form of turbine, which did find some commercial application, though it was not yet good enough to be of general significance.

The other great difficulty was an engineering one—a close fit of comparatively fast-moving parts was necessary if the turbine was to be reasonably efficient. The engineering experience of the eighteenth century provided at last the possibility of sufficiently accurate workmanship and so it is in the early nineteenth century that we find the turbine fast becoming a practicable proposition, as a result of the efforts of many workers, almost all in France. Then in 1823 came the offer by the *Société d'Encouragement pour l'Industrie Nationale* of a prize for a perfected turbine, and with this added incentive the efforts of inventors were redoubled. Part of the prize was awarded to Burdin in 1827, but the real credit for the perfected turbine belongs to Fourneyron. His first turbine, of 6 h.p., was produced also in 1827. By 1832 he had built a perfected version (a 50 h.p. turbine, used to drive a forge-hammer), and was awarded the prize of 6,000 francs. The turbine thereafter expanded very rapidly in size, reaching 800 h.p. by 1855. It later found its main application in electric power generation.

Electricity: Telegraph and Telephone

The story of electricity, whose application to many uses is one of the greatest achievements of the nineteenth century, is likewise one of long evolution, the result of the efforts of many men. Here we must skip the early developments and begin with the discovery of the Voltaic cell in 1800. This gave for the first time a continuous current, the prime essential for practical application and the basis on which scientists could discover the properties of electric currents and then learn how to apply their knowledge. Thereafter development was extremely rapid. The principle of the arc lamp was demonstrated by Davy in 1808; Faraday discovered the fundamental principles of the electric motor in 1821 and of the dynamo in 1831. Also in those years were discovered the fundamental properties on which the telegraph, the telephone and many other applications were to be based. But electricity was no easy tool to master and decades passed before really practical results were obtained.

The first important application to be brought to success was the telegraph—partly because the practical problems here were simpler than, say, for electric lighting, partly because the need was more obvious and insistent. With the growing commerce of the times, speedy means of communication were much to be desired and after the advent of railways the need for some method of informing the signalman ahead of the train's progress was a very pressing one. Various methods of rapid communication were in use—carrier pigeons, or telegraphs based on the sending of visual signals along relays of stations, but none was satisfactory.

From the beginning of the century and, in a desultory way, even before, many men sought for an electric telegraph but it was not until 1837 that success was achieved independently in the U.S.A. by Samuel Morse and in England by Cooke and Wheatstone. In the following year the latter system was installed on the 13 miles of railway between Paddington and West Drayton, while in 1844 Morse completed a line connecting Washington and Baltimore (40 miles). In the U.S.A. four years later telegraphs were in use in all but one of the states east of the Mississippi, while Britain had 16,000 miles of telegraph lines by 1868. In 1851 the Dover-Calais submarine cable was laid; and with the establishment of a transatlantic service in 1866 after many tribulations, the telegraph became a means of communication on a world scale.

If men could communicate signals over long distances by electricity, it was natural that they should seek the more convenient method of transmitting actual speech. The first to succeed was Phillipp Reis in 1861, but his apparatus, though it worked in a limited way, was little more than a curious toy. And it was not until 1876 that a practical telephone was invented by Alexander Graham Bell, a Scottish immigrant to the U.S.A. Within a few years his telephones were in use in all the advanced countries of the world. Improvements in technique came hard on each others' heels. In 1876 Bell had transmitted speech over 2 miles; by 1880, 45 miles had been reached and by 1892 the New York to Chicago line of 900 miles represented the economic limit that could be achieved until the use of inductive loading about 1900, and later of amplifiers using electronic valves, practically removed all limits of distance, so that by 1913 a line of 2,600 miles joined New York to Salt Lake City.

Electricity: Light and Power

If the telegraph and telephone changed the world by making possible instantaneous communication over the whole globe, possibilities just as revolutionary were implied in the transmission of power by electricity. It makes power available for small units—household appliances, for instance, or individual drives for factory machines, eliminating the cumbersome, inefficient and noisy shafting, ending the need to concentrate machines round the steam-engine. It provides the possibility of moving the factory out of the crowded towns, away from the coal wharf to which it was formerly tied, and into the countryside, where, in healthier conditions, it can still get its power from electricity. Or alternatively, if the factories must for other reasons remain concentrated together, it gives the opportunity to burn fuel elsewhere and transmit electric power to the city, which can thus be kept clean and healthy. These possibilities have not yet been fully utilised, though a beginning has been made; but the opportunity is there for future generations to grasp.

In point of fact the pioneers of electrical transmission of energy were not thinking of such possibilities; they were not to any great extent concerned with the transmission of power at all. Their main concern was electric lighting, perhaps partly because that problem was somewhat simpler, partly because gas lighting (London's Gas Light and Coke Company, for example, was founded in 1812) provided an obvious precedent. Edison's early meters actually recorded current consumption in cubic feet (of equivalent gas consumption)!

The dynamo, whose principle had been discovered by Faraday in 1831, was developed by a whole series of workers over the next fifty years. Davy's arc lamp was turned into a practical device by the efforts of several men in the forties and fifties. Arc lighting came to be used for special purposes. It was tried at South Foreland lighthouse in 1858, and again at Dungeness lighthouse in 1862. The appearance in 1870 of Gramme's ring dynamo (the greatest single step on the generating side) reduced the cost of electricity enough to make an economic proposition of arc lighting in many circumstances. In the next decade it was widely used and in 1878–80 it had a definite boom, being installed to light railway stations, docks, theatres, ironworks, markets and even streets.

But it was in just those boom years, no doubt partly because of the boom, that the more efficient and convenient system of incandescent lighting was established. Like many other electrical developments it had its beginning in the early nineteenth century; De La Rue produced an incandescent lamp of platinum about 1820. But it was the work of Swan in England and Edison in U.S.A., culminating about 1880, that made a practical proposition of the incandescent lamp with carbon filament. Edison's contribution was much more than a lamp. He put almost the final touches to the generator, so that by 1882 the generators in use were essentially those of today, apart from the carbon brush introduced in 1883 and certain improvements in winding and, of course, vast changes in size. Edison also worked out the by no means obvious system of distribution by cable and wiring circuits. After his work the industry expanded, possibly more rapidly than any industry had ever done before.

The first commercial installation was made in 1880 on a ship, the first on land (a private installation) in 1881. The first public lighting supply was opened at Appleton, Wisconsin, in the same year, with an output of about 1 h.p.! The first station in England was opened in 1881 at Godalming in Surrey to light three street lamps. Then in 1882 Edison's company opened stations in London, Milan, Sunbury (Pennsylvania), and—most important—the famous Pearl Street station in New York, which finally established the method of electric supply to any consumer in a district. By the end of the year nearly eighty electricity companies had been founded in England, though few had yet begun to operate.

Hydro-electric generation had been used at some of the earliest stations, including those at Appleton and Godalming, and others followed. But the station that fully established the value of hydro-electric power was that at Niagara, which in 1896 was transmitting power to Buffalo 25 miles away. Soon the generation of electricity became the principal application of the water-turbine.

It was in the transport industry that the convenience of electricity for transmitting *power* was first seriously developed. Siemens and Halske demonstrated a miniature electric railway at the Berlin Exhibition of 1879, and in 1881 built a public electrified line at Lichterfelde in Germany. In the British Isles a short electric railway was opened in 1883 on the beach at Brighton, to be followed a few weeks later by the Portrush and Bushmills line in Ireland,[2] some 5 miles in length, which was the first to use hydro-electric power. Main-line electrification began in 1895 with a 4-mile tunnel in Baltimore. London's electrified underground system started with the opening of the City and South London Railway in 1890.[3]

Electric tramways, which were to provide the main form of urban transport for many years, effectively began with those in Glasgow and Frankfurt-am-Main in 1884 and Richmond, Virginia, in 1888. Tramways, and later petrol-driven omnibuses were instrumental in changing the shape of the city. Housing need no longer be concentrated round the factories. The dense central slums began to dwindle—though it is a sad commentary on our times that they have not yet disappeared—and suburbia, with all its advantages and disadvantages, rapidly developed. In like fashion, underground and suburban electric railways have turned the great capital cities into uncontrollable sprawls.

Transport is, of course, a very specialised application of electric power; and most of the early systems had their own generating stations, independent of public electricity supplies. Power in factory or home, derived from public distribution systems was slower in coming, and made little impact till about 1890. The use of the polyphase system (developed by Tesla from 1887 on and first applied on a large scale at Niagara in 1897–8) made electric power available for heavier industrial purposes. For small-scale

[2] Later extended to the Giant's Causeway.

[3] The underground system as such began with steam trains on the Metropolitan line in 1863.

use, the direct current motor was greatly improved before 1900, while alternating current commutator motors developed rapidly after key inventions made in 1891. By 1900 individual electric motors in progressive factories were replacing the clumsy, noisy and dangerous system of overhead shafting and belt drives. At first the motors were merely adapted to existing types of machines as required, but already some machine tools were being produced with built-in motors.

Tesla's marketing of a small fan driven by a $\frac{1}{6}$ h.p. motor in 1889 was perhaps the first hint of the role electric power was to play in the home. But though many types of electric vacuum cleaners, washing machines and refrigerators were invented—and even sold in small quantities—from about the turn of the century, electric power made no serious impact on the domestic scene till after 1918.

The early central stations, working on direct current at low voltage, could distribute over a radius of only a few hundred yards. The station had to be in the centre of the area served. To gain the full advantages of electric power it should be generated at some convenient point where fuel or water-power is easily accessible, and thence transmitted to the area where it is to be used. This requires alternating current, generated at a high voltage. A lead was given by Ferranti in 1889 with his 10,000-volt generators at Deptford, whence power was transmitted to Central London. But small local stations remained common for decades. Indeed it took Government action, in the form of the Act of 1926 which set up the Grid, to secure anything like general adoption of Ferranti's policy in Britain, while other countries showed little if any more progress. The greatest benefits of all arise when the electricity can be transmitted over really long distances—up to a few hundred miles. Marcel Duprez experimented very early on long-distance transmission and in 1882 covered nearly 40 miles. The system was adopted in such cases as the Niagara power station, but its general use belongs to the inter-war period.

The Steam-Turbine

One of the most important elements in modern electric power technology is the steam-turbine. It will be recalled that two of the earliest schemes for steam-engines (neither of any practical significance) were for turbines—those of Hero and of Branca. With the success of the reciprocating engine, attention was diverted from the turbine, and by the same time good engineers, with their increasing knowledge, had come to realise the tremendous difficulties of making a workable machine of it. Speeds would have to be enormously beyond anything then feasible, and the engineering difficulties of ensuring a close fit at such speeds remained beyond practical possibilities until the late nineteenth century. James Watt put the matter neatly when he replied to fears expressed by Boulton concerning the effect of a proposed turbine on their business; after a few calculations he remarked 'without God make it possible for things to move 1,000 feet per second, it cannot do much harm'.[4]

Nevertheless, the turbine, if it could be made practicable, had certain obvious advantages—it promised higher efficiency and greater power, it would eliminate the rather roundabout process of converting the energy of steam into rotary motion via reciprocating motion. Thus several attempts were made in the latter half of the nineteenth century to produce workable turbines, but none was successful (except for specialised uses) until that patented by Charles Parsons in 1884. Parsons developed the turbine chiefly in relation to electricity generation (though his patent shows that he had other purposes also in mind from the beginning). The first turbine (Plate XIII) was used to drive a small generator and gave satisfactory results. Many turbo-generators were built for small installations in factories, ships, and so on. After the incorporation of condensers in 1891 and other improvements, the turbine rivalled the reciprocating engine in efficiency and was rapidly adopted for central generation of electricity. Thereafter it soon surpassed in both size and efficiency the utmost limit possible with the reciprocating engine. By 1912, turbo-generators of 25,000 kW. (about 33,000 h.p.) had been reached, whereas the maximum ever attained by a reciprocating engine was 20,000 h.p.

Only electricity generation and shipping required such great quantities of power. And it was to marine engines that Parsons

[4] The gearing in Branca's proposal (Figure 19) may indicate that even he had some vague idea that high speeds were involved.

next turned his attention. He constructed a small launch, the *Turbinia,* which created a sensation at the Naval Review of 1897 by reaching a speed of 34 knots, against the 27 knots of the fastest destroyers in existence. In the following years turbines were tried in various vessels of the Navy, with such success that in 1905 the Admiralty took the decision that they should be used exclusively on all classes of warships. Meanwhile the first merchant vessel with a turbine was built in 1901 and soon turbines were accepted as the best drive for all fast ships—the *Lusitania* and the *Mauretania* were launched in 1906, each with four turbines totalling 70,000 h.p. From 1909 onwards Parsons developed the system of driving the propellers through reduction gearing and thereby made possible the use of turbines in slow cargo vessels.

The Internal Combustion Engine and the Car

To use fuel directly in a cylinder is a simpler idea than the more complex cycle of fire, boiler and cylinder involved in the steam-engine, so that the earliest attempts at internal combustion engines occurred in the period just before the practical steam-engine arose. Huygens' effort to produce a gunpowder engine about 1680 has already been mentioned in Chapter 6. But if the concept of an internal combustion engine is simpler than that of a steam-engine, the practical problems of making it work are much greater; thus the arrival of the practical steam-engine put an end (for a time) to work on the other.

Nevertheless the internal combustion engine presents certain features which were bound to be attractive to inventors—its greater simplicity in principle, the possibilities of lightness and smallness arising from the elimination of fire-grate and boiler, the promise (not to be so easily realised) of greater efficiency through eliminating the loss in the chimney, boiler and steam-pipe system, and the possibility of conveniently producing engines in smaller units, suitable for the small factory or workshop (whereas the economical use of steam was confined to larger establishments). For these reasons renewed attempts were made from the last decade of the eighteenth century onwards to construct internal combustion engines of various types. The coming of coal-gas provided a suitable and readily available fuel and from the twenties the gas-engine became more and more practicable, attaining gradually increasing commercial success from 1860 on, till the Otto 'Silent' gas-engine of 1876 completed its main evolution. The gas-engine, with its adaptability to small-scale use, allowed power mechanisation of many smaller industries, just as the steam-engine had done for the larger ones a century before. However, the growing use of electric power around the turn of the century largely replaced it in this important field. Very large units using blast-furnace gas were developed, with efficiencies greater than steam in suitable circumstances. But in the long run the gas-engine was significant chiefly as a step towards the petrol and oil engines. All its principles were embodied in the latter, which have thus a more rapid evolution.

Petroleum in large quantities had been discovered in 1859 in Pennsylvania, and from 1873 onwards attempts were made to build engines using various petroleum fractions (petrol, paraffin oil, heavier oils) as fuels. All the early models ran at slow speeds, like the gas-engine from which they were derived. It was Gottlieb Daimler who realised the advantages of developing power from a high speed of rotation, and the modern petrol engine derives from the one which he had working in 1885. Karl Benz's engine of the same year, though of the slow-running type, introduced the electrical system of ignition which subsequently became standard. Wilhelm Maybach added the float-fed carburettor in 1893. By the end of the century all the main features of the modern petrol engine had appeared.

About the same time useful engines working on heavier oils were developed. The first to achieve commercial success was that of Dent and Priestman, patented in 1886, which worked on fairly heavy oil fractions. The Ackroyd-Stuart engine about 1890 successfully used still cruder oils. But all the earlier attempts pale into insignificance compared with the diesel engine, using ignition by compression (like some of its predecessors), and much more scientifically designed so that it could work on the crudest of crude oils—or indeed on almost any liquid or pulverised fuel. Diesel's main patent was dated 1892, though it was several years before a workable engine was produced. The diesel engine realised at last the dream of an oil engine which should be more efficient than steam, and was soon expanded to sizes where it could rival steam in electricity generation and ship propulsion, except in the very largest units. By 1930 a considerably greater tonnage of new shipping was being powered with diesel engines than with steam.

The effects of the petrol engine were most revolutionary in the field of transport, first on the roads and later in the air; its lightness made it pre-eminently suitable for this field. Mechanical road transport does not, however, begin with the petrol engine. The steam-carriages which we mentioned on page 115 began to reach a reasonable degree of practicability almost at the same time as the railways. By 1831 there were twenty such carriages operating for public transport in or near London with speeds of from 5 to 30 m.p.h. The growth of the railways, however, made such transport uneconomic. And, when about the middle of the century, steam-carriages had been sufficiently improved to become once more a rival, the combined opposition of railway and coaching interests succeeded in obtaining restrictive legislation in England, which made steam transport by road well nigh impossible. The Act of 1861 required that each vehicle should carry at least two drivers, and restricted speeds to 10 m.p.h. in the country and 5 m.p.h. in towns. The Red Flag Act of 1865, as amended in 1878, reduced these speed limits to 4 and 2 m.p.h. respectively and required that a man carrying a red flag or a red lantern should walk 60 yards ahead of the vehicle. In this way the interests of the railway companies were protected. A hardly surprising result was that the main initial inventions in the story of the motor-car were made elsewhere. Britain could not compete till the Red Flag Act was repealed in 1896.

Attempts to make petrol-driven vehicles date from 1864. The first of importance was that of Karl Benz in 1885. But the motor-car as we know it derives from Daimler's application of his high-speed engine to a bicycle in 1886, and later the same year to a four-wheeled carriage. In 1889 came the first Daimler to be built integrally as a car. Several cars by other inventors followed quickly, and petrol buses and lorries appeared about 1904. The further development of the motor-car is less a story of invention than of the application of mass-production methods to make widely available machines; we shall return to it in Chapter 8.

Man Takes to the Air

With many of the inventions we have described it is clear that they were achieved at some particular period largely because general social conditions had fairly suddenly established a great need for them; many inventors responded with efforts to satisfy this need, and one or a few of them were successful. The history of flight is different. It is, of course, true that there was more practical gain to be achieved from flight in the industrial era of A.D. 1900 than at any previous time. Nevertheless, man's desire to fly has been in most periods so great that we have to say that the reason why practical flight arrived no earlier than it did was not a lack of general desire, implying lack of incentive for the inventor, but lack of ability. The technical problems of flight, more than any previous mechanical achievement, were such that their solution could only be built on the results of centuries of engineering experience and scientific analysis.

Mankind first sought to fly by magical means. Then, with the great change from faith in magic to faith in machines that took place in the Middle Ages and early modern times, came a change of tactics. Thereafter men tried to construct suitable machines. They worked logically, though their attempts remained very inadequate, for lack of the requisite knowledge. Thus early in the eleventh century Eilmer of Malmesbury[5] attempted to fly with wings attached to his arms and legs. Thus Leonardo at the close of the Middle Ages carried out thorough and penetrating studies of the flight of birds and attempted to construct a flying machine on this basis. But, as scientific analysis progressed, it was realised (and stated by Borelli in 1680) that human muscles were inadequate, and heavier-than-air flight had to await the coming of a suitable motor.

Lighter-than-air flight came much sooner. After many proposals and experiments, from the early seventeenth century onwards, flight in hot-air balloons was achieved by the Montgolfier brothers in France in 1783; and in the same year the first flight in a hydrogen balloon was made. Immediately ballooning became a craze. Many flights of considerable daring were made. The Channel was crossed in 1785. Balloons were used by the

[5] As a result of a fourteenth-century copying error, he was till recently called 'Oliver' of Malmesbury.

French Army for observation in 1794. The year after the first successful flight, a proposal was made for a dirigible balloon (airship) but the first successful airship did not come till 1852, when Henri Giffard's machine with a 3 h.p. steam-engine covered 17 miles at 4 or 5 m.p.h. This was far from a practical airship—it had not got sufficient power to fly against the wind—and practical development begins from about 1884. Zeppelin began building his first ship in 1898 and made his first flight in 1900. His ships were rapidly successful. His fourth in 1908 crossed the Alps. Between 1910 and 1914 Zeppelins carried 35,000 passengers and covered 170,000 miles without serious mishap. In the 1914–18 war airships were widely used for military purposes, but not long afterwards a succession of disasters, which stood out in sharp relief because the practical alternative of the aeroplane was being developed, put an end to airship construction, except for very special purposes.[6]

A critical step towards the creation of the aeroplane was taken when Sir George Cayley published in 1809 and 1810 the results of some thirteen years of investigation. He accurately formulated the principles that must govern heavier-than-air flight, and in particular made it clear that the main problem was to obtain a suitable motive power and that the steam-engine was not likely to fill the bill. Steam (or clockwork) would serve, however, for models and from about 1840 there was considerable experimentation with power-driven model planes, the first to rise under its own power and land again safely being constructed in 1857.

Further developments now depended on a thorough scientific analysis, of which the basis was the study and practice of gliding flight. Cayley continued to investigate and construct gliders, with increasing success, till near the time of his death in 1857, but his later work was ignored by the rest of the world. Many others contributed, but the most important work was that of Otto Lilienthal in Germany, who constructed his first manned glider in 1891 after some twenty-five years of research and subsequently made hundreds of controlled glides, which thoroughly illuminated the basic principles of a flying machine and its controls. Then in the nineties came renewed attempts at power flight on a more rational

[6] In the early 1960s, with the safe gas helium becoming more available, there are signs that interest in airships is reviving.

basis, many of them almost achieving success—machines that rose a little from the ground, others that flew a few hundred yards but were clearly not under full control and ended by crashing.

In 1900 the Wright brothers began extensive gliding experiments, coupled with painstaking scientific and mathematical analysis of the problems involved. They developed a system of lateral control by independent flexing of the wings, a system which, in the form of the aileron, eventually proved to be the key to successful flight. Then they turned their attention to power flight. The recently developed automobile engine provided the basis for a suitable motor, but the brothers took equal pains in designing their particular motor and propeller. Their thoroughness was rewarded on 17 December 1903, when their machine flew for twelve seconds and covered 40 yards (Plate XIV). Larger distances had been covered before, but the point was that this time the machine was fully under control. Progress thereafter was rapid. Their fourth flight lasted 59 seconds; in 1904 they flew 5 minutes 4 seconds; in 1905 they covered 20¾ miles in 33 minutes 17 seconds. By 1908, when many others besides the Wrights were flying successfully, the duration record was just over three hours; the distance 112 miles; and the speed record 50 m.p.h. In 1909 Blériot flew the Channel.

Till 1914, nevertheless, flying remained something of an adventurous sport. The forcing house of war, with technicians, factories and Government funds all made available, turned the plane into a reliable machine. Between 1914 and 1918 maximum speeds rose from 70–80 m.p.h. to 140–155 m.p.h.; air-cooled engines developed from weights of 4 lb. per h.p. to 1·9 lb. per h.p. and water-cooled from 4·05 to 2·2; the average ceiling rose from 7,000 feet to 30,000 feet. The crossing of the Atlantic in 1919 by Alcock and Brown demonstrated what a reliable and useful machine had emerged from the war. Regular air services were quickly established and even in 1920 they flew a total of nearly 3 million miles.

Radio

Wireless communication, which also came into being about the turn of the century, arose from two main sources. The incentive to attack the problem came from the same social needs for rapid communication that earlier gave birth to the telegraph and telephone, plus the promise that wireless would provide one great advantage that these two never could—communication with ships. The basis for the solution was provided by the theoretical researches of Clerk Maxwell, published in 1864, and the experimental work of Hertz from 1886 on, which demonstrated the existence of electro-magnetic waves, the basis of radio. In the nineties this problem interested a number of inventors—particularly Popov in Russia and Rutherford and Lodge in England—who made some progress and at least demonstrated the possibility of radio-communication. But the only outstandingly successful system was that of Marconi, who arrived in England from Italy in 1896, transmitted radio signals over 3 miles and patented his invention the same year. Rapid development followed. In 1899 the British Navy on manœuvres used radio telegraphy over 75 miles and in 1901 Marconi bridged the Atlantic, while only seven years later a regular transatlantic radio telegraph was established.

Experiments in radio telephony started almost immediately on the success of telegraphy. By 1900 Fessenden of the U.S.A. had achieved some success. In 1906 he claimed to have transmitted speech across the Atlantic. In 1909 de Forest, also of the U.S.A., transmitted Caruso's voice from the Metropolitan Opera House.

But progress was slow, because the transmission of speech depended on ability to radiate *continuous* waves and the systems then available for doing so were of very limited value. Ultimate success of radio telephony depended on the 'valve' or thermionic tube. The diode, which would act as a detector but not for other purposes, was invented by the English physicist, Fleming, in 1904. The triode, the real key to modern radio, was the invention of de Forest in 1906. Nevertheless, it was not until 1913 that the radio valve and associated circuits were advanced enough to be ready for general use.

As in the case of flying, it was the war of 1914–18 that gave the incentives and means for the rapid mastery of the critical problems. Radio telephony was used widely by the fighting forces. Valve techniques were developed rapidly, especially for aircraft, in which they were used for both transmission and reception. Sets of less than ten pounds in weight in reconnaissance planes transmitted speech up to 200 miles. The development and perfection of radio techniques during the war was such that it took only two further years of systematic experiment by scores of workers all over the world (among whom Marconi remained one of the most successful) to pave the way for the beginning of regular broadcasting in 1920. Radio direction-finding began about 1907 and again was greatly developed during the war.

The Production and Preservation of Food

Aeroplanes and radio were perhaps the most startling and romantic developments of the century before 1918. But the standards of human life were much more greatly affected by the mechanisation of agriculture. The change-over from hand methods to machine methods of farming, which began to be marked in the second quarter of the nineteenth century, provided for the first time in the world's history the possibility of abundant food for all. More than that, it was the essential basis for the growth of a highly industralised civilisation.

In the early nineteenth century the advanced countries completed the change-over to the all-iron plough. This in itself meant a notable increase in productivity. Steam-power was applied to ploughing after 1850 when John Fowler introduced the system of cable-ploughing—in which steam-engines at either end of the field dragged the plough across by means of cables. This remained the main method of power ploughing until 1918 and even after that it was only slowly displaced by the tractor.

Whereas ploughing had used animal-power from the early Bronze Age, reaping until the nineteenth century remained a job entirely for human muscles. One exception to this is an extremely crude ox-power reaper described by Pliny as being in use in Gaul in Roman times, but this does not seem at any stage to have been widely used. From 1780 onwards attempts were made to construct reaping machines. The first to achieve any success was that of Patrick Bell, in 1826, which was fairly widely used in Scotland for some years. But south of the Border mechanical reaping made no progress till after the introduction of the superior machines developed in America.

The great fields of the U.S.A. provided the ideal conditions for mechanisation and it was there that the modern reaping machine developed. Several reapers were invented in the thirties, by far the most successful being that of Cyrus McCormick, patented in

1834, which cut the labour involved in reaping to one-third (Plate XV). By 1851 McCormick was making a thousand machines a year. From then on more and more automatic harvesters appeared. The American Civil War of 1861–5 created a great manpower shortage and thus gave a boost to mechanisation. After several steps the completely automatic sheaf-binding harvester appeared about 1878, cutting the labour required to one-half or one-third again. In 1880 four-fifths of the U.S. wheat harvest was cut by this machine.

The next step was the combine harvester—a machine to reap the corn and thresh it at the same time. The idea appeared in patent specifications as early 1828, and a machine was built in 1836, but the practical development of the combine does not begin till about 1860. By the eighties combines hauled by twenty to forty horses were reaping 25 to 45 acres a day in California. In the nineties, drawn by steam tractors, they had an even greater capacity. By 1930 a combine required 3·3 man-hours of labour to produce 20 bushels of wheat, compared with 57·7 man-hours with a sickle and flail in 1830. Nevertheless, the combine did not spread outside California till after 1914, when man-power problems caused its introduction east of the Rockies. It did not appear in Great Britain till 1928 and even then spread but slowly.

Meanwhile other aspects of agriculture were being mechanised. A grass tedder was invented in 1814, and the horse-rake towards the middle of the century. After 1850 the use of these simple machines spread rapidly. The mowing machine—a not very difficult adaptation of the reaper—came into use in America in 1856. Hayloaders, which first appeared in 1876, were taken up rather slowly. And with the advent of the swathe-turner in 1896, the essentials of hay-making machinery had been completed. The baler was an American invention of 1881.

Before the end of the century the potato-plough and spinner types of potato harvesters were in use. The latter throws the potatoes clear of the soil, but scatters them widely, after which they must be picked up by hand. The elevator-lifter type of harvester, which does not eliminate hand-picking, but does lay the potatoes conveniently in narrow rows, began to develop in the early twentieth century. Potato-planting machinery was developed about the same period. However, machinery for crops other than cereals and grass was not sufficiently perfected for general use till after 1918.

Apart from threshing (see Chapter 6), cable-ploughing, the use of steam tractors with combines in the nineties, and a few experiments in other directions, the horse remained the main source of power in agriculture till the end of the nineteenth century. But about 1890 in the U.S.A. and a few years later in Great Britain the first attempts to use tractors with internal combustion engines were made. The tracklaying ('caterpillar') type was improved in the early twentieth century and the arrival of the light petrol tractor about 1910 paved the way for the displacement of the horse. In the U.S.A. the transition began just before 1914, but in Britain the horse was not seriously challenged until the introduction of the Ford tractor in 1917.

These machines, with other advances in agricultural technique, provided, as we have remarked, the possibility of a highly industrialised civilisation. In 1787 it took the surplus food produced by nineteen farmers (these are U.S.A. figures) to feed one city-dweller. About 1930 these same nineteen farm workers produced enough surplus to feed sixty-six other people. At the first level it was impossible to spare sufficient workers from the land to create a large-scale industry; at the latter, for every worker on food production there could be 3½ producing manufactured goods, transport services and the like, all of which contribute to a high standard of living.

Equally important for feeding industrial populations was the development of methods of preservation which permit food to be brought right across the world or stored for long periods, to supply industrial regions that cannot be agriculturally self-supporting. In an effort to solve the problem of feeding the Revolutionary armies of France, François Appert invented in 1795 a method which is essentially the one used by the housewife of today to bottle fruit. The idea of canning in tin-plated iron canisters was patented by Peter Durand of England in 1810 and used two years later for supplying the Navy. Canned meat was brought from Australia in 1847. About this time the process became fairly common, but the product was never very pleasant and large amounts of it went bad. Much scientific research was needed to give an understanding of the conditions required for thorough sterilisation and to make canned foods safe towards the end of the century. And meanwhile the American meat-packaging industry, centred on Chicago, had made great practical advances in mechanising the canning process.

The alternative to canning was refrigeration. After some forty years' development, mechanical refrigeration became a practical proposition in the seventies, the most important step being Linde's ammonia compression refrigerator of 1873. Frozen meat was first imported into Europe from South America in 1877 and from Australia in 1880. Refrigeration has many other industrial applications. For example, oxygen, used for a variety of purposes from oxy-acetylene cutting to chemical synthesis, is best obtained by distilling it from air that has been liquefied by cooling. Linde produced an economically practical method of liquefying air in 1895. His process depended on compressing the air and then expanding it through a valve to cool it, making use of a property of gases known as the Joule-Thompson effect, which is, however, quite small. It was early realised that better results could be obtained if the air were made to do external work, that is to drive an engine. This was technically difficult but by 1902 Claude succeeded in producing a liquid air machine in which the air was cooled by making it drive a reciprocating engine. The process was later improved by Heylandt.

The Slow Mechanisation of Coal-Mining

Just as agriculture provides the food for the industrial worker, so does coal-mining provide the food for the industrial machine. It was during the nineteenth century, and long remained, the most important source of power. Naturally, therefore, much attention was given to the problem of the mechanisation of coal-mining. Under-cutting the coal face prior to breaking it down with explosives or other means, is one of the most laborious of all tasks, and attention was first devoted to the substitution of machines for men at this work. In 1761 Michael Menzies (who has already been mentioned in regard to threshing) invented a coal-cutting machine, with a swinging pick imitating the miner's action, driven by a horse and a man. In 1768 appeared 'Willie Brown's Iron Man' operated by the power of two miners. A patent of 1843 for a cutter based on a circular saw action foreshadowed the modern disc-type cutter. In this exploratory period the main difficulty was to find a suitable power source. Steam-engines were both too cumbersome and too dangerous. Various proposals were made for drives using man-power, animal-power, or even water- or steam-power at the pithead connected to the machine by ropes. Compressed air was first used in a British colliery in 1849 and quickly became the power source on which further attempts at mechanisation were based. Chain- and bar-type cutters were patented in 1853 and 1856 respectively, and a moderately practical disc-type machine appeared in 1863. But a great deal more experimenting and pioneering had to follow before the stage was set for rapid development about 1890 (Plate XVI).

In the U.S.A. the percentage of bituminous coal mechanically cut rose from about 4 per cent in 1890 to 51 per cent in 1913. Great Britain, in spite of the fact that most of the pioneering had been done there, was much slower and in 1913 only 8 per cent of British coal was cut by machine and only 676 mines out of 3,267 used coal-cutters. Meanwhile electricity, proposed as a source of power in 1863, was used in practice from about 1885 on and by 1918 was almost as common as compressed air.

Mechanisation of other mining processes was slower. The face-conveyor first appeared about 1902 and all the main types had been developed by 1913. But the spread of their use was even slower than with cutters, and in 1913 Britain had only 359 of them. The loading of coal at the face involves lifting 2 to 5 feet and casting horizontally 6 to 12 feet—no light task; yet serious attempts to mechanize it came surprisingly late. The first loader to attract general attention appeared in 1903, but was not adopted in practice. A few loaders of various design were in use in the U.S.A. by 1918, but the general adoption of power-loading did not begin until some years later.

Machines for Everything

In all the above we have only mentioned some of the outstanding lines of mechanical development in the century before 1918. But in point of fact machinery came to enter into almost every branch of industry in this period. To recount all the inventions of those years would alone take several volumes, and we can do no more than list a few examples. If the reader, as he notes each date, will pause to think what life would be like without that particular machine or without its cheap and plentiful products, he will gain some idea of the changes that machinery brought in the nineteenth century. Many branches of manufacturing were mechanised: steel-pen making, 1828; match-making, 1848; shoe-making, by McKay's shoe-sewing machine of 1861 and Goodyear's welt shoe-sewing machine in 1871. A cigarette-making machine appeared in 1876. Owen's bottle-making machine, which was soon producing 2,500 bottles an hour, arrived in 1898.

In the general field of communications many now familiar devices appeared towards the end of our period. After repeated attempts at mechanical type-setting from 1822 onwards, Mergenthaler's linotype was first used in 1886 to set a New York newspaper. Typewriter inventions, from 1843 on, are numerous, but the modern machine derives from that which Sholes produced in 1867. The first models of his design were sold by the Remington company in 1874 at $125 (about £25). Edison invented the phonograph in 1877, and over the next twenty years Berliner developed it into the gramophone, as well as inventing most of the essential techniques for the multiple reproduction of records. Cinematograph pictures became practical during the nineties. Calculating machines, after an evolution starting from 1642, became reliable and economic, and began to be regularly manufactured in the last few years of the century.

Turning to a more miscellaneous collection of items, workable sewing machines were invented from 1829 on, but the machines that are used in the home today are descended from those created by Elias Howe in 1846 and Isaac M. Singer in 1851. The time-lock was invented in 1847 and Yale's now familiar lock was perfected in 1865. E. G. Otis exhibited his passenger lift, with safety devices, in 1854 and one was installed in a store in 1857. The electric lift dates from about the end of the century. The first effective steam-rollers appeared in 1866. X-rays were discovered in 1895. Sperry invented in 1905 the gyroscopic compass, which has now largely replaced the magnetic. Many experiments from 1818 onwards culminated in the 'Rover' bicycle, invented in 1885 by Starley; Dunlop added the pneumatic tyre in 1888. By 1896 there were 4 million cyclists on the roads.

The Economics of Later Capitalism

Machinery now entered into almost every aspect of production. The material wealth available for the good of mankind was enormously increased, at least in the advanced countries. Wealth had become better distributed too, though this had taken a bitter struggle to achieve, The machine-wrecking tactics by which the workers had formerly hoped to alleviate their distress were abandoned, though there were still occasional outbursts up to the middle of the century. This was not the way forward, for the machines did create more abundance. It was the uneven distribution of wealth that had caused the misery of the factory workers—that and the concentration of the ownership of the factories, tools and machines in the hands of a comparatively small number of employers, giving them the power to decide the terms of employment. To this power the workers found a partial answer in trade unionism, which grew in strength throughout the nineteenth century and adopted new tactics more suited to the maturing capitalism in which it now operated. As individuals the workers had been powerless to prevent the degradation of their working and living conditions. But united in the trade union they could challenge the industrial magnates and wrest from them a greater share in the wealth that the new machinery had brought. They learned also to take political action to protect themselves. The pressure of the factory workers, with the help of the more humanitarian of the richer classes, produced the passing of the Factory Acts between 1802 and 1847, which abolished the worst features of the early factory exploitation. Here we cannot go into details, but merely note that the period covered by this chapter sees a general rise in the living and working conditions of the common people, but a rise that was only achieved by continual vigilance and struggle.

Since the capitalist type of economy had first appeared, there had been an era of tremendous technical progress. New inventions had almost yearly increased the efficiency with which men wrested a living from nature, and these inventions had been used almost to their maximum to provide an ever-expanding flow of commodities. In the middle of the nineteenth century it might have seemed as if this unparalleled progress was destined to go on uninterrupted for ever. But towards the end of the century interruptions did take place. Slumps or depressions of unprecedented severity occurred, in which apparently the goods produced could not be sold, though there were still millions in need of them. The manufacturer, unable to sell his products, closed (or partly closed) his works. Workers became unemployed. And only after a lapse of some years did the economic machine begin to work properly again—only to slow down once more in a new slump a few years later. After 1918 the situation worsened. Unemployment and inability to sell what could be produced became chronic features of the economy—so much so that some came to believe that too much was being produced (in spite of the fact that most people obviously could not get the things they wanted) and coined the phrase 'over-production' to account for the troubles.

Connected with these difficulties was the growth of two new features in the economic system : monopoly and imperialism. A monopoly was formed when one firm succeded in gaining control of a large part of the production in one industry; or when many of the firms in an industry came to an agreement covering the amounts they would produce and the prices they would sell at (in this case the combination of the firms is called a 'cartel'). Monopolies sought to avoid the effects of economic depression by restricting production below the level that was possible and setting artificially high prices. Formerly, any industry was composed of hundreds of small firms; and free competition between these, by giving a great advantage to the producer who used the most advanced methods, had been the main spur to invention. Monopoly did not eliminate the stimulus of competition, but it did reduce it, with effects that will be apparent later.

Nevertheless, this development of monopoly was inevitable and could not be reversed. It was brought about by many forces, most of them economic, and so outside the scope of this volume. But one cause lay in the development of the machines themselves. In the early nineteenth century or before, when the cost of building a factory and equipping it with adequate machinery would be only a few thousand pounds, any monopoly would have been quickly broken by some new entrant into the industry. But after all the mechanical developments described in this chapter and the next, the cost of setting up a business to compete with already existing firms would in many industries be hundreds of thousands of pounds at least. No small man, on the basis of his life's savings, could hope to enter the field. Many spheres of industry became closed shops, in which only those already established could exist. And even among these the increasing cost of the most advanced equipment gave tremendous advantages to the largest firms, putting them in a position to squeeze out or absorb their smaller competitors.

Imperialism and War

It is outside the scope of this volume to discuss the effect of monopolies on the growth of imperialistic rivalries and the consequent drift to war. War, however, had been a growing phenomenon all through the latter part of the nineteenth century. As the various powers grew in industrial strength without any overriding plan and sought for markets, as political forms failed to keep pace with improvements in transport and communication which were making the world more and more an indissoluble whole, so clashes became inevitable. There were other types of war too—the American Civil War, for instance, to decide whether America should be an industrial capitalist country or an agricultural slave-owning one. But all these are as nothing compared with the colonial wars at the end of the nineteenth century and the beginning of the twentieth, and the culminating struggle of 1914–18. It is therefore fitting that we should end this chapter with a note on a few of the many military inventions that mark the period.

The resources of nineteenth-century science and industry were used to make practicable many weapons, like the breech-loading cannon, which had been conceived earlier but had remained mere ideas for lack of adequate production methods, or to make suitable for general use weapons like the rifle (as opposed to the smooth-bore musket), which had been in use in the late eighteenth century but only in the hands of expert marksmen. Many new military inventions were added: the revolver by Samuel Colt in 1835, the machine-gun by Gatling in 1861, the torpedo by Whitehead in 1866 (though because of many practical difficulties it did not become important till the Russo-Japanese war of 1904–5). The submarine as a military weapon was the object of many inventors. A submarine, propelled by man-power and intended to fix mines to ships, was constructed during the American War of Independence; it succeeded in 1776 in travelling under water, but failed in its main object. The idea was revived during the American Civil War and, after many failures, a submarine did succeed in fixing a mine and sinking a ship. The modern submarine was developed competitively in several countries during the eighties and nineties. In 1916 appeared the tank, which takes so prominent a place in warfare today. These are but a few of the more outstanding military inventions. We have already noted, also, how the needs of war gave a tremendous impetus to the development of aeroplanes and of radio, which had previously been advancing comparatively slowly. Only after the aeroplane had served its turn as an agent of destruction and had been made efficient for that purpose, was it used to any notable extent in peaceful contexts. In the next chapter, which deals with the fundamental industries on which all mechanical development is based, we shall again note that much progress has been in response to the call of war.

CHAPTER 8

MATERIALS, MACHINE TOOLS AND PRODUCTION METHODS BEFORE 1939

IN the last two chapters we have almost completely ignored three very important aspects of machines: the materials from which they are made and the tools and methods used in making them. These are so vital that they deserve a special chapter.

If the reader will look back at the illustrations to Chapter 5 he will note that most of the machinery of that period was made of wood and until almost the end of the eighteenth century wood remained the chief material for industrial machinery, metals being usually confined to bearing parts, cutting edges and other positions where their special properties were absolutely essential. During the eighteenth century the steam-engine had, of course, to be constructed largely of metal (though boilers, for example, were at first often made of wood bound with iron hoops on the lines of a barrel, and brass was used more than iron in the early engines). Iron remained a rather costly material to be used only where it was essential. This was largely because no major technical improvements had taken place in iron-smelting since the first production of cast iron towards the end of the Middle Ages.

The Transformation in the Iron Industry

Iron-smelting, since its earliest days, had been carried out by means of charcoal. The scale of iron production was therefore limited by the size of the forests. When industry entered the period of comparatively rapid advance from the sixteenth century onwards, this factor severely restricted the expansion of the iron industry and therefore limited the progress of machinery in general. England, being but poorly wooded, particularly felt the shortage. Between 1540 and 1640 the price of firewood rose nearly three times as fast as general prices. At one time it might have seemed as if the British iron industry was doomed to extinction, and with it the, by then, very promising growth of British industry in general.

It was early realised that coal was a possible alternative and in the sixteenth century many industries learned to use this fuel instead of wood. The problem of using coal for iron-smelting was, however, a more difficult one. Patents for such processes were obtained by Simon Sturtevant in 1612, and Dud Dudley in 1619, and other attempts were made. But success had to await the work of Abraham Darby at Coalbrookdale in Shropshire, who developed the method of coking the coal before using it in the furnace. His first favourable trials seem to have been made in 1709, though it probably took some years to reach a commercially valuable process. Others were at first very slow to adopt the method, and even by 1760 there were only seventeen furnaces that used coke for smelting. The method was not yet generally applicable, because it depended on a very careful selection of the ores and coals, and because the product was of a quality that made it unsuitable for conversion to wrought iron. From about 1760 onwards various improvements were made—in the preparation of the coke, the power of the blast (a key step being Wilkinson's introduction of a Watt engine in 1776 to drive his bellows), and in the subsequent treatment of the metal. The number of coke-fired furnaces in Britain rose from thirty-one in 1775 to eighty-one in 1780, by which date coke had conquered charcoal in the progressive sections of the industry.

For the production of cast iron as such, coke smelting had an advantage over charcoal from a quite early date. For example, the superior strength of coke allowed the use of taller furnaces, giving a more liquid metal and so allowing finer casting. But the brittleness of cast iron, arising from its high carbon content, makes it unsuitable for many purposes. From about 1748 onwards Abraham Darby II began to produce coke-smelted metal that was more suitable for conversion to the tougher wrought iron. But the available methods of conversion, inherited from the late Middle Ages, required great skill and could only deal with small quantities. Large-scale production of malleable iron only became possible in 1784, when Cort, building on the partial achievements of earlier workers, perfected the method of puddling in a reverberatory furnace, using coal as fuel, but so arranged that only the flames came into contact with the metal.

Now the British iron industry was set for a great expansion. The production of pig-iron rose from 62,000 tons in 1788 to 125,000 tons in 1796, 250,000 tons in 1806 and, after the introduction of hot blast by Neilson in 1828, by leaps and bounds to figures of about 3 million tons a year in the middle of the century and about 8 million tons near the end of it. Iron became available in quantities sufficient for the construction of machinery wholly of that metal, and so paved the way for such developments as railways, iron ships and the many machines which we discussed in the previous chapter.

The late eighteenth century saw also considerable development in the machinery for working up wrought iron by hammering and rolling. The water-powered forge-hammer, dating from medieval times, was rapidly increased in size and in 1783 John Wilkinson first used steam to work a tilt-hammer of 7½ tons. The powerful, but very delicate, modern steam hammer was invented by Nasmyth in 1839 and introduced into practice three years later (Plate XVII). The hydraulic press, invented by Bramah in 1796, was applied about 1850 to give an even more powerful forge-hammer. Small water-driven rolling-mills, for finishing iron sheets already hammered roughly into shape, were in use in Germany early in the fifteenth century. Grooved rollers for making iron bars were developed by Polhelm in Sweden in 1745, but to Cort in England belongs the credit of devising, in 1783, a rolling-mill in which the sheets or bars were rolled directly from the bloom without previous processing. Wilkinson was once more the first to use steam power for the process, in 1796.

The Coming of Cheap Steel

An essential material for the construction of machines involving great stresses, like the electric generator, the steam-turbine, the internal combustion engine, motor-cars, and so on, which came into use near the end of the nineteenth century, was steel —a metal whose special properties arise from the fact that it contains an amount of carbon intermediate between that of cast and wrought iron. In the Middle Ages methods of production were such that steel was almost a precious metal. Even after Huntsman's development of a process[1] for making cast or crucible steel in the 1740s, it remained too costly for most purposes, and was in fact mainly used for cutlery. If steel was to be used for structural purposes and in all parts of machinery where its favourable properties (tensile strength, toughness, and so on) made it desirable, then it must be produced cheaply in far greater quantities. It was Henry Bessemer who first made this possible, in 1856. A couple of years earlier he had invented an ingenious form of artillery shell, grooved on the outside in such a way that the reaction of the propellant gases would cause it to spin, thus making it unnecessary to rifle the bore of the cannon. But no available material would make a gun strong enough to fire it. Investigating this problem, he invented his method of producing steel from pig-iron by burning away the impurities with a blast of air in a vessel that came to be called the Bessemer converter.[2] During the 1860s Siemens followed with his open-hearth method of steel-making, which is slower but gives more control over the final product. The 'basic' process, which allowed the more common phosphorus-bearing ores to be used, was invented by Thomas and Gilchrist in 1875. Though its practical introduction was delayed for several years, it effectively doubled the steel-making capacity of the world.

The characteristics of steel are vastly improved and much greater variety of properties made available by alloying it with small quantities of other metals. Although Faraday had made systematic experiments in this field in 1822, his work did not influence industrial practice and the effective history of alloy steels begins in 1871 with Mushet's invention of a tool-steel containing tungsten, vanadium and manganese, which allowed cutting at much higher speeds. Other alloys followed, such as the high manganese steel of Hadfield (1882) and the nickel steel of Schneider (1888). With the exception of Mushet's tool-steel, these were intended for use in armaments and were only later applied to more constructive purposes. Then in 1898 came the invention of high-speed tool-

[1] Similar to, and perhaps based on, a method that had been used for centuries in India.

[2] Bessemer had been anticipated by William Kelly in the U.S.A., who had developed the same process by 1851. But Kelly failed financially and his work had no influence.

steel by Taylor and White, of which we shall have more to say below. Stainless steel was invented by Harry Brearley in 1913.

The end of the nineteenth century is also marked by the introduction of various light alloys based on aluminium. Aluminium did not become a commercial proposition till C. M. Hall in America and P. L. T. Héroult in France independently invented in 1886 the electrolytic method of production. Thereafter it was used for special purposes where lightness was of prime importance —for example, in airships from 1895. Duralumin, an alloy of aluminium and copper remarkable for its high strength-weight ratio, appeared in 1909, and thereafter various alloys of aluminium and later of magnesium have been playing an ever-increasing part in engineering. The later nineteenth century also saw the beginnings of the plastics industry, though plastics did not have much effect on engineering practice till the inter-war years.

The Demand for Accuracy

The pioneer engineers of the eighteenth century had the utmost difficulty in getting their machines constructed with adequate accuracy. Smeaton had to tolerate errors of about half-an-inch on twenty-eight inch cylinders for Newcomen engines. These were made to work only by the device of using a layer of water on top of the piston as a seal. This trick was not applicable to the Watt engine and so Smeaton was led to remark that 'neither the tools nor the workmen existed that could manufacture so complex a machine with sufficient precision'. Perhaps the Watt engine could not have been a success if it were not for Wilkinson's timely invention of an adequate cylinder-boring machine. As late as 1830, it is said, a fitter who could work to one-sixteenth of an inch was a good workman.

Machines for boring pump-barrels and water-pipes from solid tree trunks date back at least well into the Middle Ages. In the early fifteenth century the same principle was applied to the boring of cannon, though only for finishing off hollow castings. An improved borer designed by the Swiss, Maritz, in 1740 was capable of boring cannon from the solid. When the Newcomen engine arrived, it was natural that the cylinders should be bored by such machines. But the diameters involved were much greater than in the case of cannon. The heavy drill-head worked effectively only on the bottom of the cylinder and very great inaccuracies resulted. Various methods were tried to improve the state of affairs, but none was successful until John Wilkinson, having invented an improved cannon borer in 1774, followed this up with an improved cylinder borer in 1775 (Plate XVIII). He placed the drill-head on a long stiff bar passing right through the cylinder and supported at both ends. This machine solved Watt's cylinder troubles, and in 1776 he wrote to Smeaton, 'Mr. Wilkinson has improved the art of boring cylinders so that I promise upon a 72-inch cylinder being not further from absolute truth than the thickness of a thin sixpence in the worst part'. Others gradually improved on Wilkinson's machine and by about 1830 the cylinder-boring machine had reached an essentially modern form.

The Development of the Lathe

The lathe, with its many variant forms, is the most important of the machine tools and the possibility of most of the nineteenth-century advances was closely tied up with its development into a robust machine of high precision. Before the middle of the sixteenth century, the only form was the plain centre-lathe, on which the work was turned between fixed centres, the drive being applied to the work itself, through a cord wound round it and usually attached to a treadle below and a flexible beam above. The earliest known illustration of the mandrel lathe, with the drive applied to a live spindle (the mandrel) to which the work is bolted or clamped, appeared in 1568. Lathes with screw-guides in the mandrel, for the purpose of screw-cutting, appeared before the end of the seventeenth century and this method, in which the work traverses and the tool is stationary, was widely employed in the eighteenth. In the modern method it is the tool that traverses, while the work merely rotates. Besson, who died in 1569, provided a picture of a crude screw-cutting lathe on these lines (Figure 23), while Leonardo[8] had earlier made a drawing of a similar idea, but it is unlikely that either of these projects influenced general practice, or even that the machines were ever constructed. During the eighteenth century clock- and instrument-

[8] Leonardo took considerable interest in lathes and sketched, for example, one with treadle-and-crank drive—a form which (so far as is known) did not come into use till after his death.

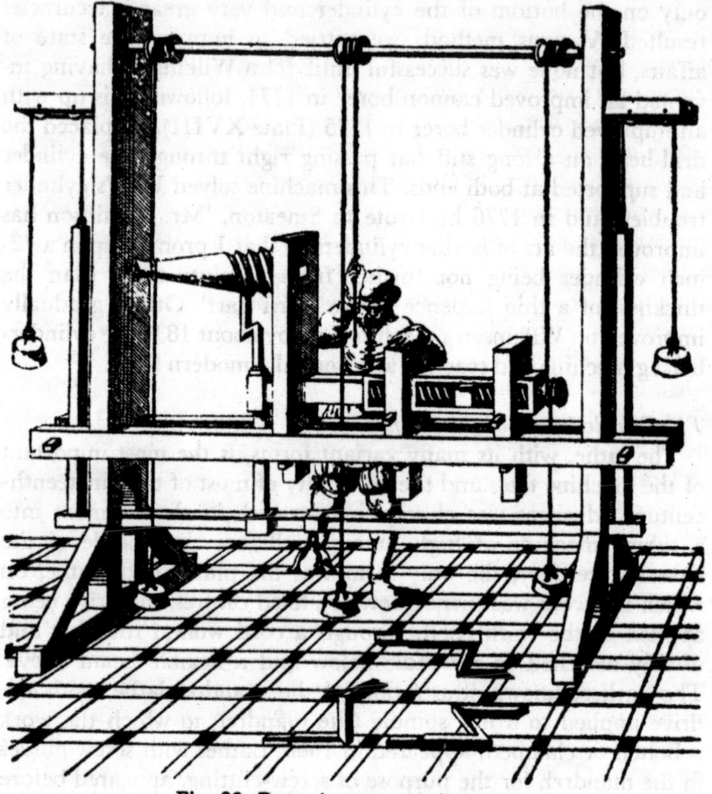

Fig. 23. Besson's screw-cutting lathe.

makers used the traversing tool in small screw-cutting lathes. Their machines embodied the elements of the slide-rest, but only in a form suitable for light work.

Till the end of the seventeenth century, the lathe was used only for turning wood and similar soft materials, and sometimes the softer metals. During the eighteenth century clock-makers and ornamental turners (who produced highly decorative patterns through intricate motions controlled by cams and templates) applied it more widely to metals, but only for small-scale work. Towards the end of the century, when the growing complexity of machinery increased the demand, a number of workers constructed lathes to turn metallic parts of greater size. But the story is complicated, and we can only give attention to the crucial work of Henry Maudslay, which created, in its essentials, the industrial metal-working lathe of today.

The highly ingenious lock invented by Bramah (pages 109-10) required standards of accuracy far higher than those then current, but was nevertheless to be manufactured in large numbers. Bramah employed Maudslay and it was while working on the problem of producing this lock that the latter began his work on the lathe, which he carried on after 1797 in his own workshop. His lathe of 1797 (Plate XIX) and more especially the improved version of 1800 marks the beginning of a new era in engineering.

Maudslay is commonly said to have invented the slide-rest. That statement greatly distorts and undervalues his work. A rudimentary slide-rest was already in existence, but it was used only for light work such as clock-making, and the construction of large lathes was too crude to accommodate it. Maudslay greatly improved the slide-rest and made it suitable for heavier work. But his really important contributions to the development of the lathe were three improvements which greatly increased its accuracy and, as it were, turned the lathe as a whole into a fit vehicle for the slide-rest. These critical improvements were: all-metal construction, the production of accurate plane surfaces for guiding the tool movements, and the technique of cutting accurate lead-screws of sufficient length to allow the use of traversing tools on large work. The construction of an all-metal lathe, instead of mounting metal working parts on a wooden base, may not seem at first sight to be of great importance; yet the rigidity it gave was the foundation of all further progress in accuracy. The plane guiding surfaces translated this potential accuracy into reality. And Maudslay's constant and painstaking work on methods of making lead screws after 1800 entirely changed current practice. He also brought change gears into general use.

There is hardly a feature of Maudslay's lathes that had not been anticipated by some other engineer. And yet so complete was his synthesis that the machine which emerged from his hands was totally different from all that preceeded it. He had created a lathe that could easily be developed to undertake the heaviest work on the hardest metals with as high a degree of precision as could be required.

Further great advances in screw-cutting and other aspects of high-precision work were made from about 1833 onwards by Joseph Whitworth, who began as one of Maudslay's workmen. Meanwhile the planer, the other basic tool of precise engineering, was developed from its crude ancestors by a number of British workers between 1814 and 1840. But the rise of precision work as a general practice was largely associated with mass-production on the principle of interchangeability, to which we now turn.

Mass-Production and Interchangeable Manufacture

Mass-production is the basis on which today we can have many machines (and other conveniences) manufactured and sold in large quantities and for reasonable prices. Consider any cheap family car of our time. If only 10,000 of the model were produced, they would cost several thousand pounds each; if but a single car were made, to the same standards of reliability and comfort, its price might approach a hundred thousand pounds. But in fact hundreds of thousands are manufactured, all identical apart from minor variations. Every process of production has to be repeated hundreds of thousands of times. Thus it is economical to build a special machine to do each process efficiently, and as a result this car costs only a few hundred pounds. The same goes for most things we use today: ball-point pens, vacuum cleaners, washing machines, radio sets.

Mass-production presents no great technical difficulty when it is applied to articles consisting of one part only (a nail, a pen nib, a pin), or to articles requiring no great engineering precision (textiles). In such cases there is no need for two samples of the product to resemble each other closely—so long as they are near enough to standard to satisfy the customer. It is not very difficult to arrange for the mass-production of such articles, provided the demand is large enough to justify either the cost of building special machines, or the wage bill for a factory of many workmen each specialising in one small part of the process. And indeed there are very early examples of mass-production of this kind. The casting of metal type at the close of the Middle Ages is perhaps the earliest. Another is a special stamping machine, worked by a treadle used at Nuremberg about 1680 for fixing heads on pins. Christopher Polhem, of Sweden, ran a factory for mass-production of many articles on these lines from about 1700 onwards. He employed about 100 men and used water-power at every possible stage of manufacture. He had special machines for nail-making, for cutting iron bars or metal sheets, presses, rolling-mills, and so on. And he turned out in mass quantities such articles as ploughshares, harrow teeth, hammer heads, tin plates and vessels. The textile machinery of Chapter 6 gives another example of the growth of mass-production in industries where accuracy is of small importance.

But now suppose that the problem is to mass-produce a machine consisting of many parts. Each component might indeed be separately mass-produced by methods which were established by the eighteenth century or earlier. But when the moment came to build the complete machine, it would be found that none of these components quite fitted the others. It would be necessary either to sort through thousands of samples to find sets that would go together, or to employ skilled fitters to file, hammer or otherwise alter the parts until they would fit. All the savings in cost achieved by mass-producing the components would be lost at this assembly stage.

To overcome this difficulty it is necessary to arrange the production of the individual components in such a way that *all* samples of each will conform to certain standard sizes (within permitted ranges of variation, known as 'tolerances'), so that any set of parts chosen at random can be assembled into a finished article. The parts, in fact, must be interchangeable—for which reason this more refined system is called mass-production on the principle of interchangeability, or more briefly interchangeable manufacture.

A notable early example of this type of mass-production was the factory for producing pulley blocks for the Admiralty, which began work in England about 1808. This scheme was the joint product of Marc Brunel and Samuel Bentham. Henry Maudslay executed the machinery, which was divided up into specialised groups for each of the processes involved. There were forty-four machines in all, of thoroughly modern design (Plate XX), and so good was the production method that ten unskilled men did the work that formerly required 110 skilled craftsmen. The output was about 130,000 blocks a year, greater than the previous output of the six largest dockyards. For a capital expenditure of £54,000, this scheme saved the Admiralty £17,000 a year. Yet despite this spectacular demonstration of its effectiveness, the method of interchangeability was not further pursued in Britain.

Before the nineteenth century there were not many types of article which were required in such quantities as to justify interchangeable manufacture. The one great exception was firearms. The lock, especially, of the musket or pistol is a delicate mechanism which will only work if it is accurately adjusted. Gunmaking was a highly skilled job and the demand for arms was very great. England, with more skilled workmen than any other country, had in 1811 a stock of 200,000 musket barrels, which were useless for want of gunsmiths to repair the locks. As early as 1717 and again in 1785 attempts were made in France to produce firearms by interchangeable manufacture. Thomas Jefferson, while U.S. Minister in France, wrote home that Le Blanc, the author of this last attempt, presented him with parts of fifty locks taken to pieces. 'I put several together myself,' wrote Jefferson, 'taking pieces at hazard as they came to hand, and they fitted in the most perfect manner. The advantages of this when arms need repair are evident.' Ultimately the French ventures seem to have failed, and it was in Jefferson's own country, where a desperate shortage of skilled labour made it specially attractive, that the method was first successfully applied.

Machine Tools for Interchangeable Manufacture

Eli Whitney began in 1800 to make muskets by mass-production methods, and several other small-arms manufacturers followed suit in the next few years. They used water-driven machinery on a large scale for such work as forging, rolling, boring, grinding and polishing. But the accurate finishing to precise measurements was done by specialised workmanship and by filing in special jigs. Soon, however, special machinery capable of working at high speed and with great and unvarying accuracy was developed for this purpose. The milling machine was in use in several of these establishments by 1818.[4] In that year Blan-

[4] Its invention was formerly attributed to Whitney, but this now seems far from certain.

chard invented the 'gun-stocking lathe', the first important example of a lathe for turning irregular shapes by copying a pattern. The capstan or turret lathe, which enables an unskilled operator to do about eight operations repeatedly after a skilled man has set the machine for him, appeared in the forties. Samuel Colt, when planning in the years 1849–54 a factory to make his revolver, employed Elisha K. Root, a brilliant organiser and mechanic, who designed many new tools (including a much improved form of drop hammer). Root also used all the best tools already available and thus indirectly gave a new impetus to others to create yet better.

The labour shortage which resulted from the American Civil War (1861–5) further stimulated the drive for more productive machine-tools. The universal milling machine (Plate XXI) appeared in 1861–2. The cylindrical grinder was first commercially produced in 1864. The automatic lathe (in which several tools in succession are automatically brought to bear on the work and the operator has only to feed in the raw material in the form of rods—Plates XXII and XXIII) developed during the war, and became well established a few years later. The multi-spindle lathe (in which the work is passed automatically to several stations and subjected to one or more different processes at each) appeared in 1895. This in turn gave birth to highly automatic machine-tools, such as the 'Mult-Au-Matic' (Plate XXIV), which appeared just before the First World War, and in which the work is moved through a series of six or eight stations, at each of which it can be subjected to such operations as boring, turning, facing, threading, grooving or drilling. Automatic gear-cutters appeared in the seventies and hobbing machines in the eighties.

The arms-makers for a long time led the field in mass-production techniques, but clock-makers were not far behind. Eli Terry of Connecticut began mass-production of wooden clocks in 1809 and by 1814 had reduced their price from $25 to $5. Mass-production of brass clocks started a little later, and by 1855 these were being produced at the rate of 400,000 a year, the price coming down eventually to 50 cent apiece. Mass-production of watches was first tried in 1848 and was successful in the fifties.

By 1850 mass-production methods were fully established. They were fundamental in making a success, in the fifties, of the sewing-machine, which was mass-produced almost from the beginning. A little later they made possible the widespread use of agricultural machinery. In this last case the property of interchangeability was important to the user as well as the producer—repairing agricultural machinery was beyond the powers of a village blacksmith, so that the availability of replacements which could be fitted into place without any skilled adjustment was an essential condition for the use of the machines. This contrasts with the position in clock-making, where interchangeability is only of importance to the manufacturer—because it simplifies his production problems. Mass-production was applied to typewriters in the eighties and to bicycles in the nineties, making possible the production of cycles at a rate of several hundred thousand a year.

The Coming of the Conveyor Belt

Let us now turn to another side of modern mass-production: continuous flow production, which is most familiar as the assembly line. With this method, in its full development, each piece of work passes successively through a series of stations, at each of which one or a few operations are performed on it. The whole factory becomes a single highly organised entity, in which raw materials flow in at several points and the work in various stages of manufacture flows along several streams which gradually come together, until the finished car (for example) is driven off the end of the main conveyor, ready for testing and the road.

Elements of the system can be traced well back into the nineteenth century. It is found in 1833 in a British Admiralty factory for baking ship-biscuits. Machines were used for kneading and other operations, but the chief novelty was that the work passed from each workman to the next on trays running on power-driven rollers. One or two more attempts on the same lines can be found in Britain, but—as with interchangeable manufacture—the crucial developments took place in America.

The assembly line principle made its first full appearance at Cincinnati in the sixties, even though it was there applied not to assembling machines, but to disassembling pigs—in other words, to cutting them up for the meat-packaging industry. The carcasses travelled by overhead conveyor past a series of workers, each of whom had to make a single cut or remove only one specified piece. Many ingenious devices were incorporated, including a station for weighing the carcasses without removing them from the conveyor. As fully developed in the eighties this 'dis-assembly line' included a device for automatically catching the live pig by a hind leg, hoisting it onto the conveyor and carrying it to the slaughterer—all within half a minute. Similar efficiency was shown at every stage. The system was organised to make use of everything the pig could provide—it is even said in jest that its dying squeal was piped off to work the factory whistle.

Something approaching the assembly line was also used in the nineties in making railway freight trucks. But the full appearance of the method in the engineering industry was associated with the motor-car.

Motor-Cars and Mass-Production

All the early cars were *built*, in the same sense that an early steam-engine was built. Then about 1902 some firms started using interchangeable manufacture. Olds produced about 2,500 of his little runabouts in 1902, 4,000 in 1903, 5,000 in 1904. Ford's production passed 10,000 a year by 1909. By 1913 there were about 200,000 motor vehicles in Britain and 600,000 in the U.S.A.

The car industry used the techniques of interchangeable production more intensively than ever, and in its turn promoted the development of a host of new machine tools: precision gear-cutters, precision grinders of many types, a great variety of presses for stamping and forming the chassis, bumpers, body panels and other parts, broaching machines, precision die-casters, drilling and tapping machines. Some of these had existed before, but the mass-production of cars led to their perfection and their use on a much greater scale. The tendency towards automatic machines was intensified.

Then Henry Ford introduced the assembly line. In 1913 he experimented with a line for assembling magneto flywheels. He split the engine assembly into eighty-four stages, reducing the labour used to one-third. He placed the chassis on rails and had it towed past a series of stations where assembly work was done. By the end of 1914 the assembly line was fairly fully developed. We cannot trace its further progress or its gradual spread to other industries, but must simply note that this flow-line method (applied not only to assembly, but also to machining the components) has become the key to efficient and therefore cheap production, and is only slowly being replaced in our time by automation.

Other Changes in Production Methods

Two new materials for tools contributed greatly to the progress we have been describing. One was the production of artificial abrasives—carborundum for example, synthesized in the electric furnace, from about 1893 on. These could be made much harder and finer than the natural emery previously used. They allowed grinding as a machining process to spread greatly and, for many purposes, to supersede cutting almost completely. Grinding, which gives greater accuracy and a much smoother finish than cutting, is now indispensable for the manufacture of internal combustion engines. The other new material was high-speed tool-steel, to which we referred earlier. It allowed cutting speeds to be increased four or five times. It has been estimated that as a result of its introduction the annual production of all industries in the U.S.A. increased by about 8 billion dollars (say £1,600 million) and this by the use of only about 20 million dollars' worth (£4 million) of the new steel per year, plus, of course, the new machine tools to use it.

All these improvements in machining methods were necessarily accompanied by parallel improvements in methods of measurement. We have no space here for a full discussion of this topic. Whitworth, who was mentioned above, played a very great part in the development of precise methods of measurement (for though America ran away with mass-production, Britain still led in many types of high-precision construction of machines only required in comparatively small numbers). The rise of interchangeable production in America was necessarily accompanied at every stage by the progressive refinement of measuring methods and the various types of gauges used.

Other processes of great importance that must be mentioned are electric welding (1886) and thermit welding (1908), which have played an increasing part in construction ever since and in many cases have done away with the clumsier methods of riveting or bolting. Oxygen cutting (oxy-acetylene and similar combinations) came into use about the turn of the century.

American manufacturers on the whole maintained a clear lead till 1914 in mass-production methods and the corresponding machine tools. Even in Britain manufacturers were slow to use the new methods. A beginning was made only after 1853, when a British Small Arms Commission recommended the adoption of what they called the 'American system'. And in 1914 shops could still be found where lengthy and laborious hand filing was used on processes admirably adapted to milling or machine grinding. The war of 1914–18, with its unprecedented demand for huge quantities of accurately produced armaments and other products, changed all this. As Cressy puts it : 'Hundreds of shops in which high-speed tool-steel was little more than a name began to use it regularly. Many automatic machines, and especially millers and grinders, crept into small and obscure engineering works and came to be regarded as essential elements of equipment. The use of jigs for machining or drilling objects of awkward shape, and of gauges for the production of interchangeable parts, spread to an enormous extent under the stress of military necessity.[5]

Developments after 1918

In the years between the two world wars, the variety of materials available for engineering was greatly extended. New alloys came into use, particularly a wide range of light alloys based on aluminium. Plastics underwent rapid development and proved superior to metals for some engineering purposes.

The various types of machine tools which had been developed over the previous century were steadily improved and more widely employed, but rather few radical innovations were made in this field. There was a notable increase in the use of oxygen flame cutting, which made it possible to cut thicknesses of steel well beyond the possibilities of mechanical methods. At the same time the flame began to take over some of the work of cutting tools in operations equivalent to planing and boring. Its precision increased greatly, till, for example, it could even be used for certain types of gear-cutting, and fairly automatic flame-cutting

[5] E. Cressy, *A Hundred Years of Mechanical Engineering* (London, 1937), p. 212.

machines were developed. In the late thirties the flame began to be used instead of a cutting tool for some types of turning operations—only on a limited scale and for coarse work, but implying considerable possibilities for the future.

Grinding, as a substitute for cutting in producing high-precision finish, continued to spread rapidly. Centreless grinding, which first appeared (though not in its modern form) in 1916, came increasingly into use from the twenties on.

We referred on page 156 to the revolution in industry that was brought about by the introduction of high-speed tool steel. When tungsten carbide, second in hardness only to diamond, came into use as a tool material about 1926, it led to a similar revolution, which received further impetus from the introduction of mixtures such as tantalum and tungsten carbides about 1939. As a result cutting speeds increased once again by six or seven times, implying vast increases in production potential. Unfortunately this material, of German origin, came under the control of international cartels which greatly restricted its production and use outside Germany.[6] To the people of other countries this meant loss of potential wealth. To the monopolies involved it doubtless meant no more than the protection of vested interests and the maintenance of high prices, but to Germany it meant the ability to rearm quickly with efficient tools, while ensuring that the peace-loving nations would be comparatively unprepared for war.

Automatic Machinery

The most interesting development of the inter-war period was an increasing tendency to explore the possibilities of highly automatic machinery—a portent of the widespread automation of our own time. Lathes and similar equipment were fitted with devices to measure the work and stop the machine automatically when the right size was reached. On a larger scale was the plant for making car frames, installed in the late twenties by A. O. Smith

[6] For details see *Germany's Master Plan* by J. Borkin and C. A. Welsh and the U.S. Government publication, *Economic and Politic Aspects of Cartels*, by C. D. Edwards (Washington, 1944), which shows how the cartel raised the price per pound of tungsten carbide from its 1927–8 level of $50 to $453 and kept it above $200 till, after an anti-trust indictment in 1942, it fell again to between $27 and $45.

and Co., Milwaukee, which could turn out one completed frame every eight seconds, or about 10,000 a day, virtually untouched by human hand. It was run by a staff of 120, mostly supervisory or maintenance, so that one car frame was the product of about sixteen man-minutes of work. This machine made 75 per cent of the car frames used in the U.S.A., other than those used by Ford, who had a similar plant of his own.

One of the most useful automatic machines is the automatic die-caster, a development of the die-casters which the automobile industry brought into being early in the century. In such machines objects are cast in permanent metal moulds with great rapidity. The machine is not highly specialised—mere changing of the die or mould converts it to the production of a new object—and, because of its simplicity, it can be made highly automatic. A typical example cost about £1,000 between the wars and, attended by one man, could cast eight pieces per minute or over 4 million a year, if it ran all the time. Of course, it had to stop for repairs, but two such machines running only half time could produce radiator caps for the entire motor-car industry of the world. Developments like these naturally prompt consideration as to whether full use can be made of modern technique when industry is run in several competing units. Die-casting is restricted to certain alloys, but automatic moulding machines of a rather different type, larger and more complicated, will cast almost any metal. A remarkable example was the automatic moulding machine at Klimovsk, U.S.S.R., for iron castings. Its output was 10,000 in a two-shift day. It cut labour requirements by 60 per cent, auxiliary metal cutting machines, which would otherwise be used for finishing, by 75 per cent, and the cost of production by 50 per cent.

The simplest processes to make automatic are those in which the raw material is uniform (casting for instance), so that the machine has to exercise no function comparable to judgement. Next come those in which 'judgement' is required (for example, to determine when sufficient metal has been removed in a cutting process), but this can be exercised through contacts of moving parts comparable to the sense of touch. However, human judgement in production is usually employed through the sense of sight. For that reason probably the most revolutionary development of the period under review was the application to a wide variety of processes of the photo-electric cell or 'electric eye', which transmutes variations in light into variations of electric current and thence, through amplifiers and relays, into mechanical action. The earliest type of photo-cell depended on the discovery in 1873 that the electric conductivity of selenium varies with the amount of light falling on it. But cells based on this principle are slow in response, and the modern extremely sensitive photo-cell, based on the fact that certain substances emit electrons when light falls on them, is mainly a post-1918 development, though again it depends on fundamental discoveries made from the eighties onwards.

By 1939 photo-cells had found wide application in such processes as grading and sorting commodities like rice, beans and cigars, detecting and rejecting tins with labels missing as they come from an automatic labelling machine, reading a drawing and controlling the tool making a copper engraving of it for printing. But more significant as foretastes of later developments were some applications to the basic production processes of metallurgy and engineering—reversing the rollers in steel rolling-mills, removing metal bars from the furnace at a given temperature, automatic inspection of the articles coming off machine tools, and so on. One such inspecting machine for camshafts was reported from the U.S.A. to have enabled four men to do the work formerly requiring eighteen. A British example of about 1939 was an automatic machine for drilling and reaming crankshafts, controlled by a beam of light acting on a photo-cell through slotted discs, instead of the usual cam mechanism. A further step towards the programme-controlled machines of the post-war period was a Soviet lathe of 1940, in which a photo-cell read the blue-print and controlled the actions of the tools on one or several lathes accordingly. A similar application, made during the last war in the U.S.A., was to the control of an oxygen cutting machine by a photo-cell reading a scale drawing.

Such applications of the photo-cell, and of other similar devices for measuring temperature, chemical composition, and the like, promise the possibility of entirely eliminating all those monotonous forms of labour in which human judgement is used merely to decide whether or not an article conforms to a given standard.

The ill-effects of such monotonous work, repeated endlessly day after day, form one of the most serious problems of mass-production methods. The developments discussed provide the means of solving it, but, to quote C. C. Furnas, 'as a first guess I would say that there are at least a million workers in America doing routine tasks of sorting, inspecting or controlling, who could be cheaply and successfully replaced by devices actuated by photocells'.[7] We shall take up this theme again in Chapter 14.

[7] *The Next Hundred Years* (London, 1936) pp. 179–80.

CHAPTER 9

BETWEEN TWO WARS
(1918–39)

THE years between the two wars were marked not so much by startling new inventions as by remarkable advances in the efficiency of already familiar machines. This resulted from a multitude of small inventions and detailed improvements, the work of thousands of engineers, inventors and scientists. In 1918, for example, the best power stations required about 1½ lb. of coal to generate one unit of electricity; by 1939 the best stations had reduced this figure to about ¾ lb. In the same period improvements in ship design reduced the power required to carry a given cargo by some 15 to 20 per cent, while the fuel consumption of engines of the same power was reduced by 50 or 60 per cent; so that the overall fuel consumption on the most up-to-date ships was reduced to one-third of its former value. Improvements over industry as a whole were such that the productivity of labour (i.e. the output per man-hour) in the U.S.A. increased by 39 per cent between 1920 and 1935.

But at the same time these improved techniques were not always used to the best effect. The *average* amount of coal used to generate a unit of electricity in Great Britain or the U.S.A. was about 3 lb. in 1918 and a little under 1½ lb. in 1939. In other words, the average efficiency of power stations in 1939 was only about half of the best possible and was just about equal to the best in existence in 1918; average efficiency lagged twenty years behind the best. The advance of 39 per cent in productivity, referred to above, was not used to provide 39 per cent more goods and services. Actual production rose only 14 per cent in the same period and the remainder of the increased efficiency was offset by increases in unemployment. And similarly (as we shall see below) it was frequently the case that various industries failed to use the best machinery available.

It must be remembered in this connection that it is not possible to introduce each new technique instantaneously over a whole industry. The new machines have to be constructed and installed. Whether this can be done or not depends, in the last analysis, on whether hands are available to do the work. If there had been a scarcity of labour, the lag in efficiency would have been inevitable. But actually there were millions of unemployed and the fact that these available workers were not used for bringing efficiency up towards the best possible indicates a failure of economic organisation.

The U.S.S.R.

One exception must be made to these remarks. The U.S.S.R. found it possible to abolish unemployment entirely.[1] The efficiency of industry there was by no means the best that was technically possible, but at least it was the best that was attainable in practice, since the whole of the available man-power was used to advance it. The U.S.S.R. began as a very backward country. It had a few islands of advanced industry, but in general pre-revolutionary Russia was an agricultural country and a very backward one at that, with almost medieval equipment. In 1910 there were 10 million wooden ploughs and 18 million wooden harrows in use in Russia, compared with only 4½ million iron ploughs, to say nothing of the almost complete absence of more modern agricultural equipment, which elsewhere had come into use since about 1800. The war of 1914–18 and the destructive wars of intervention greatly worsened the situation. It took till 1928 to restore production even to its pre-war level, and then began the struggle of the Soviet people to raise their technique to a level comparable with the advanced countries.

There followed the most rapid and most conscious industrialisation known in history. From 1913 to 1938, the volume of industrial production increased by a factor of *six and a half* in the U.S.S.R., compared with some 40 to 50 per cent in the rest of the world. In the decade 1930 to 1940, Soviet industrial production increased by an annual average of 18 per cent, as against 2·8 per cent in the U.S.A., 3·5 per cent in Britain and 2·5 per cent

[1] From about 1930 onwards, when the struggle to reconstruct after the effects of the revolution and the wars of intervention had been completed.

in France. In output of electric power the U.S.S.R. moved from fifteenth place in the world in 1913 to third in 1936; in coal production from sixth to fourth; in the production of agricultural machinery from fifth to first. Tractors and combine harvesters were not made at all in Tsarist Russia; by 1936, Soviet production led the world in both.

These results were achieved by a conscious approach to the problem of mechanisation. The objective of plenty for all could be reached only through increasing production by the most advanced techniques. The raising of the technical level was not left to individuals, but was undertaken by the State and became one of its main political tasks. Inventors were given every possible encouragement; apparatus, laboratories, and so on, were lavishly provided. Education was directed to producing a maximum of skilled engineers, scientists and inventors. Workers were given facilities to enable them to use their intimate knowledge of the job for the purpose of suggesting improvements. Hundreds of thousands of inventions came from ordinary workers. The Stakhanovite movement epitomised the conscious struggle to make the best possible use of technology.

The figures given can, however, be misleading. Though in total production the U.S.S.R. had by 1939 become comparable with many other industrialised countries, its output was still low in relation to population. In 1937 its production *per head* of pig iron (which can be taken as a rough index of industrial strength) was 86 kilograms, against 292 for the U.S.A., 234 for Germany and 183 for Great Britain. Although the U.S.S.R. was being industrialised at a more rapid pace than any other country at any time, the Soviet industrial and political leaders still reckoned at the end of the decade that some fifteen further years were required to catch up with the more advanced countries of the world. The destruction wrought in the Second World War greatly extended that period.

The Progress of Electricity

Mechanisation had now become so widespread that we cannot hope to do more than describe some of the general trends of the period, and choose a few examples for more detailed discussion. We may well begin with the electric power industry, because of its increasing role in all aspects of industrial advance, as well as the change it brought about on the domestic scene.

The output of electricity in Great Britain, for example, rose from about 125 million units a year at the beginning of the century to 9,927 million in 1928 and 26,409 million in 1939. Efficiency improved enormously, as we have already noted. Large power stations, generating at high voltages and transmitting their power in high-tension cables over distances up to 200 or 300 miles, replaced the tiny local direct-current stations of the early part of the century. Nevertheless, this progress did not come easily. Mr. S. B. Donkin, then President of the Institution of Civil Engineers, said in 1938 :[2] 'The earlier technical developments were accompanied by no commensurate improvement in the organisation of the supply industry as a whole, nor is there any evidence which might be put before an impartial observer to suggest that the undertakings had any broad policy for the future or conception of the part which might be played by electricity in national life'. The electric supply industry, in fact, was almost the first[3] in which the forms of organisation that had played so great a part in developing world resources for more than two centuries clearly proved themselves inadequate to carry that development further.

The strain of the 1914–18 war showed great weaknesses in the industry and after some years of investigation the Government decided that it could only be properly organised by nationalising the transmitting section and co-ordinating the generating section.[4] This was done by the Electricity Act of 1926, which provided for the setting up of the Grid, one of the greatest engineering achievements of the period. The result was a very remarkable improvement in the efficiency of the industry. Previously each individual station had to maintain sufficient plant to cope with its peak

[2] *Transactions of the International Engineering Congress, Glasgow*, 1938, p. 49.

[3] A much earlier example, of course, was the electric telegraph, which in Britain had to be nationalised in 1870, because of the poor and inefficient service given by the telegraph companies and the high prices charged. When the Post Office took over, the number of messages sent trebled in five years, while the technical efficiency of the equipment improved by leaps and bounds.

[4] The completion of the process of nationalisation had to await further exposures of inadequacy during the Second World War.

load (though that operates for but an hour or two a day), besides a considerable amount of reserve plant to allow for breakdowns. Now a station on peak load could be helped out by another which was slack; the best plant could be kept running continuously and the older generators used only at the peak, thus lowering the overall cost of power; and the linking up enabled one set of reserve plant to deal with emergencies in several stations. In 1928, when construction of the Grid was just beginning, generators as a whole ran on an average only 1,127 hours in the year; by 1939 they ran 2,701 hours. Each generator, therefore, was lying idle for a much shorter time, so that a truly enormous saving was made in capital cost. By 1937, this amounted to £27 million and had paid —in less than ten years—for the original cost of the Grid.

Similar trends occurred elsewhere. In the U.S.A. much of the electricity industry remained (and still remains) in private hands, but the most outstanding advances were made in Federal schemes, like that in the Tennessee Valley, where hydro-electrification provided the pivot for the development of a backward area into one of the most advanced industrial districts in the country. Average domestic consumption of electricity rose by 146 per cent in two years.

Planning is the key to an efficient electricity supply. The U.S.S.R. with its fully planned economy had therefore a special advantage—though this had to be set against the disadvantage of having to start from an extremely backward electric power system. Though the U.S.S.R. had still a long way to go before overtaking the other major powers in the *per capita* consumption of electricity, nevertheless the advances made were truly amazing—from 500 million units generated in 1920 to 4,205 million in 1927, 13,540 million in 1932 and 36,400 million in 1937. The planning of the whole of industry allowed a much more efficient use of the plant than elsewhere. Thus the generators in district power stations in the U.S.S.R. were able to work 4,300 hours in 1935, against 2,300 hours, for example, in Great Britain.

The technical progress of the electricity industry since 1918 was mostly a matter of gradual improvement, increases in efficiency, higher transmission voltages and so on, the details of which would be out of place here. Apart from some experimental progress towards the realisation of high-tension direct-current transmission, which would allow transmission over much longer distances, the only outstandingly new technical development was that of combined heat and power generation. In this system the heat which necessarily emerges from the condensers of the steam-turbines and which was formerly wasted, is transmitted as hot water or steam through pipes to factories or blocks of flats to be used there instead of local heating apparatus. A fuel economy of some 30 per cent is obtained. Though district heating unconnected with electricity supply was not uncommon in the U.S.A., it was the U.S.S.R. that led the world in the development of combined heat and power systems in the thirties; and in recent years about one-third of Soviet thermal stations also supply district heating. The method was also tried in Pimlico (London) in the fifties, but has not found any general application in Britain.

Agricultural Machinery

By 1918 machines had been developed which mechanised the agricultural processes of ploughing, cultivating, sowing, reaping and threshing cereals, the various hay-making processes, and some of the processes connected with root crops, besides various miscellaneous machines which we have not mentioned. The tractor was already beginning to replace the horse. It was subsequently greatly improved, while about 1924 there appeared tractors with high clearances suitable for cultivation between rows of young plants. The use that was made of tractors and other machinery varied enormously from country to country. In the U.S.A., where the development was most rapid, the number of tractors in use rose from 80,000 in 1918 to 1,600,000 in 1939. That amounts to somewhere about fifteen per hundred workers on the land.[5] But in Great Britain the number in 1939 was only 55,000 or about eight per hundred workers. The U.S.S.R., starting from the very primitive agriculture we have already described, had only 700 tractors in 1920 and from this developed to 483,000 in 1938 and 523,000 in 1940. In relation to land workers this was still very little—rather less than one tractor per hundred workers. On the other

[5] These figures, however, fail to show the extreme unevenness of development. The large mass of small farms did not have the benefit of machinery. Only about one farm in six had a tractor. while one in five was without even animal-power.

hand, the organisation of agriculture in collective farms permitted a much more efficient use of the machinery than elsewhere. Expressing the work done by a tractor in terms of the equivalent of ploughing an acre, the average output of a Soviet tractor in 1936 was 1,210 acres, against 225 in U.S.A. That meant that, although the U.S.A. had four times as many tractors as the U.S.S.R. the actual work got out of them was only the equivalent of some 350 million acres of ploughing, against near 600 million in the U.S.S.R. Similarly it has been estimated[6] that the output of British tractors could easily have been trebled. In 1940 some 90 per cent of Soviet ploughing and sowing was done by machine and 50 per cent of the grain harvested by combine. This last figure was also reached by the U.S.A. in 1938.

Mechanisation in other parts of agriculture was still at the pioneering stage. Machines for ditching and making drainage channels were successfully developed. Progress was made in applying machinery to vegetables and root crops. The potato-harvesting machines referred to on page 133 were considerably improved, though even by 1938 the elevator-lifter required favourable soil conditions. Attempts were made to mechanise beet lifting, with a degree of success which is well estimated by the contemporary comment in the *Journal of the Ministry of Agriculture*:[7] 'Several beet harvesters are available, and some of them, at any rate, are worth serious attention.' Machines for transplanting young vegetables were successfully developed. Attempts to pull flax mechanically were not in general successful, though reports from the U.S.S.R. about 1940 indicated the favourable development of a combine which pulled, cleaned and bound three acres of flax an hour. In the U.S.S.R. machines were also in the experimental stage for some jobs hitherto done entirely by hand, such as picking and pressing tea leaves and pruning tea bushes.

Mechanical cotton-picking has had a singularly unfortunate history. The first patent for a mechanical cotton-picker, in the U.S.A., dates from 1850, and by 1937 over 900 patents had been filed. Yet cotton was still picked almost entirely by hand. Concerning a machine developed in the thirties, which could pick

[6] D. N. McHardy, *Power Farming for Crops and Stock* (Reading, 1938), p. 9.

[7] Volume 45 (1938–9), pp. 593–4.

in 7½ hours as much as a good hand picker in five weeks, while reducing the labour required by 75 per cent, the U.S. Government report *Technological Trends*, published in 1937, commented (p. 58) that 'Fear of over-production with consequent shattering of existing price levels, and of dramatic displacement of cotton pickers, is deterring the introduction of the automatic cotton picker invented by the Rust brothers. . . . The inventors, cognisant of the revolutionary consequences attending their invention, are themselves withholding its application, except for its trial use on a co-operative farm in Mississippi and in the Soviet Union, where the problem of unemployment does not exist'.[8] In the last analysis the root cause of the trouble was the cheapness of hand-picking labour consequent upon the low standard of living at which the Negro population of the Southern States is forced to exist.

Mechanisation in the Mines

In Chapter 7 we saw that mechanisation had become established by 1918 in two important aspects of coal-mining, namely undercutting and conveying the coal from the face. Here again the relative rates of progress in various countries are of interest. In the U.S.A. the percentage of bituminous coal cut by machine rose from 51 per cent in 1913 to 79 per cent in 1935 and 88 per cent in 1939. Britain on the other hand, starting from 8 per cent in 1913, reached the American 1913 level only in 1935, and even in 1939 reached only 61 per cent. Similarly in 1939 only 58 per cent of Britain's coal was carried from the coal-face in conveyors. In the U.S.S.R., where the backward Tsarist régime cut only 1·7 per cent of its coal mechanically in 1913, the rate of mechanisation of the industry was truly remarkable. By 1940 just under 95 per cent was cut by machine and the industry was said to be more highly mechanised than in any other country in the world (though the figure was higher in particular coalfields elsewhere, for example, the Ruhr with over 97 per cent).

The serious lag in the mechanisation of British mines naturally

[8] The more intense Soviet interest in mechanical cotton-picking during the experimental phase has shown results in the post-war period. It is expected that in 1965 the whole cotton harvest of Uzbekistan will be picked by machine.

meant that the productivity of labour remained low and prices high, and, since almost the whole of industry depended on coal for its power, this was a very serious drag on British industrial progress. The events of the Second World War brought these facts home, and the Government set up a Technical Advisory Committee on the Coal Industry under the chairmanship of Mr. C. C. Reid. Its report (1945) was illuminating. Different natural conditions, it said, invalidate any comparison of the British and American industries, but natural conditions in Britain are 'comparable with those of the Ruhr and Holland, and, therefore, afford no explanation of the much lower O.M.S. in Britain'. (O.M.S. is the Report's abbreviation for 'output per man-shift', which in 1936 was only 23·54 cwt. in Britain, compared with 35·94 cwt. in Holland and 33·66 in the Ruhr—in spite of the fact that in 1913 Britain was slightly ahead of both these.) The explanation of this low O.M.S., said the Committee, lay not only in the failure to mechanise the mining processes, but more fundamentally in the poor general planning of mine layout and systems of underground transport (which depend largely on layout). Questions of general mine planning are beyond the scope of this book, but we have to note the fact of the British industry's backwardness in this respect, because, as the Reid Report stresses, the outdated layout and haulage systems were unable to deal with the greater potential output of mechanised methods at the face, and were therefore an important factor in retarding the introduction of machine-cutting and conveying. The report made recommendations for a drastic technical reorganisation of the industry, and said, '. . . we have come to the conclusion that it is not enough simply to recommend technical changes which we believe to be fully practicable, when it is evident to us, as mining engineers, that they cannot be satisfactorily carried through by the Industry organised as it is today'. Thus, other considerations apart, the post-war nationalisation of the coal-mining industry was an elementary step towards its urgently required technical rehabilitation—which has in fact resulted.

We turn now to more recent developments in mining machinery, whose value could not be regarded as fully established in this period. By 1918, we have seen, some preliminary attempts had been made at power loading on to the conveyor at the coal-face. But perhaps the real beginning should be dated from J. F. Joy's design of 1922. Yet the applicability of loaders remained very restricted, and even by 1937 only 17 per cent of American bituminous coal was loaded mechanically, while Britain had only about twenty of the machines in 1939. More modern versions, like that shown in Plate XXV, began to make serious progress towards solving the problem shortly after the war.

In 1937 a mine at Sverdlovsk in the U.S.S.R. tried out the new method of hydraulic mining. The coal, in this process, is smashed up and carried away by high-pressure jets of water directed at the face. The water not only wins the coal, but also transports it in troughs, and the smaller particles are even pumped to the surface in the water. It was estimated that the method increased the productivity of labour three-fold and cut production costs to half.[9] By 1940 it was being applied in several other mines.

The greatest Soviet innovation, however, was the underground gasification of coal. This is neither a 'tool' nor a 'machine' and so is strictly outside our terms of reference, but because of its potential affects on power production it must have some discussion here It eliminates mining altogether and turns the coal seam into an underground gasworks. Air or steam or a combination or alternation of the two is pumped down one shaft to the burning coal seam and up another comes the gas, which can be varied in composition at will. The idea of this method was suggested early in the century by William Ramsay, an English chemist, but it was not tried out till Soviet experiments began about 1933. Many difficulties had to be overcome, but by 1940 the first full-scale industrial station was established and several more followed it. The method shows several advantages over mining, at least for some types of seams. It abolishes the dangers of underground work. It extracts 80 to 90 per cent of the coal, as against 60 per cent by mining methods. It makes economical the exploitation of seams which are too thin and of too low quality for ordinary methods (it is to these that it has so far been applied, and it may prove to be less advantageous for rich seams). The gas which emerges is used for electric power generation and as the basis

[9] Post-war experience suggests that these original estimates were over-optimistic. In typical cases the productivity increase is about 1½ to 2 times, and the saving in cost some 25 to 30 per cent.

for synthetic chemical industries, besides being distributed to consumers in the same way as ordinary town gas.

Cautious experiments on underground gasification were begun in Britain in 1949. Ten years later they were approaching success and a pilot plant was contributing a few thousand kilowatts of power to the Grid. But by this time increasing efficiency in orthodox mining, coupled with a contraction of the market in an economic recession, had led to the accumulation of large stocks of unwanted coal. And so, to avoid possible unemployment underground, the experiments were abandoned. Some experimental work was also done in the U.S.A. after the war. But the leadership in developing this technique remains in Soviet hands.

Refrigeration and Heat-Pumps

The quality of the gas obtained by underground gasification can be greatly improved by pumping oxygen (or oxygen-rich air) down the shaft instead of ordinary air. In addition the synthetic chemical industries mentioned in the last paragraph but one, and indeed many other industries, require a cheap and abundant supply of oxygen, which is obtained by distilling liquid air. We have already mentioned (page 135) the Linde and Claude processes for liquefying air. But, just as a steam-turbine is more efficient than a reciprocating engine, so also a turbine should be more efficient for liquefying air than Claude's reciprocating engine. This fact was early understood, but the difficulties of design were such that no progress was made till Kapitza in the Soviet Union produced a practical machine in 1939, in which the cooling is done in a turbine rotating at 40,000 revolutions a minute. The Linde process requires air to be compressed to 200 atmospheres, and the Claude process needs 40. Kapitza's only needs the low compression of 5 atmospheres, thus reducing the size and cost of the compressor plant. Early models equalled the efficiency of the established processes, and later versions have considerably improved on it, so that the method has since come into regular use.

One of the most remarkable inventions of the inter-war years was concerned with the less violent refrigeration for food preservation (as in the domestic refrigerator). All the early refrigerators required a pump as part of the mechanism. The invention (patented in 1923 by a Swedish firm) of a refrigerator driven entirely by heat and using no pump was a piece of outstanding ingenuity.

The heat which a refrigerator withdraws from the object it is cooling is given out into its surroundings. In other words, a refrigerator will act as a heater, and in this form it is called a 'heat-pump'. When using electricity it is much more efficient than the resistance heater. And the same apparatus can be used for heating in winter and cooling in summer. All this was realised by Kelvin in 1852, but only towards the end of the inter-war period did it become possible to put the idea to practical use. Because the capital cost is high, early installations were confined to public buildings. After the war, such uses became rather more common, and towards the end of the fifties small-scale versions for domestic use came within the range of the well-to-do, mainly in America. It has been suggested that a dual-purpose plant, produced in Britain in the late fifties for simultaneously cooling the larder and heating water, would have been cheaper than separate refrigerator and water-heater, were it not for an illogical differential application of the purchase-tax.

The Gas-Turbine

Compared with, say, the period 1875 to 1895, which saw the perfection of the gas-engine, the development of the main types of petrol and oil engines, including the diesel, and the development of the steam-turbine, the twenty years between the two wars were not remarkable for the invention of prime movers. There were great increases in efficiency, of course, such as those we mentioned at the beginning of the chapter, and one fundamentally new form of prime mover appears to have passed through the critical stages of its development shortly before the Second World War—namely the internal-combustion turbine, which uses the expansion of burning gas (or atomised liquid fuels) directly to drive a turbine. There are obvious advantages to be expected from such an engine—chiefly low initial cost, small size and weight for a given power output, quick starting (compared with steam), independence of water supply and simplicity of construction. The chief disadvantage is that in order to attain reasonable efficiency the turbine has to work at a very high temperature which implies stringent demands on the materials of construction.

Curiously enough, the first known proposal for an oil engine, that of John Barber in 1791, was for a crude type of turbine. This, of course, was a freak, of no practical importance, but towards the end of the nineteenth century more practical attempts were made. The first to reach any success was that of Holzwarth, designed in 1908, which after trials and improvements was used industrially to a limited extent. This, however, was an explosion turbine, the burning of the gas taking place intermittently. It thus avoided many of the problems associated with a continuous turbine, but in doing so it sacrificed the advantage of simplicity—it was, in fact, a highly complicated machine. The development of the continuous-combustion turbine belongs largely to the inter-war period and was done chiefly by the Swiss firm of Brown-Boveri. It was first used for auxiliary purposes, where waste gaseous fuel was available, so that efficiency was less important: for example, exhaust gas-turbines to super-charge diesel engines and later for charging Velox boilers and other processes. But as its efficiency increased (to some 17 to 20 per cent, compared with 30 to 35 per cent for the best steam cycles), it became feasible to use the turbine for the primary production of power in certain cases where its special advantages outweighed its comparatively low efficiency. By the late thirties it had become an economic proposition for taking the peak load in electricity generation, where the engine may only run for some three or four hundred hours a year, so that low capital cost and quick starting are more important than efficiency. The first[10] installation (4,000 kW.) for this purpose was made in 1938 at Neuchâtel in Switzerland. Again, the gas-turbine had obvious advantages for use on railways, where lightness is important and where the efficiency of the steam locomotive was very low (8 to 12 per cent). The first gas-turbine locomotive—yielding 2,200 h.p. at an over-all efficiency of 18 per cent—was ordered for the Swiss Federal Railways just before the war and completed in 1941.

Progress in the Air

The war of 1914–18, as we have seen, found the aeroplane at

[10] Gas-turbine generating sets, up to 6,000 kW., had been used some years earlier in American oilfields; but this is not a parallel case, since cheap fuel was available.

little more than an experimental stage and left it as a reliable machine capable of development as a useful servant. In 1919, the year the Atlantic was first flown, regular air services were established covering 3,200 miles of route. By the next year the figure had risen to 9,700 miles and nearly 3 million miles were flown. By 1938 there were 349,100 miles of regular air services in operation, and the mileage flown was nearly 234 millions, an expansion of seventy-eight times in eighteen years! In May 1939, Pan-American Airways began the first regular transatlantic air mail. The expansion is an indicator of the increased efficiency and safety of aircraft, brought about by a multitude of detailed improvements as well as some outstanding inventions such as the Handley-Page slot (1919), flaps, the application of the supercharger (earlier used on racing cars) and the variable-pitch propeller (developed by a series of inventors between 1924 and 1934). The last two enabled aeroplanes to fly at great heights, thus reducing air resistance and greatly increasing speed.

The auto-gyro, which made some approach to the solution of the problem of long runways appeared in 1923 and was quite widely use in the thirties. Many attempts were made to produce practical helicopters, which would completely solve this problem by allowing take-off and landing on a few square yards. Limited success was obtained from about 1935 on, and the Sikorsky machine, which was to be the basis of future progress, first flew on 14 September 1939, but the really practical development of the helicopter was one of the by-products of the Second World War.

The Electronic Industries

Radio, like the aeroplane, had passed its most critical barriers in the 1914–18 war and thereafter it too developed with extreme rapidity. The advance from the first tentative broadcasts in 1920 to the important part that broadcasting plays in life today and the reliability with which it plays that part, is a reflection of the great improvements in technical efficiency. Ideas for beam transmission had been put forward from 1905 onwards. But its practical achievement dates from 1924, when work by Marconi and Franklin culminated in the setting up in Britain of a radio telegraph station for communication with the Dominions and India using short-wave beams. Beam transmission provided the basis for much wider use of the radio telephone, which in some circumstances gives better telephonic communication over great distances than do the land-line and cable. A public transatlantic radio telephone service was opened in 1926.

Television in its turn approached practicability shortly before the Second World War. Its history actually goes back a surprisingly long way. Telegraphy of single pictures was achieved experimentally before 1850 and a workable system of radio picture telegraphy was devised by Korn of Germany in 1907. A transoceanic commercial radio photogram service was in operation in 1926, though the process did not become important till about 1935. The basic principles of television transmission by wire were enunciated by Casselle in 1855 and an apparatus was built by Senlecq in 1877—only four years after the discovery of the principle of the selenium photo-cell. Nipkow patented the scanning disc in 1884. In 1901 Fessenden designed a radio television system. By 1911 television had been achieved, crude and imperfect, certainly not fit to have any aesthetic or entertainment value, but nevertheless a portent of what was to come.

The first really practical system was that which J. L. Baird first publicly demonstrated in 1926, and which the B.B.C. used for regular experimental transmission from 1929 onwards. This, however, was a low-definition system based on mechanical scanning, and the future lay with more subtle methods using cathode ray tubes in both camera and receiver.

The cathode ray oscillograph had been invented by Braun in 1897 and rapidly improved by others. Boris Rosing, a German working in Russia, applied it in 1911 to a television receiver, and about the same time Campbell Swinton in England made definite proposals as to how it could be used in the camera—a much more complicated matter. Following up this line of development, Vladimir Zworykin (a former student of Rosing, but now working in the U.S.A.) made his first Iconoscope camera in 1923. By the early thirties this had become a practical piece of apparatus, as had the Emitron camera developed by the British company, Electrical and Musical Industries, on the basis of Zworykin's work. With the opening of the B.B.C's transmissions on the Emitron system late in 1936, television had arrived in principle. To make it suitable for everyday use required much detailed development of electronic techniques, and this came largely from the use of electronic devices for many purposes during the war, so that when peace came everything was ready for the remarkable flowering that has made television one of the most potent influences for good or evil in our time.

Radio (except in its crudest form), television, and the use of photo-cells for the control of machinery (pages 160-1) are all applications of the science of 'electronics'—the science of manipulating electrons. This is a field that typifies an important new trend of the twentieth century. Formerly the process of invention and technical improvement was largely carried through by practical engineers and craftsmen, who used science only occasionally and incidentally. From the seventeenth century onwards, fundamental science had been playing an increasing role in industrial progress (for example, in creating the steam-engine, pages 91-2). But even in the nineteenth century most technological advances were still made on a largely empirical basis, with science used now and again to solve particularly knotty problems. In the twentieth century, by contrast, most important inventions have originated from discoveries in fundamental science, which are only later applied for practical purposes. Thus the science of electronics, together with all its applications, derives from the researches of J. J. Thomson from 1897 onwards, and of many who followed in his footsteps. Limitations of space prevent us from giving adequate stress to this basic role of science in modern technological progress. But these notes on the electronic industry—whose development was the main contribution of the inter-war period to the history of machines—must serve to remind us that from the twenties or thirties onward the inventor as such became steadily less important, and the fundamental scientist standing behind him came more and more to be the real innovator.

Another product of electronic technique is the 'talking picture'. A 'talkie' system was designed by Ruhmer in 1900, while in 1906 Eugene Lauste produced a system which was essentially modern in form and apparently satisfactory in most respects. It failed however, from lack of amplification. Nevertheless, it was in the same year that the triode valve, the essential constituent of the amplifier, appeared and amplifiers for radio were rapidly developed thereafter. It might have been expected, therefore, that a combination of Lauste's system with the amplifier, plus some improvement and refinement, would have produced satisfactory 'talkies' within a few years. But development was, in fact, remarkably slow. It was not till after de Forest's patent in 1923 that any significant progress took place, and the first public sound picture was 'The Jazz Singer' of 1928. Coloured films came a little later. Between 1934 and 1940 the Soviet inventor, Ivanov, developed a stereoscopic cinema, not requiring coloured spectacles or such aids, which gave satisfactory results. In Britain work on similar lines was carried out about the same time by Dennis Gabor, but was not taken up by the entertainment industry, and the stereoscopic cinema (except for trick performances with coloured or polarised spectacles) has not been used outside the U.S.S.R.

Before we leave this field a word on sound recording and reproducing apparatus will be in order. The gramophone was greatly improved by the introduction of electrical recording in 1924. The system of magnetic recording—the fore-runner of the tape-recorder of today—was invented by Valdemar Poulsen of Denmark in 1900 and greatly developed by Stille and others from 1924, to yield the Blattnerphone and later the Marconi-Stille recorder of 1933. Its usefulness was now clearly proved, and a few years later magnetic recording was widely used, for example inside broadcasting organisations. But tape-recorders were not made available to the general public till after the war. It has been alleged[11] that the use of this and other new recording methods was intentionally restricted by the powerful gramophone monopolies, seeking to protect their own interests. Since magnetic tape is also useful in a wide variety of industrial processes, for controlling machines, this charge is a serious one.

Machines in Everyday Life

A large number of the machines and appliances that we have discussed in the last few pages are related to life in a fundamentally different way from the machines of earlier times. They are

[11] For example, by O. W. Roskill in *Engineering 156* (1943), p. 385. It has similarly been suggested that the introduction of long-playing records was delayed by companies having vested interests in the old 'seventy-eights'.

used for the direct satisfaction of some need of the consumer, instead of for the production of some article which the consumer desires. Till the nineteenth century almost every machine or tool worthy of discussion was an instrument of production. It made the cloth the consumer would use, or carried it from the factory to the shop. There were exceptions, of course, like clocks or passenger transport. But towards 1900 there began to appear machines intended for the consumer to use directly for his personal benefit—the telephone, the cinema, the gramophone, the bicycle, the motor-car. This tendency grew strong after 1918. Motor-cars became fairly common. The 'talkies' came to be an essential part of life. In the home, machines became familiar—the vacuum cleaner, the washing machine, the refrigerator, the radio, etc., where earlier perhaps the only important machines found at home were the sewing machine and the mangle. The use of advanced machinery in production remained, of course, the basis of a high standard of living, but machines used for pleasure or personal convenience came to play an important role in life. The number of telephones per thousand people in the U.S.A. was less than 5 in 1895; by 1910 it had reached 82; by 1930, 164. Thereafter it declined to only 130 in 1939. This last draws our attention to the fact that, widespread as they were, telephones (apart from those used in business, which formed about one-third of the total) were confined to a small section of the population, the comparatively well-to-do. A saturation point was reached at which all those who could afford telephones possessed them, and as a result of the depression in the thirties the number actually declined.

It was the same in other cases. Of the homes in the U.S.A. wired for electricity in 1936, only 48 per cent had vacuum cleaners, only 34 per cent refrigerators. We quote American figures because these problems have been seriously studied by a number of committees set up by the U.S. Government; similar figures for Great Britain are difficult to estimate, but they would almost certainly be lower. Referring to these and other electrical appliances, the official U.S. Government publication, *Technological Trends*, remarked in 1937: 'The wonder is not that so many homes are now employing these electrical servants—but rather that so many are failing (usually for economic reasons) to utilise these conveniences' (p. 325). Considerations similar to those we mentioned in discussing failures to make full use of up-to-date techniques (page 163) apply again in this case. If there had been a shortage of man-power, then these electrical and mechanical appliances could have been manufactured no more quickly and it would have been natural and necessary that only a proportion of the people should have them. But, as there were many millions of unemployed, it would have been possible to manufacture at a higher rate and provide at least a higher proportion, if not all, with modern conveniences and labour-saving devices.

Progress Slows Down

Those who lived through the period between the wars gained the impression that this was a time of great innovation in mechanical matters. Indeed to the casual observer it seemed to be the period of most rapid progress that had ever been known. Yet sober examination of the facts does not confirm the impression. Let us, by way of illustration, compare the decades 1930–9 and 1880–9. The 1880s witnessed the perfection of the incandescent electric lamp, followed quickly by the establishment of public electricity supplies, electric railways and tramways, the polyphase system and the first examples of high voltage generation and transmission. In the field of prime-movers they saw the appearance of the steam-turbine, effective petrol engines and engines using heavier oils. The motor-car made its appearance. The first alloy steels (other than Mushet's) were developed, and electrolytic production of aluminium started. And by the time one comes to consider 'second class' inventions like electric welding, the Linotype or practical bicycles, the list would extend to several paragraphs.

Against this the 1930s can claim as first-class inventions only the gas-turbine and the helicopter (both of which only just managed to squeeze in at the end of the decade), a significant but limited application of electronics to industrial processes, some development—equally limited, if equally significant for the future—in automatic machinery, and the establishment of practical television. To pad out the list, one has to add minor inventions like the gyro-tiller,[12] improvements to inventions already

[12] First tried as early as 1868, but only perfected in this decade.

established, as with the variable-pitch air-screw or magnetic recording (noting the limited use that was made of this last), or preliminary steps in things like power-loading in coal-mines. And to be quite fair to the period, one must note that Whittle was already developing his ideas on jet-propulsion, and that radar had achieved some limited success though secrecy prevented any practical use of it until the war came.[13]

When this comparison is made, it becomes clear that progress in the thirties was considerably slower than it had been fifty years earlier. It is not difficult to extend the survey to cover other decades, say from 1750 onwards. And when this is done, the conclusion that emerges is that the rate at which important inventions were being made rose steadily throughout the eighteenth and nineteenth centuries, but reached a peak about 1895 and thereafter declined fairly steadily till 1939.[14] The period between the wars, far from being a time of accelerated progress, was actually one in which progress slowed down considerably.

How then did the illusion that this was a time of rapid advance arise? First, there are a large number of cases in which, although the fundamental inventions were made several decades earlier, they had no serious impact on the life of the man-in-the-street until after 1918. Such were the motor-car, radio, the aeroplane, and for most people even electric lighting and the telephone. Though the years before the Second World War were not so highly inventive as they seemed at the time, yet they were years in which earlier techniques became widely diffused and began to have easily noticed effects on the process of living. Naturally this greater use of earlier inventions depended on a steady flow of improvements in detail; and while fundamental invention slowed

[13] The discerning reader will notice the omission of some half-dozen inventions of the late thirties. The reason for this will appear later.

[14] In the first edition of this book (Cobbett Press, 1948) an attempt was made to put such comparisons on a statistical footing, not only for these periods, but for the whole span from the invention of agriculture to 1945, by devising an index to measure technological progressiveness. This material is omitted from the present edition. But if the reader is interested in the problem of measuring technological progress and in the light which such measurements can throw on its relations to social conditions, he may care to consult at a library pp. 182–92, 204 and 207–26 of the first edition.

down, the stream of patent literature for inventions concerned with minor improvements swelled enormously.

The second reason for the illusion lies in the point we have already made, that a great proportion of the mechanical and electrical devices now coming into use had a direct impact on the consumer. One does not notice—unless one has some special interest—that one's shirt is slightly cheaper because the yarn was ring-spun and the weaving done on a Northrop loom. Still less does one appreciate that the loom and spinning machine would have been more costly and less efficient, were it not for advances in steel-making and machine tools. But between the wars people could not help becoming aware of the cars, talking films, broadcasts and vacuum cleaners—and could not help wondering at the progress of science and engineering which they represented.

We have explained the illusion. But now what about explaining the reality? So far as fundamental inventions (rather than minor improvements) are concerned, progress went on at a steadily increasing pace throughout the eighteenth and nineteenth centuries. And then in our century it slowed down. Why? Not because 'Almost everything has been discovered',[15] as several writers thought in the thirties; nor because the process of further invention was becoming much more difficult—for progress suddenly accelerated again after 1939. Some other explanation is needed.

Now we have already met some previous cases in which a slowing down followed a period of comparatively rapid advance—after 3000 B.C., about 400 B.C., and again in the Roman Empire. And in each one of these cases we found social causes: various trends arising from the social structure of the times, the ways in which production and consumption were controlled, acted in such a manner as to discourage further invention.[16] This suggests that there may be social causes behind the new decline that we are considering. We can begin by noting what new social and

[15] C. C. Furnas, *The Next Hundred Years* (London, 1936), p. 294.

[16] There is another slowing down between A.D. 1300 and 1700, though this is not apparent until one does a statistical analysis. This can similarly be related to frustrations arising from the inability of feudal society to make use of the new technology of the time. The recovery starts with the victory of capitalism in England.

economic phenomena have arisen in the period under review. Some of these have already forced themselves on our attention earlier in this chapter and towards the end of Chapter 7—the permanent difficulty that manufacturers found from the late nineteenth century on in selling their products, chronic unemployment, and the formation of cartels and monopolies. We have already mentioned in passing some examples of how these things can retard progress. Chiefly they act by restricting production; but that means less incentive to instal the latest types of machinery, which in turn implies less encouragement to invent yet better. Sometimes they go further and actively discourage new invention.

Faults in the Distribution System

An outstanding (but by no means untypical) example of how the chronic difficulty of selling products discouraged invention is provided by the case of the Rust brothers' cotton-picker (pages 168-9). This invention was not brought into general use (except in the U.S.S.R.) because of a fear of what *Technological Trends* calls 'over-production', meaning, of course, the curious situation in which people who obviously need cotton goods are prevented by mal-distribution of purchasing power from buying them. It is not often that inventors foresee this difficulty and deliberately restrict the use of their machines as the Rust brothers did. More usually it happens that the producers fearing 'over-production' simply do not use the machine.

The difficulty of selling products leads to huge and wasteful competitive advertising campaigns, to the employment of enormous sales staffs to search for customers. In a pre-war motor-car costing £600 there was about £90 worth of direct factory labour, whereas about £240 went to the cost of selling it. Now it quite clearly does not cost anything like that sum merely to convey the car to the consumer and provide a man who will hand it over in exchange for his money. The reasons for the disparity are clearly put by Norton Leonard[17] when he says that the trouble 'starts with the development of a machine or method which cuts to a fraction the cost of making some useful article. All the established manufacturers who can afford it buy the machine, increas-

[17] *Tools of Tomorrow* (London, 1935), pp. 155–6.

ing their potential output many times. To pay for their investment they all calculate that they will have to capture larger proportions of the available market. Therefore they advertise widely and expansively. They increase their sales forces, allow larger commission, resort to all the tricks known to commercialism. The price of the product may fall to some extent, but most of the advantages of the new method have been cancelled by the cost of selling and the enforced idleness of the over-numerous machines. In many cases today the retail price of an article produced chiefly by automatic machines is three or four times the cost of production.' The community thus loses most of the potential value of the improved machinery. But more than that, he continues, 'One effect of this is to slow down the introduction of the newest and most efficient equipment. The manufacturers look ahead, see trouble approaching, and so they do not invest their money in machines which would certainly cut their legitimate production costs, but might not yield tangible profits.' And if the best existing machinery is not being used, what encouragement is there to invent yet better? All this is, of course, purely artificial. There is no lack of real market for the products, in the sense of people who need them. The difficulties arise from the distribution of purchasing power in such a way that those who need the goods cannot buy them.

The Effects of Unemployment

Unemployment is merely this same faulty distribution looked at from the other side. The goods are not sold, production is cut down and therefore men are thrown out of work. And possible unemployment was the other reason given for restricting the use of the Rust cotton-picker. It is again true that few inventors will act with such complete consciousness of the potential effects of their work, but in a less conscious way they will be deterred by the fact that their invention may increase unemployment. In attempts to employ some of the workless, a retrogression to more primitive methods has sometimes occurred. W. I. Sirovich, speaking in the U.S. Congress, said: 'One of the western states last year entered into a number of contracts for paving roads containing the specific stipulation that labor-saving machinery should not be used, with the intention of increasing the number of jobs provided.

I am not informed whether the men were required to dig up and remove the dirt with their hands, or whether they were allowed to do two or three times as much work with a shovel.'[18]

Unemployment retards technical progress in another way. The mass of men eager to find jobs depresses wage-rates, so that it is often cheaper to use primitive methods involving much hand-labour than to introduce automatic machinery. Men are retained, because they are cheap, on soul-destroying monotonous repetition work which could be better done by automatic machinery. That is one of the reasons for the failure to make full use of photo-cells in production (page 161).

The Role of Monopoly

The formation of cartels and monopolies also restricts production—indeed, one of the reasons for forming them is to maintain high prices by agreed restriction of output—and therefore holds back technical progress in the way we have been discussing. But monopoly often acts in a more direct manner. This problem much concerned the Government of the United States during the thirties. Under the New Deal policy a number of Government committees considered it and issued reports from which we quote. One of them[19] says: '. . . opposition has always come from vested interests which could see their property and income menaced by new inventions. Railroads were opposed by the owners of turnpikes and stagecoach lines. The use of gas for lighting was opposed because it would destroy the whale-oil business. Later electric lighting was fought by the gas companies. The telephone came into existence over the bitter opposition of the telegraph companies. The radio telegraph was fought by the telegraph companies. The radio telephone was fought by the telephone, telegraph and radio telegraph interests. Although corporate organisations do develop and utilise many inventions, sometimes corporations will fight successfully against the passage of laws requiring them to adopt modern improvements. . . . As Charles F. Kettering, vice-president of General Motors, said in an address in 1927:

[18] Quoted by Bernhard J. Stern in 'Frustration of Technology', *Science and Society 2* (1937).

[19] U.S. National Resources Committee, *Technology and Planning* (Washington, 1937), pp. 5–6.

"Bankers regard research as most dangerous and a thing that makes banking hazardous due to the rapid changes it brings about in industry." A banker who finances a new development that will destroy his present investments is asleep at the switch. Progress depends, therefore, to some extent on free resources of capital that cannot be controlled from any central point. With the tendency to centralisation of control in business and banking the openings for free initiative are more and more restricted.'

Opposition by vested interests to progress that threatened to supersede them was, of course, something that occurred long before the twentieth century. The resistance to the railways (pages 116-7) was an early example, and the quotation of the previous paragraph reminds us of several others. Even these early cases occurred mainly in industries like transport and communications which tend strongly to monopoly. However, while capitalism was still truly competitive—that is, till near the end of the nineteenth century—it was comparatively easy to overcome such opposition. The inventor could usually obtain the backing of people independent of the vested interest; there was always one of the many competing producers who would invest in the new technique. But the growth of monopoly as a general feature of economic life strengthened the forces of resistance. A monopoly of the twentieth century type had power of a quite new order of magnitude—a power well described by Henry A. Wallace, at that time Vice-President of the U.S.A., when he said in September 1943 : 'The peoples and the Governments of the world had unwittingly let the cartels and the monopolies form a super-government by means of which they could monopolise and divide whole fields of science and carve up the markets of the world. The people must get back their power to deal with this super-government. This super-government has misused the peoples of the United States, not only with regard to rubber [here he is referring to secret agreements between American monopolies and the German chemical combine I.G. Farbenindustrie, which greatly restricted America's pre-war development of synthetic rubber], but in a host of other critical industries as well. . . . These cliques have their own international government, by which they arrive at private quotas. Their emissaries are found in the Foreign Offices of many of the important nations of the world. They create their own system of tariffs and determine who shall be given permission to produce, to buy and to sell. . . . This secret agreement [on synthetic rubber] between an American monopoly and a German cartel was subject to no public authority. It was far more important than most treaties, but it was never acted upon by the U.S. Senate.'[20]

Such is the power of monopoly. It controls a whole industry. If it refuses to use an invention, there is no rival to whom the inventor can turn. The huge capital investment required for efficiency in modern industry prevents any new competitor from entering the field in order to exploit a new method. Of course, a monopoly is seldom absolutely complete, but even so it has plenty of power and plenty of methods by which it can prevent technical innovation. The introduction of an invention will usually depend on the utilisation at some stage of a technique already in use. The monopoly may have patent control of the latter and so prevent the introduction of the former. Another common method is to buy patents with no intention of using them, or even to undertake research in order to obtain patents that will stop others using a new device but will merely be shelved by the monopoly. The patent law of most countries in theory forbids this; in theory, if a patent is not used, anybody can bring a legal action and obtain permission to use it. In practice the costs of such action are so great that the monopoly can in fact suppress the use of a patent. For example, in 1934 the American Bell Telephone Company controlled 9,234 patents, of which they were using only 4,225. In spite of arguments put up by the Company, the Federal Communications Commission investigating the situation concluded that 3,433 of the remainder, which might have been socially useful, were suppressed by the Company to protect their own interests against competitors.

Sometimes the monopoly merely restricts the use of a new method, as with tungsten carbide (page 158). Sometimes it prevents its use at all. *Technological Trends* (one of the New Deal publications) says (p. 53): 'Changes within the electric industry have been retarded by the buying and supressing of patents by the large corporations which dominate the field. . . . A superior

[20] The story of these cartel agreements concerning synthetic rubber and of the great damage they did to the Allied war effort is very effectively told by Guenter Reimann in *Patents for Hitler* (London, 1945).

electric lamp, which it is estimated will save electric light users $10,000,000 a year, has been invented but has not been put on the market.' Later in the same document (p. 353), C. C. Furnas says: 'The author knows of one metallurgist who made his own safety-razor blade, sharpened it, and nitrided it. It has been used daily, without re-sharpening, for two years. Naturally the razor-blade manufacturers are not interested.'

In Great Britain concrete examples are difficult to come by, partly because there have been no Government inquiries, partly because the libel law endangers anybody who publishes a specific instance. British companies have several times been mentioned in connection with charges of entering into restrictive international agreements brought against various American corporations by the U.S. Government. The accusations have naturally been denied in Britain but there has been no opportunity to decide the matter, judicially or otherwise. While proven cases are lacking, general statements have been made by many authorities who are in a position to know the truth; for example, by Sir Alexander Gibb in his presidential address to the Engineering Section of the British Association in 1937: 'Of course, here, as always in research, it is the case that the greater the success of research, the more immediate and drastic the effect on existing plant and equipment. That is where the rub sometimes lies . . . and many valuable inventions have been bought up by vested interests and suppressed. . . . It is therefore not surprising that there is not always an enthusiasm for unrestricted research.'[21]

A specific example in Britain was provided by the railway companies, whose monopoly position was so strong that they did not even need to buy patents, but had merely to ignore new developments. The Government appointed a committee to consider railway electrification. Its findings were summarised by Mr. S. B. Donkin, President of the Institution of Civil Engineers: 'The finding of the Weir Committee, published in 1931, was unanimous in favour of complete main line electrification. The Committee emphasised that comparison between such electrification and either suburban electrification already in operation in this country or main line electrification undertaken in many countries abroad, would be misleading. Nevertheless the Committee found

[21] *Report of the British Association*, September 1937, pp. 158–9.

that under the conditions of railway working in Great Britain, electrification would reduce the cost of operating the railway system, and therefore increase the efficiency of utilisation of the coal resources of the country; it would reduce the average schedule running time of main line trains; by increasing the bulk use of electricity it would have a most favourable effect on the cost of electricity for other purposes; and finally, the cleanliness of an electrified system would have an effect on the health and well-being of the urban population which could not be assessed in terms of money alone. . . . It is unfortunate that up to the present the recommendation of the Committee in favour of complete main line electrification has not been accepted.'[22]

The growing complication and sophistication of modern technology, with innovation becoming continually more difficult and more costly, tends further to increase the power of monopoly. The resources of civilisation also grow, of course, and so provide the means for overcoming the increasing difficulties. But for success these resources have to be concentrated. Modern industrial research requires large staffs working co-operatively, great laboratories and expensive equipment. In the inter-war period, apart from a few small state-owned institutions the only organisations who could afford such staffs and equipment were the great industrial corporations. So the position was that the monopolies controlled a large part of the resources required for research leading to further technical advance, but these same monopolies had interests which tended to reduce their enthusiasm for invention, especially for fundamental inventions which revolutionise the methods of industry. As the American Government document, *Economic and Political Aspects of International Cartels*, referred to above, puts it (p. 32): 'Desiring to limit expansion of output and avoid the development of uncontrolled substitute processes, cartels are necessarily suspicious of new technological developments. They readily undertake research to discover new uses for their old products but often discourage the development of new processes or new products.' This explains the fact, noted above, that the number of detailed improvements increased rapidly between the wars, while the number of fundamental in-

[22] *Transactions of the International Engineering Congress, Glasgow*, 1938, pp. 52–53.

ventions was on the decline. In a word, the greatest opportunities for invention lie with the enormous resources of large concerns, but these have often very little incentive to use their resources to produce major technological changes. The effect is shown in W. M. Grosvenor's calculation[23] that only twelve out of seventy-five of the most important inventions between 1889 and 1929 were produced by research carried out by large corporations. The rest, we may suppose, depended on some more or less fortunate set of circumstances putting the necessary resources in other hands.

To summarise, we have found at least three social factors that tended in the years between the wars (and indeed from about 1900 onwards) to restrict the use of the most advanced methods and ultimately to slow down the progress of invention. First, the faulty distribution system, which created the chronic difficulty of selling products and therefore reduced the incentive to introduce advanced techniques. Second, mass unemployment, which discouraged invention through the fear of displacing labour and, by depressing wage-rates, often made it cheaper to use monotonous hand labour instead of introducing highly automatic machines. Third, monopoly with its tendency to protect its own interests even at the cost of progress. These were not necessarily the only retarding factors at work, but at least they were three important ones.

Another piece of evidence may be added. In the list (pages 180-1) of inventions of the decade 1930–39, we omitted several items : underground gasification of coal, Kapitza's turbo-expander for liquefying air, hydraulic mining, combined heat-and-power electricity stations, the stereo cinema and the Rust cotton-picker. These all have one thing in common : they were widely used *only* in the U.S.S.R. (at least till well into the war or after, when other countries began to employ some of them). Not all of them were Soviet inventions (the cotton-picker was American); but only in the Soviet Union did the conditions exist where they could be introduced into practice and further developed. Now the U.S.S.R. was the first country to change its social structure in such a way as to rectify the faults of the distribution system,

[23] 'The Seeds of Progress' in *Chemical Markets 24* (1929), p. 24. Quoted in Stern, op. cit.

eliminate unemployment, and abolish the control of industry by privately owned monopolies. The inference is clear: that these three factors were responsible for slowing down progress in the rest of the world. Further confirmation of this view will be found in the next chapter.

CHAPTER 10

THE SECOND WORLD WAR (1939–45)

THE troubles that had retarded advance before 1939 were largely swept away by the necessities of war. Private interests were subjected to the national need. Wasteful competition on the one hand, and the restriction of production by monopoly on the other, were over-ridden by national control. The *Handbook of U.S.A.*, issued by the U.S. Office of War Information, tells us: 'In pre-war days, the intricate maze of cartels (international commercial agreements), while protecting private interests and profits, tended to limit production. After the United States entered the war, alien-held patents came under the control of the Alien Property Custodian, and thus helped to speed U.S. production'—and similar steps were taken in Great Britain. The State took control of production and insisted on the use of the most efficient methods possible (with some unfortunate exceptions). Joint Production Committees, by giving the workers a share in policy formulation, played a big part in the drive for efficiency. Research and the development of new inventions were also subjected to Government control. Indeed they were largely carried out in Government establishments, for states that had shown little interest in the application of science for human betterment in times of peace were suddenly forced to undertake great efforts to promote technical efficiency for war. The insatiable demands of the armed forces also solved, even if in a terribly hurtful way, the problem of 'over-production'. Unemployment gave place to a serious labour shortage, which created strong incentives for the introduction of labour-saving machines and methods. The result of all this was a very great raising of the technical level in many industries, as the best possible machines were introduced. And at the same time there came a number of major new developments.

The Dawn of the Nuclear Age

The most important of these new developments—one of the most important of all time—was the release of nuclear energy. The chain of events which had its first culmination in the atomic bomb began in 1896, when Becquerel discovered radio-activity. There is no space here to describe the research carried on by scientists in all parts of the world, and most notably by Rutherford and his associates, which led to the discovery by Hahn and Strassman in 1938 of the particular property of the uranium atom which was to lead to the release of nuclear energy. They did not fully understand their experimental results, but the correct explanation was given in 1939 by Frisch and Meitner. It was found that when a particular kind of sub-atomic particle, the neutron, enters the nucleus of a uranium atom,[1] this nucleus splits into two roughly equal parts, a vast amount of energy is set free, and more neutrons are produced, which in the right conditions could be made to split more uranium nuclei, thus giving a 'chain reaction' that would build up into an enormous release of energy.

Then came the war. Scientists in Great Britain and the U.S.A. convinced their respective Governments that this process of *nuclear fission* (as it is called) was likely to yield a bomb thousands of times more powerful than any previously known. Vast research projects were set in motion by the two Governments, at first separately, later jointly. About £500 million was spent on research, development, construction of the plant, and the eventual manufacture of atomic bombs. A point that emerges is the magnitude of the results that are obtainable, the rate at which technical advance can be pushed forward, when full financial facilities are given to scientists and engineers. As Sir John Anderson said, 'In four years our scientists have solved a problem that in peace might have taken twenty-five to fifty years'.

The first nuclear reactor (then called a 'pile'), constructed by Enrico Fermi and his team in Chicago, started work on 2 December 1942. It produced only half a watt of heat to begin with, later 200 watts. But—besides being a step on the way to atomic bombs—it demonstrated the principle on which the nuclear power stations of the fifties and after were to be based. Less than a year later another reactor was producing 1,000 kW. of heat, and

[1] More precisely, an atom of one uranium isotope, uranium-235.

by the end of 1944, 100,000 kW. had been reached. The first atomic bomb was tested in July 1945. And in August of that year came the tragedies of Hiroshima and Nagasaki.

The atomic bomb, we all hope, marks but a passing phase in the history of the world. But in those few years men had taken, even if in a perverse way, their most fundamental step forward in their control of nature since they learned to use fire, perhaps a million years ago. That is not just a dramatic statement made for effect. It is based on the scientific nature of the discovery. There are, to the best of our knowledge, three fundamentally different kinds of natural forces—gravitational forces, chemical or electro-magnetic forces, and nuclear forces. Along with tool-making, it is the mastery of chemical forces—by controlling and using fire—that marks the beginning of the human story, the transition from some ape-like creature to the earliest form of man. In one sense technical history since then has been the story of how man learnt to make better and better use of his control over gravitational forces and chemical forces (and this book, apart from the first page of Chapter 1, is a mere snapshot of the last hundredth of that story). Man learnt, for example, to use gravitational forces to drive water-wheels. He learnt to use chemical forces to drive steam-engines. Although it is not at first sight obvious, all the forces involved in electrical machinery and electronic devices are of the same fundamental nature as chemical forces. During all this time men were merely finding new ways of using old forces. But now—with the first 'pile' of 1942, they had at last started to master a third, fundamentally different and far more powerful, type of force—that which binds together the particles of atomic nuclei. These nuclear forces are enormously more powerful than the others, because they are, as it were, nearer to the centre of the basic plan of the universe.

When men first discovered how to use fire, they can have had no conception of the many uses it would eventually be put to—they would not have foreseen steam-engines, alloy steels, plastics, electric railways or television. All they would see at first would be possibilities of applying fire, as a substitute for something else, to do something that was already familiar—to warm them when the sun failed, to give light on moonless nights. Only gradually they learned the other possibilities of fire—cookery, pottery, metals, steam-engine, and so on. In the same way, we today cannot foresee what will be the consequences of this equally fundamental conquest of nuclear forces. We can only say that it will probably transform the life of humanity just as fundamentally as did that ancient discovery of fire. But there will be one big difference. It took a million years to work out the consequences of the control of fire. Nowadays progress is incomparably faster, and it will probably only take a few generations for nuclear energy to make corresponding changes in human life. In Chapter 12 we shall look at man's first few hesitating steps along this new road.

The development of atomic energy provides an excellent illustration of a trend (already mentioned on page 177) that has been growing strongly in recent years. For atomic energy in practice was the result of fifty years of scientific research, much of which was done without any reference to possible applications, followed by five years of applied science and engineering directed to the solution of a particular practical problem. It is more and more becoming true that the best way to produce technical advances of great benefit to humanity is not to devote the largest possible amount of research to the immediate practical problems, but rather to ensure that a large amount of fundamental scientific research is undertaken and that full use is made of its results by applied scientists and industrialists. Quite apart from other reasons (such as cultural ones) for doing fundamental scientific research, it is now the case that the community as a whole is likely to benefit more from it than from most other human activities (with certain obvious provisos, which the alternatives presented by the atomic bomb well illustrate).

The war years just failed to produce another step forward of perhaps as great significance as nuclear energy, namely electronic computers. For here again the urgency of war greatly speeded up what had previously been a dead slow advance, and computers were on the verge of becoming practical devices when the war came to an end—for which reason they will be considered in Chapter 13.

Jet-Planes and Helicopters

Some other wartime inventions, though less significant than nuclear energy from a long-term point of view, have led in the post-war years to more immediate practical benefits. The most notable of these were in the air—the jet-propelled plane, practical helicopters, and (again in a perverse way) the German V-2 rocket. The last was a key step on the road to the conquest of space. The first practical helicopter (as we saw on page 175) flew a few days after the outbreak of war. Its further development might have continued as slowly as in the past. But its promise as a weapon led to the liberal provision of the resources needed to transform it rapidly into the reliable machine of today —useful in many phases of transport, in emergency rescue work and as a mobile crane.

The story of jet-propulsion is very clearly one of frustration in peace, followed by immense effort and quick success for war. Proposals for jet-propelled aeroplanes go back to 1920 or earlier. During the thirties several workers in various countries tackled the problem. In Britain, Whittle began his work about 1928, but could get no support from the Air Ministry. By 1937 engines of his design were run successfully on the test-bed. But still almost nobody was interested, and it was not till 1939 that orders were placed for trial planes for development work. Thereafter progress was rapid. In 1941 full-scale trials were successful (Plate XXVI) and by early 1942 the first planes were coming off the production line. Developments in other countries were in some cases only slightly behind Whittle's work.

The Beginnings of Radar

Not strictly 'in the air', but closely connected with it, is radar (formerly known as 'radio-location'—the use of radio to detect and accurately fix the position of invisible aircraft and other objects). Radio-location had by the outbreak of war advanced farther than the other developments so far mentioned. Sir Robert Watson-Watt and his team started investigating its possibilities in 1930. By 1935 they could detect a plane at 50 miles. And in 1938 Britain's south-east coast had a chain of radar sentinels. By contrast, Dr. Lyman Chalkley, chief economic analyst to the U.S. Government's Board of Economic Warfare, alleged that radar was not adequately developed before the war in the U.S.A. because it did not appear to have any profitable peacetime uses. On the outbreak of war, he said, America 'had to start practically from scratch, meanwhile losing ships and planes and men, because the profit motive had not guided up to the development of radar from a state of laboratory curiosity to the manufacture of practical instruments'.

During the war the technique was carried to new heights. The refinement that goes by the name of 'centimetric radar' was the result of brilliant research and (like all radar advances) of fine team-work. It depended in particular on the cavity magnetron valve, invented in 1939 by a team at the University of Birmingham, and rapidly developed in the following years. The new technique increased the accuracy of radar in its primary application to detecting enemy aircraft, and greatly extended the range of circumstances in which it could be used. But it did far more than that by making possible the application of radar for many other purposes—to begin with, such things as accurately guiding bombing planes to their targets and even arranging the release of the bombs at the right moment. Radar moved on from the status of a particular method of solving a particular problem, to the far higher status of a technique of very wide applicability. Safety and efficiency of ships and aircraft has been enormously increased by numerous radar devices, including the one illustrated in Plate XXVII, which gives the navigator a map of his surroundings even in thick fog. Other applications have included accurate determinations of distances for map-making and scientific investigations of the surfaces of the moon and the planets.

To these vital advances—the crucial step in nuclear energy and the bringing into practical use of jet-propulsion, helicopters and developed forms of radar—must be added many other lines in which war-time researches led to success in the immediate post-war period (we have mentioned computers as the outstanding example). As a result, the war years stand out as one of the periods—perhaps even *the* period—of most rapid technical advance in all history.

Of course, each one of the outstanding wartime inventions depended to a considerable extent on work carried out before the war. Nevertheless, while granting credit for prewar efforts, we must note that the war years were remarkable for bringing to perfection and putting into practical use far more outstanding inventions than any comparable period in the previous fifty years. This would seem to be more than a coincidence. It confirms the view, stated in Chapter 9, that in the inter-war period progress was being held back by social and economic restraints. The twenties and thirties did not lack inventive ability, but society gave little help or encouragement. This is exemplified in the Whittle story and confirmed by Dr. Chalkley's remarks about radar. The same idea was expressed by G. G. Smith in discussing, before the announcement of Whittle's success, the prospects for jet-propulsion. He wrote: 'Under the stress of war conditions, funds are available for research and experiments, the best equipped brains can be applied to problems and vested interests are not allowed to impede developments'.[2] The statement by Sir John Anderson, quoted above, points to the same sort of conclusion.

Advances in Production Methods

Less spectacular, but probably equally important, were advances made in production methods. Between 1940 and 1943 American industrial production nearly doubled. In Britain, even under siege, production increased by more than 40 per cent between 1939 and 1943—that is at an average yearly rate of about 9 per cent, as contrasted with the 3·5 per cent of the previous decade. All this was in spite of the difficulties of importing essential machinery and materials in wartime, in spite of the effects of bombing, the strain on transport, and the 4,500,000 men in the Forces.

Only one-twelfth of the British increase came from working longer hours. The rest arose from the better organisation of industry under Government control and the subjection of sectional interests to national need, from full employment and the recruiting of new workers to industry, and from increased efficiency arising from the more widespread adoption of modern machines and up-to-date methods. The rise in the technical level of industry was shown by the increase in labour productivity (output per man-hour), estimated at some 15 per cent (more than twice as fast as in peacetime) over all industries and some 30 to 35 per cent in the munitions industries.

[2] *Flight*, 9 October 1941; reprinted in his *Gas Turbines and Jet Propulsion for Aircraft* (3rd edition, London, 1941), p. 40.

Most of the improved efficiency in engineering arose from the spreading throughout the industry of the modern machines and techniques that had been developed during the past few decades, but had not previously been widely applied. Tungsten carbide tools, whose spread before the war had been restricted by the policy of international cartels (page 158), came into general use. The machine-tool industry played a valiant part in providing, on an enormously increased scale, the various types of highly productive machines for which demand arose, and especially the more robust and rigid models required for using carbide tools. In America the expansion of this basic industry was unparalleled. Before the war sales of machine-tools reached a peak of about $200 million in four separate years (1918, 1929, 1937, 1939). In 1942 sales were $1,300 million and the average for the years 1940–3 was over $900 million, or four-and-a-half times the pre-war best. At the end of 1939 the U.S.A. had 1,500 million dollars' worth of machines which were less than fourteen years old; by the end of 1943 she had 4,500 million dollars' worth. Large-sections of industry, formerly using obsolescent equipment, had been rapidly modernised.

Much of the increased productivity, in industry generally, arose from the wider application of mass-production methods and from a multitude of refinements and improvements in these methods. Among the latter is the outstanding innovation of 'quality control'. The essence of interchangeable production is that the measurements of each piece must be identical within certain permitted limits of error, called 'tolerances'. Owing to wear of tools and other factors, a machine which is set to produce the pieces to specification will gradually lose its accuracy, until eventually the errors will exceed the tolerances. Any further pieces produced will then have to be rejected as 'scrap'. The old method was simply to inspect occasional samples and when these were found to be outside the required limits, the machine would be adjusted. But meanwhile many pieces would have been produced with too great errors and these would all be wasted. Quality control uses the science of statistics to avoid this. From the permitted tolerances a new set of inner limits is calculated; when the errors on more than a certain number of samples exceed these, the pieces are still sufficiently good for use, but it is a warning to the inspector that the machine is liable soon to become so inaccurate as to produce scrap. It is therefore stopped and adjusted immediately, and wastage of time and material is avoided. The statistical principles on which quality control is based had been known for many years, and in limited fields the method had been used for a couple of decades, but it was only during the war that quality control was widely applied and the full possibilities of the method were developed. The effects of this and other improvements in production methods are shown by the case of the Sten gun, which was made so cheap as to be classed as a 'consumable store' to be thrown away when no longer serviceable. Its cost was reduced to about thirty shillings, as against about as many pounds for a similar article before the war.

Mass-production methods were also applied to work of an entirely new order of size—for example, in the U.S.A. to the prefabrication in factories of complete parts of a ship, ready for rapid assembly on the slipway. A single American factory in 1943 was producing parts enabling a shipyard to launch two 10,000-ton ships a week. By these and similar methods the U.S.A. was able to reach the amazing production of 3,876 merchant vessels in three years—an average of twenty-five a week.

British Agriculture Mechanises

Before the war, as we saw on page 167, British agriculture had been backward in its use of machinery. The situation was completely changed when agriculture came to be one of the pivots of the war efforts. By means of guaranteed prices and other aids, the Government encouraged farmers to aim for maximum output —which required, among other things, greater mechanisation. The number of tractors in use more than trebled from 55,000 in 1939 to 175,000 in 1944; the number of tractor implements rose from 200,000 in 1939 to 1,175,000 in 1943; and the number of combine harvesters from 150 to 1,500. On the basis of the number of machines to a given area, Britain's agriculture became the most highly mechanised in Europe. The previous tendency to use machinery to less than its full capacity was partly overcome by pooling schemes.

In war conditions sugar-beet and potatoes became especially important (because of their high energy content). Much attention was given to the improvement of machines for dealing with them. About 1943 the latest beet-harvesters, which lifted the beet, topped it and deposited it in piles at intervals, were said to be completely effective in most circumstances. Potato-planters and lifters were also improved. Advanced types of planters in 1943 saved 80 per cent of the labour involved. Lifters which dug the potatoes, picked them up, sorted and loaded them were brought to success, though not used on a wide scale. Another example of wartime inventions was a machine for picking up sheaves of corn, carrying them to and loading them on to the stack. The result of this mechanisation, together with other improvements, was a 70 per cent increase in Britain's agricultural production between 1939 and 1943. In the latter year home-grown products supplied two-thirds of food requirements, against one-third before the war.

. . . and British Mining Fails

There were unfortunately some industries in which these remarkable increases in efficiency did not take place in Britain. The most notable was coal-mining. Coal, always the life-blood of industry, became even more important in war. Every aspect of production depended on it. Yet, instead of increasing to satisfy the call for more fuel, the production of coal actually *decreased*—from 231 million tons in 1939 to 193 million in 1944.

The causes operating to reduce output included some that were unavoidable, such as the loss of man-power in the call-up and the increasing age of those that were left. But greater use of machinery could have compensated for these losses, as it did in other industries. Yet the mine-owners held to the policy of pre-war years. There were only forty more coal-cutters in use in 1943 than in 1939, though the number increased by another 424 in 1944; and the quantity of coal cut by machine actually decreased from 142 million tons in 1939 to 132 million tons in 1944. Similarly, although the number of face and gate conveyors rose from 8,271 in 1939 to 9,492 in 1944, the use of them was such that the amount of coal conveyed fell from 134 million tons in 1939 to 127 million tons in 1944 (after reaching a peak of 137 million tons in 1940). Power loaders might have helped greatly to solve the man-power problem; yet only 192 of them were in use in 1944. American experts, visiting the mines, found over a million pounds' worth of machinery lying idle and estimated that its use would have increased the output by 12 to 15 million tons a year. As a result of this policy, the supply of coal fell well below Britain's needs. In their homes the people suffered from the shortage. Factory supplies had to be rationed and no doubt production was held back and the war prolonged.

The U.S.S.R. in the War

In Chapter 9 we saw that the U.S.S.R., having struggled from a position of extreme backwardness to turn herself into a modern industrial country, was beginning to take her place as an innovator in a few lines of development. In Part Three we shall, of course, be studying how that country jumped into the lead in several fields. But during the war itself, no invention of outstanding importance emanated from the U.S.S.R. This appears to have been the outcome of a considered policy. Research of a radical or exploratory nature was abandoned or drastically reduced. Work in nuclear physics, for example, was virtually stopped, so that the U.S.S.R. had no part in the early work on the release of nuclear energy. Instead, all efforts were concentrated on using available techniques (naturally with a multitude of improvements) to increase production.

At first the destruction of plant by the German invaders severely reduced productive capacity. But when the counter-offensive began, it was accompanied by increases in production which outdid even those of the thirties. The output of pig-iron increased by 20 per cent between mid-1942 and mid-1943 and by another 34 per cent from then to mid-1944. Coal production rose by 32 per cent between July 1943 and July 1944. The output of steam-driven power stations in 1943 was 20 per cent more than the total for 1940 and 1941. The capacity of new generating plant installed in 1944 was reckoned as nearly 3 million kW., which is almost as much as the new installations in Britain in the first ten years of the Grid.

These statistics give us little idea of how the *efficiency* of Soviet industry increased during the war. We learn a little more from figures on labour productivity, which for industry as a whole increased by about 40 per cent between 1942 and 1944 and, for example, in coal-mining by 32 per cent between 1943 and 1944.

Such increases as these could not be obtained merely by working harder, though that must have played a part. They indicate that, despite the lack of major advances, a great deal was being done in the way of small inventions and improvements. Many of these came from the workers on the job, as is indicated by numerous reports, of which this is a sample : 'A two months' "rationalisation suggestions" campaign, which has just ended [in November 1944] in the factories of the Commissariat of Light Industry, has resulted in the submission by the workers of over 3,000 inventions and proposals for improvements . . . the 810 suggestions already put into effect in the factories will economise materials, power and labour to the value of 60 million roubles a year.'

And yet, though figures like those given are some help, a far more vivid indication of the expansion and increasing efficiency of Soviet industry is provided by the successes of the Red Army. No army could have withstood the long retreats of 1941 and 1942 and then advanced so rapidly in 1943 and 1944, no army could have produced such concentrations of fire power—in some cases one artillery piece per yard over hundreds of miles of front—unless it were backed, not only by a civil population determined to win no matter what the sacrifice, but also by an industry of tremendous efficiency.

PART THREE

OUR TIME

CHAPTER II

CONTINUITY AND CHANGE

RECENT events always appear in foreshortened perspective. For this reason it has been difficult to attain a proper balance in the previous two chapters; the reader of the future will doubtless find that some achievements of these periods have been underrated, others exaggerated in merit—only time will show truly the relative merits of various lines of advance. When we come to consider progress since 1945, the difficulty becomes much greater. We cannot pretend to give a complete or balanced account of the period. We can do no more than describe a few major trends and mention a few minor ones. And, rather than attempt a collection of detailed technical histories of automation, space exploration and the like, it will be more important to aim at an assessment of the social significance of the new technologies—to try to visualise their effect on human life in the years to come, to consider why advance was more rapid here and slower there, to compare policies of various countries, and to examine all these points in relation to the social, economic and political changes of the time.

These latter changes have been truly vast. Socialism, previously confined to the U.S.S.R., has been adopted as the way forward by countries comprising about one-third of the population of the world. Colonial peoples have become more and more discontented with their bondage and one by one have gained their freedom, until in the early sixties only a handful of colonial territories remain. In the capitalist world the troubles that held back progress before 1939 have, at least partially and temporarily, been overcome. The cycle of boom and slump has been moderated into a series of *comparatively* mild recessions and recoveries. Unemployment has been reduced in scale, though it has latterly tended to increase again. Monopolies emerged strengthened from the war;

we shall not know for some time to what extent they are again engaged on activities like those that frustrated technical advance in the inter-war period,[1] but it would appear on the evidence available that their role has been less restrictive than hitherto.

On the international scale, the most striking phenomenon has been the division of the world into socialist and capitalist 'camps' (with the former colonial countries and a few others taking an uneasy position between). And, in view of the familiar fact that an old order does not willingly yield place to a new, this has led to the Cold War. The atmosphere of these years has been not so much one of peace as one of preparation for war, and we shall see that this has had a strong effect on technological development. But from 1963 onwards the horizon has slightly brightened, and there are signs that the arms race will give way to economic and technical rivalry. Indeed this peaceful competition is ultimately decisive, and the socialist countries have for years been stressing that the relative merits of the capitalist and socialist systems will be decided by their respective abilities to promote technological progress and apply it for the good of humanity. An assessment of the progress of this competition must be one of the main tasks of the present chapter.

Socially and politically our time is a mixture of continuity and change—continuity, in that much of the world adheres to a somewhat modified form of the political and social system that first saw light in seventeenth and eighteenth century England; and change, in that much of the rest has adopted an entirely new system. Continuity and change are similarly interwoven in the technological realm. So exciting is the novel element in the mixture, that we might be tempted to treat the years since 1945 entirely in those terms—in terms of nuclear energy, computers, automation, space travel, transistors, and all the rest. But this would be to give a one-sided picture. For, as always, much of the progress of our time has come from the improvement and widespread use of inventions that had been established earlier. The jet fighters of the Second World War, together with their near relatives the turbo-props, became the long-distance passenger planes

[1] For it was largely the need to restrain their influence in the Second World War that led to the release of really convincing evidence of their earlier activities.

of today. Television, technically established before the war, has since become one of the most widespread boons (or banes) of domestic life. Radar has developed into a routine aid for shipping and aircraft. Britain's agriculture (to take a more parochial example) has continued to walk the road of mechanisation on to which it was forced by the demands of war. And so one might go on.

We cannot hope to make any adequate survey of the continuation in our time of earlier trends. Let us be content with two examples—electrification, which still remains one of the key issues in industrialisation, and gas-turbines, which will illustrate the progress of an invention that had just reached practicability at the outbreak of war.

Progress in Gas-Turbines

In spite of efforts to increase efficiency by raising the working temperature and to adapt it to use cheaper fuels unsuitable for other engines,[2] the gas-turbine still remains costly to run in terms of fuel consumption. For stand-by electricity generation (see page 174) its value has been fully established. The first British installation, of 15,000 kW. started work at Manchester in 1952. In 1957 a 20,000 kW. turbine was built near Moscow to use the cheap gas from an underground gasification station. And in 1962 the Soviet Union announced an experiment towards further improving the economy of the engine by using its waste heat for district heating—with two turbines running on natural gas to produce 100,000 kW. of power and a million and a half gallons of hot water per hour. Gas-turbines still remained modest in size and power—in 1962 the largest in existence were of 30,000 kW. in Switzerland and 40,000 kW. in Sweden, with one of 50,000 kW. undergoing tests in the U.S.S.R. Smaller installations have also proved their worth in stand-by water pumping (Metropolitan Water Board, 1955), the provision of ships' electricity supplies while in port, and various industrial applications.

For transport purposes the gas-turbine offers, in compensation for its high fuel consumption, the advantages of simplicity, reliability, lightness, long life and low maintenance costs. The

[2] In 1962 the American Chrysler Corporation were claiming that their small (140 h.p.) version would 'run on anything from fuel oil to French perfume'.

British Rover Company began developing a gas turbine car in 1950, and the Chrysler Corporation of America were not far behind. In the Le Mans 24-hour race of 1963, the Rover vehicle demonstrated its capabilities by covering 2,553 miles at an average speed of 109·7 m.p.h., with only nine pit stops, in a race so gruelling that thirty-six of the forty-nine starters fell by the wayside. And a little later Chrysler loaned fifty of their vehicles to private motorists to assess their performance in normal conditions. Fire engines powered by gas-turbines appear to have been successful in the U.S.A., and some attempt has been made to develop heavy lorries driven by this unit. Yet it remains doubtful if the gas-turbine will ever oust its competitors in road transport.[8] Meanwhile these researches have given a useful by-product in the form of light portable turbine-driven fire pumps and the like (the Rover model was in production in 1954). Though experiments continue with gas-turbines for railway locomotives, the question of whether they can ever be more useful than diesels or electrification remains undecided.

For military purposes, fuel economy is of secondary importance, and it appears that a good deal of attention is being paid to the possibilities of the gas-turbine as the power unit of personnel-carrying vehicles and of tanks, while at least six navies have adopted it for driving their fastest fighting ships (Plate XXVIII).

All the foregoing refers to open-cycle versions in which the products of combustion pass through the turbine itself. The closed-cycle principle, in which the heat from the fuel is transferred to a separate working gas that drives the turbine, was developed from 1947 onwards by Escher-Wyss, and promises higher efficiencies, of the order of 30 per cent. But once more its future importance as a prime mover cannot yet be predicted.

New Methods of Producing Electricity

Industrial prosperity, and therefore all technological progress, continues to depend very largely on electric power. In recent years world electricity production has been increasing by a factor of about two and a quarter each decade. But in the U.S.S.R. it increased

[8] If the familiar reciprocating internal combustion engine is to be superseded by any other, the most likely candidate would seem to be the Wankel 'rotary piston' engine, which—after years of development—was first fitted to a production model in 1964.

four times from 1953 to 1963, while in the socialist countries as a whole it increases about three and a quarter times per decade.

The rising efficiency of power production is reflected in the way its prices have resisted the general inflationary tendency. In Britain, for example, the cost of electricity rose by only 31 per cent between 1948 and 1959, although the cost of fuel had risen by 67 per cent, while the capital costs had been grossly increased by an inflation of 80 or 90 per cent in mechanical and electrical engineering and of 40 to 50 per cent in building and civil engineering, as well as a rise from 3 to 5½ per cent in the interest rate on borrowed capital. This steady improvement has resulted, not from revolutionary changes, but simply from advances in engineering techniques that have allowed generators to be built in much larger sizes with corresponding increases in thermal efficiency. In Britain generators have advanced from 30,000 kW.[4] in 1948 to 275,000 kW. in 1962. In the same period thermal efficiencies rose from 28·3 to 37·7 per cent, while the capital cost of a power station per kilowatt of capacity fell from £67 to £43. Units of 500,000 kW. under construction are expected to raise efficiency to 39·2 per cent and reduce capital cost per kilowatt to £35.

The steam temperatures and pressures involved in these large units are now approaching the critical point, above which water does not boil in the ordinary sense, but instead the whole contents of the boiler become, in effect, steam. At this stage new and difficult technical problems arise—for example, a far higher standard of water purity is required. The U.S.A. has had a supercritical boiler since 1958, and Britain's first is due in 1965. But in this field the U.S.S.R. has a small but distinct lead.[5] Plans for a

[4] It is more usual nowadays to express figures in units of megawatts, denoted by MW. (1 MW. = 1,000 kW. = 1 million watts). But, on the assumption that many readers will think more easily in terms of kilowatts (kW.)—a kilowatt being the power required by one bar of an ordinary electric fire—we shall retain that unit.

[5] Though she lags somewhat behind in the size of thermal power units in general. Her first 300,000 kW. units were tested in 1963, and regular production at this size started the following year, while work is proceeding towards 500,000 and 800,000 kW. units. We may mention in passing that the U.S.S.R. continues to lead the world in large-scale hydro-electric schemes. The Volgograd (former Stalingrad) station of 1959 (2,415,000 kW.) and the Bratsk station of 1963–4 (3,600,000 kW.) were each in turn the world's largest. Still larger stations are planned, while many smaller schemes are in operation.

small supercritical boiler were drawn up in 1937, though because of the war the project was not completed till ten years later. Two full-scale supercritical boilers were installed at the Chelyabinsk power station in 1959, working at 3,225 lb. per square inch pressure and giving 260 tons of steam an hour. A more recent installation raises the latter figure to 950 tons an hour.

These conventional means of generating electricity—by boiler, steam-turbine and alternator—seem to be getting very close to the limit of their development. Sizes will not increase by more than another factor of two, nor will thermal efficiencies rise much above 40 per cent. And so increasing attention is being paid to quite novel methods of getting electricity direct from heat, without the use of boiler and turbine. The most promising of these is the one known as magnetohydrodynamic (MHD) or magentoplasmadynamic (MPD) generation, the principle of which is quite simple. In the familiar generator wires are whirled in a magnetic field, whose action causes a current to flow in them. MHD replaces the wires with a stream of hot gas—so hot that its atoms are broken up into their electrically charged constituents; it thus becomes a conductor, in which current is induced by the motion of the gas through the magnetic field. Though the principle is simple—indeed Faraday experimented on these lines before 1840—the development of it into a practical generator involves formidable engineering problems, largely because of the very high temperatures involved. Small experimental models, producing a few kilowatts of power, worked successfully in the U.S.A. from 1959, and shortly afterwards in Britain and the U.S.S.R. The next stage is that of pilot plant experiments yielding a few tens of thousands of kilowatts. The U.S.S.R. announced plans on these lines in 1962, but no further information seems to be available. A 40,000 kW. version was at the testing stage in America during 1964, at which time Britain also announced plans for a £2 million research project intended to lead to a 20,000 kW. prototype by 1967–8. Some experts have risked the prediction that MHD generators will be producing power commercially before the end of the sixties, though the mid-seventies seems a more likely date. They will presumably be employed as 'toppers', using the heat at high temperatures and passing their exhaust heat on to ordinary steam-driven generators; and in this way overall efficiencies of perhaps 60 or 65 per cent may be hoped for. They are most likely to come into their own as a way of using nuclear energy more effectively.

Practical possibilities of other new ways of generating electricity direct from heat—such as the thermionic method—probably belong to the more distant future. But the production of current direct from chemical energy in the fuel cell seems to be reaching the verge of the practical. As a result of researches carried on since 1932, Mr. Francis Bacon of Cambridge produced a workable cell in 1959, using it to drive a fork-lift truck. His cell has the disadvantage of using gaseous hydrogen as fuel, but later developments make other fuels possible—for example, an American cell of 1963, which ran on cheap fuel oils. Intense research on the subject is being done in Sweden, where a team hopes to produce by 1966 a cell using 'cracked' ammonia as fuel and yielding 25 kW. The attraction of the fuel cell is its high potential efficiency—60 per cent seems a reasonable possibility. If only because it works at low voltages, it is not likely to play an important role in central power stations, but (with the help of recent developments in light direct current motors) it might well replace the internal combustion engine in transport. Since distribution costs are lower for gas than for electricity, it has even been suggested that domestic electricity supplies in the future might be provided by fuel cells in the home, running on piped hydrocarbon gases, and incidentally providing a 'free bonus' of waste heat to run the central heating system.

Developments in transmission

Whatever the degree of truth in that last speculation, efficient use of power for a long time to come will depend on electricity grids. The most extensive grid is that of the U.S.S.R.,[6] with Britain a good second (America, with the division of its power industry among many separate corporations, some private, some public, is not in this competition). The cheap transmission of power over long distances depends on the use of high voltages.

[6] Actually the U.S.S.R. has two main grids, a European one and a Siberian one (completed 1963). These will eventually be inter-connected; and a single integrated grid for the whole country is envisaged for 1980. The European grid is also in the course of being interconnected with those of the other Eastern European socialist countries.

Britain planned in 1951 the creation of a super-grid to connect the principal generating centres at 275,000 volts, and started construction two years later, but revised the figure to 400,000 volts at the end of 1960. A short length at this voltage was under test in 1962, and the system is to be operating in 1965. Sweden reached 400,000 volts in the fifties. But the U.S.S.R., where very long distance transmissions are essential, has steadily kept ahead. They began using 500,000 volts in 1959 and three years later had 2,500 miles at this voltage, including two 620 mile lines connecting the Volgograd hydro-electric station to Moscow. Work has begun on a line of 750,000 volts, due for completion in 1965, an experimental (50-mile) section of which was tested in 1962. This is intended to give experience for the extensive use of such high voltages. Canada has plans for about 400 miles at 735,000 volts.

All this refers to transmission of alternating current. For higher voltages still and for cables underground or under the sea at moderate voltages, the power losses involved in using alternating current become too large. Direct current must be employed for these purposes, despite the fact that this implies using huge thermionic valves to link the transmission line to alternating current systems at both ends. The first commercial-scale direct current line, 61 miles at 100,000 volts, was commissioned in 1954 to connect an island to the Swedish mainland. The 38 mile submarine cable joining the English and French grids at 200,000 volts began work in 1961. Soviet engineers, realising that direct current transmission may be the only means of coping with their vast distances, instituted a research programme in the late forties, the first result of which was an experimental line of 78 miles at 200,000 volts connecting Moscow and Kashira. The experience thus gained is being used to construct the first really high-voltage long-distance direct current lines. The connection between the Volgograd hydro-electric station and the Donbas—about 300 miles at 800,000 volts—was completed towards the end of 1964. Plans are being worked out for several lines at 1,400,000 volts and more than 1,500 miles long, which will join the Siberian grid, with its giant hydro-electric stations, to the Urals and the European grid.

If much of the last few pages seems to the reader to be little more than a dull recital of statistics, let him recall that the progress of any period is characterised as much by the development of existing techniques towards the bigger and better (or sometimes towards the smaller and better) as by the arrival of the really new and strange. Any really comprehensive history would make the same study of sizes and efficiencies over the whole field of engineering. But the reader is saved from this dreary prospect by the writer's deficiencies in knowledge. And so we may turn to some of the really novel developments of our time.

CHAPTER 12

NUCLEAR POWER IN ACTION

WHEN we discussed nuclear energy in Chapter 10, we ended with an optimistic look into the distant future. Experience since 1945 might incline one more towards pessimism. By far the greatest effort in the nuclear field has gone into the production and perfection of more and more fearsome weapons—though the limited nuclear test ban agreement of 1963 gives hope of improvement. The application of nuclear power for peaceful purposes has progressed more slowly, partly because of the concentration of effort on the military side and partly for good economic reasons. Nuclear power has proved more costly in these initial phases than had been anticipated. Coal and oil prices have not risen as much as was expected, and the improvements discussed on pages 211-2 have kept the cost of conventionally produced power below the level at which nuclear stations could hope to compete.

The First Nuclear Power Stations

We have noted that nuclear research was not carried on in the U.S.S.R. during the war. The first Russian research reactor was only completed in 1947. And yet the world's first nuclear power station started working near Moscow on 27 June 1954.[1] It was only of pilot-plant size—5,000 kW.—but served to demonstrate that the production of electricity from nuclear energy was a practical proposition.

Britain's Calder Hall was the first full-scale nuclear power station. It started working in May 1956 and delivered power to

[1] Earlier indications that the U.S.S.R. was fast overtaking the Western powers had been her successful A-bomb test of 1949 and her production in 1953 of the first practical H-bomb (though America had exploded a thermo-nuclear device, too clumsy for use as a practical weapon, a year earlier).

the grid five months later, eventually reaching an output of 37,500 kW. But Calder Hall was primarily a military plant, for making plutonium to be used in bombs, the electricity production being a mere by-product intended to reduce the cost of the former. In the same way, America's programme of civil power stations started as an offshoot of war-like projects. Work towards designing a nuclear submarine began there in 1946. The land-based prototype of the pressurised water reactor[2] that was to power the first submarine operated successfully in 1953—so that the U.S.A., had her energies been otherwise directed, might easily have won the race to produce the first peaceful nuclear power. The *Nautillus* first sailed under nuclear power in January 1955. As a result of this success, the U.S. Atomic Energy Commission decided to embark on an experimental electric power plant at Shippingport, of 60,000 kW. capacity, which went into action at the end of 1957. Its reactors are based on the one that powered *Nautillus*. But military planning need take little account of economy, so that the plant at Shippingport has small relevance to the economic production of power for peaceful purposes. It generates electricity at eight times the cost of Calder Hall, which itself could not survive straightforward competition in normal operating conditions with coal- or oil-fired stations.

The British Nuclear Power Programme

Britain was the first country to attempt to use nuclear power to generate a substantial proportion of her electricity supply. In 1955, when work on Calder Hall was well-advanced, estimates of the future prospects of such stations were more rosy than subsequent experience has justified. At the same time there were alarming prospects that coal prices would rise rapidly—for the rejuvenating effect of nationalisation was not appreciated. And there were threats that shortage of foreign exchange would make oil-fired stations too risky. In these circumstances, it appeared that Calder Hall type stations—graphite-moderated, gas-cooled

[2] It will not be possible, for reasons of space, to describe the various types of reactor—pressurised water, graphite-moderated gas-cooled (or magnox), etc.—to which reference will be made. Information on this, and a wealth of detail on particular stations will be found in *Nuclear power today and tomorrow* by Kenneth Jay (London, Methuen, 1961).

'Magnox' stations (as they came to be called)—could play an economic role in the country's power industry. In addition there were hopes of selling such stations abroad. And so in February 1955 the Government announced a programme for constructing twelve stations of this type with a total capacity of 1½ to 2 million kW. by 1965. Very soon it became clear that the sizes of individual stations could advantageously be increased by at least a factor or two, so that fewer would be needed. Contracts for four of them were placed during 1956 and 1957.

Fears of an oil shortage, engendered by the Suez affair, led to an expanded programme in March 1957, which called for nineteen stations, totalling 5 or 6 million kW., by 1965. But Britain was now running into serious economic difficulties, which the Government attempted to meet by restricting economic expansion and cutting down investment; and so in October the completion of the programme was postponed to 1966. Meanwhile the estimated cost of nuclear power was rising. Partly this derived from a revision of estimates in the light of experience, partly from the capital restrictions which made interest rates much higher than had been anticipated.[3] Coal and oil turned out to be more plentiful and conventional power much cheaper than expected. These factors, coupled with the continued Government policy of restricting investment, led to a further slowing down in the programme; in June 1960, the target became 5 million kW. by 1968.

In 1963 the first two civil[4] power stations in Britain began to operate—one of 300,000 kW. at Berkeley in Gloucestershire, the other of 275,000 kW. at Bradwell in Essex.[5] By now the economics had become clear. These stations produced power at about a penny a unit, compared with a halfpenny a unit from an efficient coal- or oil-fired station. It was now estimated that stations of this type, even with all the improvements that can be foreseen,

[3] Since the capital cost of nuclear stations is much higher than for coal or oil, while the fuel costs are lower, a high rate of interest militates against nuclear power.

[4] 'Civil' as contrasted with Calder Hall and its successor Chapel Cross (1958–9), which yield electricity as a by-product of military plutonium production.

[5] The third, at Hunterston in Ayrshire, opened two years behind schedule in 1964. It has been yielding 323,000 kW.

cannot hope to break even in costs with conventional stations until about 1975. By that time they will presumably have been superseded by more sophisticated and more efficient types so that the whole policy of building stations of the Calder Hall type may well prove to have been a blind-alley development, which did not even serve very well as a stop-gap measure. At the very best these stations can only be economic when generating the base-load (when high capital cost can be offset by running for 75 per cent or more of the time),[6] and 6 million kW. is about the maximum demand for base-load in the next few years, so that the present programme represents the absolute limit of what can be done with stations of the Calder Hall type. In the meantime, other nations have preferred to wait for more advanced types of reactor, with the result that the much hoped for export market collapsed, and only two stations were sold abroad—to Italy and Japan.

In fact nuclear power is one of those cases (and there are many in the history of technology), in which it does not pay to look for quick profitability by applying early forms on a large scale. Undoubtedly nuclear power will eventually supersede coal and oil, but only through the use of more advanced methods. It is necessary to go through a period of experimenting with a wide variety of reactors in order to find one that can ultimately be developed for economic application on a large scale.

More Advanced British Experiments

Britain's concentration on quick results restricted her resources for forward-looking experiments, but some important projects are under way. Two of these—the Advanced Gas-cooled Reactor at Windscale, and the High Temperature Gas-cooled Reactor *(Dragon)* at Winfrith Heath—are essentially developments from the Calder Hall type. The changes involved are simple in principle, but raise thorny engineering problems in practice. The Windscale plant reached its full power of 28,000 kW. in February 1963, and the Atomic Energy Authority claimed that an ambitious programme of full-scale power stations on these lines

[6] In fact, the original military-plutonium-cum-power stations at Calder Hall and Chapel Cross have run at full power for 87 per cent of the time.

would give electricity rather more cheaply than coal or oil. But the Central Elecricity Generating Board, which must eventually buy and use the stations, and the private enterprise consortia,[7] which would build them, alleged reasons for regarding these caculations as over-optimistic. It remains doubtful if stations of this type could ever be justified on the scale that would be required, or could be making a useful contribution to power supplies before being superseded by more efficient reactors developed along different lines.

The *Dragon* project is of a more ambitious and more long-term nature. Run in co-operation with other European countries, it aims to reach great efficiency by running at very high temperature, with the coolant gas leaving the reactor at about 750° C. It 'went critical' (that is, a nuclear reaction started) in August 1964, but at least two years must elapse before it will be possible to say whether a granddaughter of Calder Hall will be able to produce power cheaply enough to oust the fossil fuels.[8]

Outside the rather narrow field of Calder Hall and its descendants, Britain has only one important experiment in nuclear power[9]—the fast reactor at Dounreay (Plates XXIX and XXX). This system promises possibilities of 'breeding'—that is, besides producing power, it will convert part of the inert isotope of uranium (or thorium) into further fuel, with the prospect that eventually almost the whole of the uranium will be used, instead of a theoretical maximum of one part in 140 as at present. In addition, fast reactors can run on plutonium, which is a by-product of the Calder Hall type station, so that they offer hope of a more balanced utilisation of resources. The practical implementation of the design involved even greater technical difficulties

[7] The conflict of interests between these various bodies is a further cause of Britain's nuclear troubles. The artificial division has also resulted in effort being wasted by the duplication of development and design work, and in a too thin spreading of scarce scientific manpower. And further problems have arisen from the need to maintain profitability for the consortia when the programme had to be retarded.

[8] *Dragon* will not itself produce electricity. It is intended simply to test the possibility of designing practical and economic reactors of this type.

[9] Apart from the announcement in 1963 of a plan to build a prototype reactor with heavy-water moderator and ordinary water coolant (part of which will be turned to steam in the core). This is primarily intended to investigate the economics of the system, but will also give about 100,000 kW. of electric power. Building has begun and the target date is 1967.

than had been expected.[10] The reactor started working at low power in November 1959—twenty months behind schedule. Towards the end of 1961, it ran at power for over a month, reaching 11,000 kW. Late in the following year it started supplying a token amount of electricity to the grid, and in the summer of 1963 it reached its full power level of 15,000 kW.

At the time of writing Dounreay appears to be a success. The project is running a little ahead of parallel ones in the U.S.A. and the U.S.S.R., and may enable Britain really to take the lead which the Calder Hall stations, after their illusory promises, failed to give. Work is in progress towards designing a prototype commercial version, for which it is hoped to receive Government approval during 1965; and there is a prospect that fast reactors in the 1970s will at last be producing power more cheaply than it can be got from coal and oil.

American and Soviet Programmes

The other two major nuclear powers are well provided with sources of coal and oil, and are thus free from the pressures that pushed Britain on to the road of haste. They have constructed fewer full-scale power stations, but have experimented more widely with small versions of the more advanced systems that may provide the electricity of the seventies and after.

The American beginning at Shippingport was followed by a station of 200,000 kW. capacity, based on the boiling-water principle, which came into full operation at Dresden, Illinois, in mid-1960. Work on fast breeder reactors has been more ambitious than in Britain, though lagging a little behind in time. The Experimental Breeder Reactor Number 2 (16,500 kW.) and the Enrico Fermi plant (60,900 kW.) both began operation in 1963. Other large-scale experimental stations now in operation include one of 75,000 kW. using liquid sodium for coolant, and one of 11,000 kW. which employs an organic material as moderator. In addition, stations which use on a smaller scale the same principles as the British Magnox (Calder Hall type) and High Temperature Gas-cooled (Winfrith Heath) reactors should be in operation

[10] Less excusable was the delay of many months resulting from the transfer of staff to military work when the Windscale accident of 1957 caused a shut-down of some of the existing plants which made plutonium for bombs.

by 1965. And a great variety of other methods are being tried out.

Apart from the Shippingport and Dresden stations and a privately owned plant giving 175,000 kW. at Rowe, Massachussets, these are essentially pilot-plant experiments. But on the basis of experience gained from them, America appears to be now ready to embark on the construction of full-sized nuclear power stations in the next few years. One of 800,000 kW. is due to be in full operation in 1965, while privately owned utility companies have produced plans for the completion between 1966 and 1970 of several stations in the 300,000 to 600,000 kW. range. And American companies have secured several contracts for constructing stations abroad. It is perhaps too early to place full confidence in the claim that development along some of these lines will give nuclear power that is fully competitive with coal and oil by the early 1970s.[11] But the wisdom of the wide-ranging American experimental programme has been demonstrated by the White Paper of April 1964 concerning plans for the 'second generation' of British nuclear power stations. While calling for 5 million kW. of nuclear power to be installed in the years 1970–5, the Government found itself unable to choose between stations based on the British Advanced Gas-cooled Reactor (page 219) or on the American pressurised-water or boiling-water systems. The latter have heavier running costs than the British, but much lower capital costs. And with the high interest rates that are likely to prevail for years to come, this gives the advantage to the Americans.[12]

Based on the experience of the 1954 pilot plant (page 216), a station of 100,000 kW. went into action in Siberia in September 1958. At that time the U.S.S.R. was planning to build atomic power stations totalling some 2 or 2½ million kW. But when experience showed that nuclear power could not become an economic proposition for a decade or so, the programme was severely reduced. A station at Beloyarsk in the Urals started to feed electricity to the grid in the spring of 1964. Of 100,000 kW. capacity, it was claimed to be the first in the world to generate

[11] They should certainly be competitive before then at sites where coal and oil are costly.

[12] However, in May 1965 it was decided to use the Advanced Gas-cooled system for the first of the new stations (Dungeness B), the estimate being that its power will be 10 per cent cheaper than the American reactors could give. The criticism made above may have been too severe.

superheated steam (at 510° C) in the core and feed it direct to the turbines. A further 200,000 kW. of the same station is under construction. The first section (210,000 kW.) of a station on the pressurised-water system at Novovoronezh was completed in November, and work was continuing there on a second unit of 365,000 kW.

Meanwhile attention has been concentrated on experimental work with more advanced types of reactor that promise economic power in the 1970s, with a programme on lines similar to the American, but on a smaller scale. A small (5,000 kW.) fast breeder reactor has been operating since 1958. And towards the end of 1964 construction of a fast reactor of some 300,000 kW. was begun. Other Soviet experiments include one with heavy water moderator and gas-cooling, another using sodium cooling, and one employing a liquid fuel consisting of uranium dioxide suspended in heavy water.

By the end of 1964, Soviet nuclear power capacity had reached almost a million kilowatts, while Britain and America each had rather more than a million kilowatts, and the world total was approaching four millions.[13] It seems likely that 1964 will prove to be the turning point at which the disappointments of early years began to give place to hope and to not very distant success. By this time experts were estimating that world nuclear power capacity might reach 20 million kW. by 1970 and 100 million by 1980. Customers were now appearing among countries who did not have the resources to develop their own nuclear power, and who had hitherto been unconvinced of the advisability of buying power stations. On the whole, world opinion seemed to have decided that Britain's Magnox stations were already obsolete and her Advanced Gas-cooled reactor type not yet proven, so that the majority of orders were going to the U.S.A.

Nuclear Ships

In the foreseeable future nuclear power will only be economic (except in very special conditions) when used on a large scale.

[13] Except for one or two references below, we cannot describe the far from negligible effort of other countries. But it is worth remarking that Canada's programmes, based on heavy water as both moderator and coolant, might well prove to be one of the most significant lines of development.

Apart from electricity, the only other need for power in large enough quantities is in ship propulsion. For submarines and other warships the 'usefulness' of nuclear power is, unfortunately, well established. By 1964 the U.S.A. had a nuclear-powered aircraft carrier and frigate, and fifty nuclear submarines (four were launched in one day during 1963). Britain had one submarine commissioned in April 1963; another was lauched in December and two more were under construction the following year. The U.S.S.R. also has nuclear submarines, though the number is unknown to us.[14] A French one was under construction in 1964 and two others are to follow. Holland has decided to build an unspecified number.[15]

By 1955 the *Nautillus* had demonstrated the technical feasability of marine nuclear propulsion. But, as things stand at present, nuclear fuels cannot come within sight of competing economically with coal and oil in driving merchant shipping. It fell to the Soviet Union to discover the one role in which a nuclear ship could handsomely pay its way—as an ice-breaker. Conventional ice-breakers, with their need to return to port frequently for refuelling, can work only near the coast. But to open up the full potentialities of Arctic navigation, it is necessary to clear shipping lanes much farther north. A nuclear-powered ice-breaker, capable of working for a year or more without refuelling, is ideal for the purpose; and its higher capital and running costs are amply repaid by the facilities it provides for hundreds of other ships. Thus the *Lenin* (Plate XXXI), which was launched in 1957 and made her maiden voyage in 1959, is the one venture in nuclear power so far which can be completely justified in terms of its immediate economic yield. The *Lenin* has a displacement of 16,000 tons and her engines yield 44,000 shaft horsepower (which makes her enormously powerful for her size). She has three pressurised-water reactors, one of which is normally in reserve, and her first fuel charge lasted three years. She can

[14] *Jane's Fighting Ships* estimated twenty-six in 1963.

[15] All this effort may not be entirely wasted. The resistance of the water to a submarine is much smaller than to a surface vessel. Now that nuclear engines allow submarines to stay submerged for long periods, instead of having to surface frequently to breathe (an American one went right round the world under water in 1960), it is possible that submarine freighters will in future help to cheapen transport.

steam steadily at two knots through ice 7 feet thick, which an ordinary ice-breaker could only attack (if at all) by a process of repeatedly retreating and charging forward at full speed. As a result she has been able to open passages in places and at seasons that were unthinkable previously. She doubled the Arctic navigation season in 1962. Two more nuclear ice-breakers are to be built, the first being due for completion in 1971.

Some two or three years behind the *Lenin* came the United States nuclear merchant ship *Savannah* (Plate XXXII) which was launched in 1959 and sailed on her maiden voyage in 1962. With engines giving 22,000 shaft horse-power, she can carry 60 passengers and 9,400 tons of cargo. Her reactors are again derived directly from those of the *Nautillus*, in the planning of which economic considerations were largely ignored. She cost £18 million to build and fit out, and to this must be added about £11 million for special shore installations. When this is compared with the estimated cost of £23 million for the super-liner with which the Cunard Line intends to replace the *Queen Mary*, it will be seen that the *Savannah* cannot pretend to be even a preliminary essay towards the economic nuclear merchant ship. She is partly a prestige demonstration (with special arrangements for showing her machinery to visitors) and partly an exercise in testing the practicability and safety of nuclear-powered shipping. Doubts remain on the last point, however, since in February 1963 the U.S. Atomic Energy Commission recommended that she be confined to port, pending the installation of emergency power equipment and improved safety devices. Soon afterwards, fears of the dangers of operating the vessel led to labour disputes, and so the proposed triumphal tour of foreign ports had to be postponed till the summer of 1964.

In the middle of 1964 West Germany launched a nuclear-powered ore-carrier, with 1967 as the target date for her maiden voyage. But again this will not be an economic proposition—with operating costs perhaps 50 per cent above those of conventional ships. Japan is planning a nuclear-powered oceanographic survey vessel, with launching scheduled for 1969. Britain has pursued a vascillating policy, in which conflicts between economic realities and questions of political prestige have led to bitter arguments, but to no decision as late as autumn 1964. Other countries have also announced projects, but all are shrouded in doubts of various kinds. From all this experience it seems to be clear that nuclear power for ship propulsion cannot become a paying proposition for at least a decade or so, except in very special cases like ice-breakers and research ships.

Ideas about nuclear aeroplanes and railway locomotives have been discussed from time to time, but it is difficult to see how the danger of scattering radio-active substances in an accident could be avoided (it is surely easier to run an electric locomotive from power provided by nuclear stations). Nuclear rockets will doubtless play their part in space travel in the future, but are not likely to be practicable for some years yet.

Other Applications of Nuclear Power

There are not many other fields in which the use of nuclear power seems to be feasible for the present or near future. There is a role for small, easily transportable stations, for use in remote regions where fuel supplies are scarce. In these circumstances even costly power from a reactor may be a better proposition than the long-distance transport of ordinary fuels. Such stations have been developed by the U.S.A. and the U.S.S.R. Most of the American ones have been set up in connection with military installations, such as Arctic radar stations, but a more encouraging example is the plant at the Antarctic research base at McMurdo Sound, which gives 1,500 kW. of electricity as well as steam for heating. It was assembled in eighty days, went critical in March 1962, and began supplying power that summer. The Soviet *Arbus*, giving 700 kW. and consisting of blocks of up to 12 tons which can be easily transported (even by air) and assembled, began work in autumn 1963. It is intended for use in the Arctic and other remote regions. Another Soviet plant, giving 1,500 kW. is mounted on four self-propelled tracked vehicles—one each for the pressurised-water reactor, the heat exchangers, the turbo-generators, and the switch-gear and controls—weighing 350 tons in all. Designed to cross the roughest country, it is again intended for use in the Arctic. The prototype, by 1964, had been operating satisfactorily for three years.

Still smaller nuclear devices are required for auxiliary power supplies in space vehicles, or for use in navigational buoys, automatic weather stations and the like. Here efficiency can be sacrificed to gain the advantages of compactness and the ability to run for years without re-fuelling. America has been developing a series of such power units, under the general name of SNAP ('System for auxiliary nuclear power'). Some of them use the heat given out by radio-active isotopes (which are previously produced in nuclear reactors) and convert it thermo-electrically (or in some cases, thermionically) into current. SNAP-9A, used in the *Transit* satellites (page 294), employs plutonium-238, weighs 27 lb. and gives a few watts of power. Others with power ratings up to about 60 watts are being developed. Russia announced in 1964 an isotopic power generator capable of an output of 150 to 200 watts for a year.

Other SNAP systems involve true nuclear reactors, and of these the most important is SNAP-10A, in which the liquid-metal coolant is pumped to thermo-electric converters (thermo-couples) with an output of 500 watts. The project was in an advanced state of development at the end of 1964, but had not yet been tried out as a complete system.[16] The Russian Romashka ('Daisy'), which started work in August 1964, gives about the same power, but shows a more advanced design. It uses a fast-neutron reactor, from which the heat flows directly by conduction to the thermo-electric converters that surround it (immediately outside a neutron-reflecting screen). It works at 800° C. against the 580° C. of SNAP-10A, which promises well for future improvements in efficiency. By the end of 1964 it had operated satisfactorily for more than 3,000 hours.

As explained on page 167, the economics of electricity generation can be much improved by using the waste heat from the turbines for industrial or domestic heating. The McMurdo Sound station mentioned above is an example of the same idea in the nuclear field, but the pioneering towards a large-scale application of this principle has been done in Scandinavia. A station at Halden in Norway gives about 10,000 kW. of electricity and supplies heat to a nearby paper pulp factory. It began operation in 1959, but did not reach full power till 1962. It had also the distinction of being the first boiling heavy water plant in the world. A Swedish

[16] It worked satisfactorily in April 1965, providing auxiliary power in a space vehicle.

station which started work in 1963 supplies electricity and at the same time undertakes district heating for a Stockholm suburb. And one of the most encouraging political events of 1964 was the U.S.A.-U.S.S.R. agreement to undertake joint research on the problem of using nuclear heat to distil fresh water from the sea for the benefit of arid regions. There is every sign that this would be an economic proposition in an area that could find full use for both the electricity and the water. Several specific schemes are being studied in the U.S.A. (including one for a plant in Israel). And the new Soviet fast reactor mentioned on page 223, apart from its power output, will produce more than 20 million gallons of fresh water daily from the Caspian Sea.

Prospects of Thermo-nuclear Power

It was suggested on pages 194-5 that the control of nuclear energy is the biggest step in man's technological progress since he mastered fire. We have just seen that up to the mid-sixties very little has been achieved, and inevitably there is some feeling of disappointment. Yet if this really is the biggest technological revolution for a million years, we ought not to be surprised that its fruits cannot be picked in a couple of decades.

It seems beyond all reasonable doubt that nuclear power will become competitive with coal and oil quite soon, perhaps during the 1970s, and thereafter will become *much* cheaper than these. That will relieve our descendants of one serious worry—the prospect that resources of coal and oil might become so depleted as to retard, or even put an end to, man's progress in the use of power. For even the most cautious estimate would suggest that supplies of uranium as a nuclear fuel will last a thousand years or so.

And this is only the beginning. So far we have merely been discussing the simplest and crudest type of nuclear engineering: that which depends on the *fission* of the very heavy element, uranium (or plutonium)—on the breaking down of large atoms and the release of energy that accompanies it. Nuclear energy can also be obtained by the process of *fusion*—the building up of the lightest atoms, the atoms of hydrogen, into atoms of helium. This is the process involved in the hydrogen bomb. And a comparison of the hydrogen bomb with the uranium and plutonium bombs of 1945 shows how much more power can be got from harnessing the fusion process.

Scientifically there is no reason at all why fusion should not be used to provide power. It has in fact provided almost all our power in the past, for it is the source of the Sun's energy, which in turn is the indirect origin of the power we get from coal or oil or falling water, or from our own muscles. The Sun gives the clue to the thermo-nuclear processes that would be needed to harness the energy of fusion. In the furnace at its centre, where the temperature is something like 10 million degrees centigrade, the atoms are moving so fast that the violence of their mutual collisions forces them into fusion. In order to produce thermo-nuclear energy on Earth, we have only to create a similar high-temperature furnace containing the appropriate isotopes of hydrogen. Only now the temperature has to be much higher—several hundred million degrees—since we have to squeeze our energy source into a much smaller space.

But what sort of vessel can be used to hold a gas at such a temperature? Only one possible answer can be given at present. At these temperatures the gas takes the form of a *plasma*—that is, a gas in which the atoms are split into the component nuclei and electrons. Since these component parts are electrically charged they can be confined by a magnetic field—in a 'magnetic bottle' as it is called. But the engineering problems involved in doing so are immense. To discuss them here would involve too many technicalities. It must simply be said that, though the solution seems still to be a long way off, encouraging progress is being made, mainly in the U.S.A. and the U.S.S.R., though with Britain and other countries playing some part. There seems to be little to choose between the American and Soviet achievements up till now, but available statistics suggest that the Soviet effort is already bigger than the American and is increasing much faster.[17]

Practical thermo-nuclear power is probably still a long way off. A supreme optimist might hope for success in twenty years.

[17] The *New Scientist*, 19 March 1964, p. 744, reports from American sources that of all scientists and engineers then doing thermo-nuclear research, 25 per cent were in the U.S.A., and 35 per cent in the U.S.S.R. But between 1959 and 1963 the number of these researchers rose by 64 per cent in the Soviet Union, by only 1 per cent in America and by 34 per cent in other countries.

Even the worst pessimist could hardly refuse to believe that it will be achieved in the thousand years or so before the exhaustion of uranium supplies. And when it does come, the thermo-nuclear process will give us virtually unlimited sources of power. It has been calculated that the oceans contain enough of the fuel (heavy hydrogen) to provide for a thousand times our present power consumption for a thousand million years.

Looking Ahead

To sum up, with a first stage of power from fission and a later one of power from fusion, mankind's energy resources are henceforward virtually unlimited. Now the amount of energy or power available is one of the most important factors in determining how much each man and woman in the community can produce, and therefore in determining the standard of living. Mankind's progress has been largely conditioned by the amount of energy he was able to command—at first only his own muscles, then step by step animal-power, wind- and water-power, coal and oil. And now the prospect of virtually unlimited power offers the hope—if we do not use it to destroy ourselves—of virtually unlimited progress. Plentiful power implies plentiful everything else, for if we are short of something we can use the power to make it or to make a substitute for it.

Even this is probably only a glimpse of the future. For, as we noted on pages 194-5, we are behaving now as the first discoverers of fire must have behaved : we are merely applying our new technical powers to do the same things as before, but to do them rather better. We are using our command of nuclear forces simply to provide more of that very familiar thing, power. But just as fire implied all sorts of completely novel developments, from cookery to electronics, which its first discoverers could not foresee, so also our mastery of nuclear forces will open up to us vast new fields of achievement of which at present we have not the slightest inkling. The whole life of man will be transformed. Our descendants will be as different from us as we are from that ape-man who first took the daring step of feeding a fire instead of running away from it. And because of the way in which history continually speeds up, what previously took a million years may now require only a few generations.

CHAPTER 13

COMPUTERS IN MODERN LIFE

ELECTRONIC computers are likely to have as profound effects as nuclear energy on the future of man. They arrived on the scene almost at the same time. But whereas it is taking years of tedious plodding to make a really useful servant of nuclear energy, computers grew up very quickly and are already affecting almost every part of life. This contrast is not so surprising when we remember that nuclear energy represents the mastery of the first fundamentally new natural force since the control of fire, whereas electronics is only a very late development in using the forces that fire put into our hands.

These computers, in their pre-electronic form, have a remarkably long history. Anybody who has to do very lengthy and complicated calculations soon discovers that these must be organised into a routine, and that the routine can be expressed as a series of precise instructions which have only to be obeyed mechanically in order to produce the required result. If we imagine the results of all the successive steps in the calculation set out in rows and columns on a sheet of paper, a typical instruction would read: 'Take the numbers in the third and eighth rows of the last completed column on your paper, multiply them together and write the answer in the fourth row of the next column.' When a new column has in this way been completed, the command will be to go back to the start of the series of instructions; but now, of course, the 'last completed column' of the sample instruction above will refer to the newly completed column, so that the whole calculation will move one column forward. And—the real key to the whole matter—every now and then in the routine there will occur a special type of order, known as a *branch instruction* or *conditional transfer instruction,* which says something to the effect, 'if the number in such-and-such a position is positive or zero, proceed to the next instruction on the list; if it is negative, pass instead to instruction number so-and-so'. The complete list of instructions can always be put in such a form that mere mechanical obedience will lead to the required answer.

Since the seventeenth century, calculating machines have been in existence which can do mechanically the processes of adding, subtracting, multiplying and dividing. When such a machine is used in a long calculation, the operator does not calculate; he merely organises the calculation by deciding, according to the instructions laid down, which two numbers to feed to the machine at every stage, which arithmetical operation to perform with them, and where to write the answer. *His* work, also, is entirely automatic in principle.

It was the English mathematician, Charles Babbage, who first realised about 1833 that it should be possible to make the whole process automatic throughout. One has only to link the mechanisms that do the arithmetical operations with others that parallel the operator's actions in following the instructions, and add also a 'store' or 'memory' device that will keep track of numbers already calculated (as the human calculator does on paper) and make them available when required again. The principles governing such a machine were worked out almost completely by Babbage. But with only mechanical devices like gear-wheels and ratchets at his disposal, he failed in his attempts to construct a practical machine.

The Birth of the Electronic Computer

No further practical steps towards the electronic computer were taken till the Second World War—except that Herman Hollerith, while working on the United States census of 1890, introduced special purpose tabulating and calculating machines to which numbers were fed by means of punch-cards,[1] which were subsequently to become the normal means (along with punched paper tape) of feeding computers.

Yet any time after 1919 a practical electronic computer could have been built. In that year Eccles and Jordan invented the key device of the 'flip-flop', a circuit using a couple of valves, which can be put in either of two states and remains in that state till

[1] Punch-cards, already familiar in the Jacquard loom (page 100) had formed part of Babbage's plan.

instructed to change to the other. A suitable (if rather slow) memory device already existed in the form of Poulsen's magnetic recorder (page 178). At long last, in 1937, Howard H. Aiken of Harvard University started the construction of a machine using electro-magnetic relays, which incorporated many of Babbage's ideas (but omitted the key conditional transfer instruction). Others had been working theoretically on the subject during the thirties. But, as we have seen in so many other cases, it was only the emergency of war that could provide sufficient impetus and support for full-out development. Aiken's machine, the Automatic Sequence-Controlled Calculator, began work in April 1944 doing calculations for the U.S. Navy. It was slow by modern standards, taking one-third of a second to do an addition and six seconds for a multiplication.

Meanwhile the U.S. Army Ordnance Department had sponsored work on an electronic machine called ENIAC.[2] Completed in 1946, this was intended primarily for calculating trajectories of artillery shells, but it was soon discovered that it could be used (within certain limitations) for calculations of any type. It could do 5,000 additions a second, and calculate in half a minute a ballistic table that formerly needed 20 hours.[3] This was, in fact, the first electronic computer. But it was very complicated in design, had too small a store ('memory') and was in many ways distinctly different in principle and mode of operation from the electronic computer of today.

The latter really takes its beginning from theoretical studies carried out by John von Neumann from 1945 onwards. An American team began constructing a machine called EDVAC on the lines he laid down, but for various reasons their work was held up, and the first computer of a modern type was EDSAC, built by a team led by M. V. Wilkes in Cambridge, England, which did its first fully automatic calculation in May 1949. It took less than a ten-thousandth of a second for an addition, and under a hundredth of a second for a multiplication; and its store

[2] The early computers were known by names based on the initials of their full titles—in this case 'Electronic Numerical Integrator and Calculator'. But no purpose will be served by giving further full names.

[3] The author first learned of these figures with a feeling of deep regret. He had spent almost the whole of the war years doing similar calculations, which ENIAC could have completed in five or six hours.

could hold 512 numbers of a size up to ten million. Another team at Manchester had a prototype of a rather different machine[4] working in 1948 and produced a full-scale version (in co-operation with the firm of Ferranti) in 1951.

Some Advanced Computers

From then on the story has been one of very rapid improvement by the use of more refined engineering methods—the substitution of transistors for valves, micro-miniaturisation, the devising of better storage systems, and so on. Instead of following the details, let us examine the powers of a few of the most recent computers. The *Atlas* was developed by a collaboration between Manchester University and Ferranti Ltd.,[5] the first machine being inaugurated at the University in December 1962. The store of this first version will hold over 100,000 numbers of a size equivalent to 14 decimal digits, but the design allows for extension to over a million such numbers. The speed at which *Atlas* works is such that it will do on the average more than half a million arithmetical operations per second, and in suitable circumstances can reach a million. At such speeds the usefulness of a computer is limited by the fact that the equipment for feeding it with problems and printing out the results works much more slowly, with the danger that the computer itself may be forced to stand idle. To overcome this difficulty *Atlas* works on a number of problems simultaneously. If it is held up, for one reason or another, on one of these, it immediately switches to another and carries on till the first is ready for further attention. The problems are fed to the computer with an indication of priorities, but it revises the priority schedule in the light of the delays it experiences in order to give maximum over-all speed. It may have 200 jobs queueing up at any one time, of which perhaps a dozen will be in the 'execution phase'. And if, after all this, it finds itself with time to spare, it proceeds to undertake a systematic routine testing of itself! It has been said that the first *Atlas* can do in a fortnight more computing than has ever before been done at Manchester. In order to make full use of its facilities, it is being linked by land-line with

[4] With cathode ray tube storage, instead of the delay-line stores of EDSAC and EDVAC.

[5] But the Ferranti computer interests have since been taken over by International Computers and Tabulators Ltd.

input-output centres in several other cities. The manufacturers claim that the first five of these machines, when working fully, will double Britain's computing capacity.

Hiring *Atlas* for normal commercial use costs £750 an hour.[6] This works out at more than ten thousand 'sums' for a penny—which gives some idea of the immense increase in efficiency that computers can give. To the outright buyer an *Atlas* costs from £2 to £3½ million, according to his exact requirements. Four had been sold by the middle of 1964. The U.S.S.R. wishes to buy another four, but the so-called 'strategic' embargo on exports will prevent this sale unless the British Government changes its policy.[7]

Atlas at the time of its appearance was by far the world's most powerful computer. But unfortunately (from the British point of view) it appears to have been bettered by the System-360 of the American firm, International Business Machines. Six different levels of size and powerfulness are available, the last being more powerful than *Atlas*, together with a large range of peripheral equipment to take care of input and output. The design is such that anything can be 'plugged in' to anything else. The user can start with the smallest version costing about £75,000—which would count as a medium-sized computer—and expand his equipment as he wishes. Even programmes prepared for a smaller version will serve without change on a larger one. There is virtually no limit to the size of store available, and the speed of operation is faster than that of *Atlas*. Besides accepting information by the usual means of punched cards, punched tape or magnetic tape, System-360 can read documents printed in ordinary ink, or lead-pencil markings in specified positions on a sheet of paper. It can be interrogated about the information it holds, by dialling a code on a telephone hand-set; and the reply comes back in spoken form. While it has not gone the whole way with micro-miniaturisation (so that it could be surpassed even with techniques now available), it uses diodes and transistors only a

[6] If the hirer requires the use of the whole machine. But he will normally only want to present one of the problems on which it is working simultaneously, and his costs will be correspondingly less.

[7] So far the Soviet Union has not been in the forefront of computer development, except in one special line which will be mentioned below. But they have been enterprising in computer applications, which serves to explain their desire to buy very advanced models.

fiftieth of an inch in diameter. Its commercial success is shown by the fact that about 130 machines (mostly in the lower range of size) were ordered in Britain alone within ten weeks of the first public announcement.[8]

Giants like these are not for everybody. But going in the opposite direction, there has been a substantial development since 1959 in the production of small, slow, cheap computers, suitable for use by the medium-sized commercial firm or the council of a small town. Machines of this type are about the size of an office desk, have stores for a few thousand numbers and can work at the rate of a few thousand instructions per second. This has been achieved by the careful use of transistorised circuits. Going still farther, the employment of solid circuit micro-miniaturisation (page 309) has led to experimental versions of tiny computers a few cubic inches in volume and a few pounds (or even ounces) in weight. But so far these seem to have been developed mainly in military contexts.

An automatic computer need not, of course, be electronic. It can be based on any switching device. Very promising in recent years has been the use of pneumatic methods, in which the switching is done by interacting jets of air or liquid. Computers using this principle are slow, but they are cheap and extremely reliable, so that they are likely to be important in certain circumstances, particularly in controlling machinery. Work on them was first announced in Moscow and Washington about the end of 1959, and the U.S.S.R. seems at present to be leading, though it is difficult to make a judgement, since the American work is largely being carried out for the armed forces and much of it is on the secret list.

Computers for Clerical Work

Turning now to the applications, it should first be realised that there are very many scientific problems which are soluble in principle, but for which the necessary calculations are so lengthy

[8] System-360 was announced in April 1964, with first deliveries promised for about two years later. In September, International Computers and Tabulators announced their Series 1900, which (on the information available at the time of writing) appears to be very similar in its principle and its powers, and promised one-year deliveries. Advertised prices range from about £40,000 to £750,000 or more (Plate XXXIII).

that without computers they would occupy years or centuries, and so in practice could not be carried out. Thus the advent of the computer is revolutionising many fields of science, both fundamental and applied. In their early days, around 1950, computers in Britain were applied mainly to scientific problems, while in America military calculations took precedence, though some scientific work was done. It was soon realised, however, that a vast amount of the clerical work involved in modern industry and administration is admirably suited to the computer. Though a clerk in the ordinary way is expected to use his brains, it is usually possible to specify his work in terms of a fixed routine of instructions of the sort that a computer can handle far faster, more cheaply and more accurately. Furthermore, a computer is not just a calculating device, even though it was first developed for that purpose. It is in essence a *data processing* or *information handling* machine. That is to say, it is capable of accepting facts of any type, provided they can be precisely stated,[9] sorting them out, deducing their logical consequences, and presenting the results in any convenient form that may be specified. The combination of calculating and data processing abilities in fact provides most of the facilities that managements require from their armies of clerks.

The first to interest themselves seriously in this line of progress were J. Lyons and Company, the London firm of caterers and food merchants. After exploratory work carried out on the Cambridge EDSAC, they built their own computer, LEO I, which began routine work at the end of 1953, and soon demonstrated the advantages of the 'electronic office'. In preparing the payroll for Lyons, and later for Ford at Dagenham and other firms, it did the work of two or three hundred clerks, while itself needing a staff of only fourteen. Within a year or two computers were widely used in commercial firms for wage-roll calculations, invoicing, stock control and so on. Local authorities, nationalised industries, Government Departments, insurance companies and the like soon found similar uses for them. Banks began to employ them to keep customers' accounts up to the minute, often using automatic cheque-sorting machinery to speed the process.

[9] Precise statements also include less precise ones in which the degree of imprecision can be precisely stated!

But such accountancy applications hardly begin to show the paces of computers in commerce and industry. They use only the arithmetical powers of the machines, not their ability to process information nor their ability to take decisions (provided clear rules about the basis of decision are laid down). Within a year or two LEO was demonstrating something of what could be done when all the computer's powers are employed. Daily orders for supplies to the three hundred Lyons teashops are telephoned to headquarters and fed to the computer. Sorting and collating this information, LEO prepares schedules for the factory, so that production can be adjusted to demand. It plans the movements of stocks from warehouse to loading wharfs, even arranging them in such a way that the vans are loaded in the best order, with the goods that have to be delivered first placed nearest the doors, and so forth. Having done in an hour or so routine jobs of this type that previously took the work of fifty clerks, LEO turns to matters needing management attention. It has been told, for example, the normal sales of each tea-shop. It now compares these with current orders, ignores cases where a shop is running very much as planned, but prints out details when results are unexpectedly good or bad—so that appropriate management action can be taken. Note that here the computer is making use of its decision-taking ability, even if the decision in this instance is merely that of picking out cases that require human decision.

Computers in the Planning of Production

The methods that Lyons had pioneered were soon to be applied in production planning in many industries. No matter how efficient the individual machines or workers in a factory may be, the efficiency of the whole ultimately depends on the planning of the entire production process so that it works smoothly as a unity—so that raw materials and part finished work are promptly available when and where they are needed, so that jobs are not held up because the machine which must process them next is already occupied at something else, so that machines or operators do not stand idle or part-finished work wait a long time for completion, so that priorities imposed by customers' orders are satisfied, and so on. All this is essentially a matter of calculation. The statistics required to do the calculation and produce the perfect production plan are (or could be) available. The only trouble is that the amount of arithmetic and data processing to be done is such that it would need weeks, months, or even years of work from an army of clerks—which is hardly a practical way of deciding next week's production programme. So in practice till recently the management had to ignore the potential wealth of available statistics and rely on experience and intuition. As a result, the factory was usually working a good deal below maximun efficiency.

The speed of computers and their ability to handle large quantities of information completely changed the situation. Though a computer cannot, in most instances, work fast enough to find the perfect production plan, it can do much better than was previously possible. As an example of comprehensive development on these lines, the British Petroleum Company began in 1958 by using a computer that worked out the most efficient way of using current stocks of crude oil and available plant in a refinery to satisfy orders in hand. As a next step, five widely scattered refineries were linked in a single planning scheme, with the computer now allocating work between them in such a way as, for instance, to minimise transport costs. It dealt with crude oil and finished product movements in an area stretching from Scandinavia to Australia. With two more refineries added later, this piece of computer planning covered an annual production of about 32 million tons of petroleum products. In 1964 a parallel system was introduced to deal with another 16 million tons in the European sphere of operations—by which time computer planning covered more than three-quarters of the Company's activities. This, of course, is an unusually large-scale application of the method; but its usefulness in more common conditions may be illustrated by the case of a factory making domestic appliances at Peterborough in England, where the introduction of a computer in 1961 reduced the time to work out a production programme from seven weeks to 3 hours.

So far computers have mainly planned to make the best possible use of existing factories and equipment. But an obvious extension is to use similar methods to plan the factory itself. This was done recently for an American factory producing industrial gases. Fed with information about the geographical distribution of customers and their estimated requirements for several years ahead, and also about the costs of possible sites, power supplies and transport facilities, the computer was used to choose the best site, decide the size of the factory and even work out its building schedule.

In agriculture, similarly, a computer can use information about soil quality, available machinery and manpower, market conditions and the like in order to plan the usage of the land in the most profitable way. Tested on twenty Czechoslovak collective farms, this procedure gave an average of nearly 15 per cent increase in the protein yield of fodder crops, while a team in Moscow is investigating the much more complex problem of using computers to plan agriculture on a regional or even a national level. Again in Holland a computer which stores a vast amount of information about soil analyses and regional peculiarities takes a mere 30 seconds to advise a farmer on the best choice of fertilisers for his proposed crops.

When a factory or depot has to deliver goods to many customers scattered over an an area, it is most important to arrange the routings of its lorries in the most economical way. And this, too, can be done more efficiently by computer. In Moscow, the sand for about 500 building sites is delivered by lorries from eight wharfs at various points along the river. The problem is to choose which wharfs shall supply which sites. By a calculation taking an hour and a half, a Strela computer produced a scheme which cut transport requirements by about half a million ton-miles a day, compared with the best that a human manager can do.[10] An American computer firm will now make an analysis of such problems to the customer's order, at a cost which might be £60 in a typical case.

For large and complex construction work another type of planning, 'network analysis', has been developed. Each one of the multitude of jobs to be done depends on the completion of certain previous jobs and in turn must be finished before certain others can be started. The object of the method is to discover the

[10] As a result of this and similar experiences, an integrated system of computer control is to be applied—it is hoped during 1965—to all construction work in Moscow, covering sixty to eighty supply depots, about a thousand construction sites, more than 10,000 vehicles and over 200,000 workers.

sequence (or sequences) of jobs which will occupy a longer time than any others, and so to enable the attention of the planners to concentrate on getting them done according to schedule. The method was developed in America in 1958 for co-ordinating the work of the several thousand contractors involved in the Polaris missile project, and a little later by du Pont Nemours for scheduling the building of chemical plants. It is now widely used on large building projects, in ship-building, and, for example, in planning the construction of London Underground's new Victoria Line.

It seems evident that if computers can be used in these ways to plan more efficiently the operations of particular factories or companies, then they should be able to help with the much bigger task of planning the whole economy in a socialist country. The mathmatical problems to be solved in order to make this practicable are naturally of a far higher order of complexity. Much research on these lines has been going on in the U.S.S.R. for some years, and those concerned seem confident that the use of computers can greatly improve the accuracy and efficiency of their national planning. It is thought that the effects will begin to be felt from 1965 onwards.

Some Other Practical Applications

It will be impossible to give more than a few samples of other practical work that computers are now doing for us. The calculations involved in designing a lens system formerly took many months; and even then the designer had to rest content with imperfections that could, in theory, be eliminated by yet more calculation. Now the computation can be pushed to higher degrees of refinement and the time taken reduced to days or hours. In ship design, too, the amount of calculation involved is so great that the designer is eventually reduced to relying on experience and hunches. But computers are now taking over the task of calculating the ideal hull shape for any specified purpose, and ensuring optimum performance in varying weather conditions. They are even beginning to do the long and tedious work of breaking down the general plan into the detailed specification for each plate or other part.

Where the answer to a problem depends on collating large

amounts of information, the computer reigns supreme. Since 1963 New York has had one which scans 120,000 legal references a minute, searching for relevant cases and precedents. In diagnosing heart diseases from lists of symptoms in the same year a Tokyo computer was 90·1 per cent accurate, against a range of 75·2 to 78 per cent success for ten experienced doctors, while a Soviet medical institute reported similar results. A computer is being used to analyse maternity records of two hundred American hospitals, giving data for the improvement of obstetrical practice; and a similar project has started in England. Many other schemes are under way using computers to elicit from statistics information about the conditions that promote diseases and hence about possible methods of predicting, preventing or treating them.

Problems in which many variables have to be arranged to satisfy a large number of conditions are particularly difficult and tedious—as any one will know who has had to work out the timetable for a large school, ensuring that two classes are not simultaneously assigned to the same room or the same teacher, that every member of staff has (say) five free periods evenly distributed over the week, and that John Smith really has the option of taking physics or Spanish. In the past one has had to accept arrangements that fall well short of the ideal, but now the computer can rapidly survey all possibilities and prepare the best possible timetable. The even more complicated problem of making up railway timetables involves a large body of clerks working for as much as a year. But, after research beginning in 1957, British Railways produced their first computer-made timetable in 1963, and have embarked on a project for the regular use of computers which should reduce the time of preparation by ten weeks or so and make big savings in staff requirements. On the Soviet railway system a computer-compiled schedule for the movement of empty coaches and wagons is saving about 8 million roubles a year (roughly £3 million at the official rate of exchange).

Since 1954 air lines have been using computers to take care of seat reservations. Within a few seconds the clerk in any one of the agents' offices can consult the computer's store to discover if a seat is available; if a new booking is made, the computer alters its records accordingly. The British European Airways system, due to start work in 1964, will do away with some 500,000 record cards, 100,000 flight control sheets and more than a million booking entries during the busy months of the year.

In the last example speed is of great importance, since air lines loose heavily when non-availability of information leads to lost bookings. And perhaps computers show off their paces best (so far as practical life is concerned) when the complexity of a problem is allied to a necessity for speed. Thus to ease traffic congestion, the need is to make a rapid assessment of information (provided automatically) about traffic density at many points, decide quickly which streams are to have priority, and operate the traffic lights accordingly. A very simple computer system controlling the entrances to a New York tunnel reduced the average delay per vehicle by 70 per cent. A Toronto experiment controlling fifteen intersections cut the delay per vehicle by 25 per cent in the morning rush hour and 11 per cent in the evening one. A much more ambitious scheme is gradually being introduced there and is due to cover 500 or more sets of traffic lights by 1965. The installation will cost about $3 million but is expected to have as big an effect as $20 to $40 million spent on road improvements. New York is planning an even bigger scheme costing a million dollars in design and twenty times as much in execution. The Ministry of Transport embarked in 1963 on a detailed survey to decide if 4 square miles of London's traffic should similarly be put in the hands of a computer.

Computers aid the Scholar and Scientist

Turning to a completely different field, computers have now invaded the field of literary research. Any scholar finding a fragment of papyrus with a few words on it which he thinks may be part of the New Testament has only to consult a machine at Birkbeck College, London, which will either tell him that they are not, or give the exact reference. Soon the whole corpus of Greek literature will be on tape there, and ready to solve similar identification problems. Another computer in Milan has been indexing the works of St. Thomas Aquinas and the Dead Sea scrolls. A work of a million and a half words can now be indexed completely—every word of it—as an aid to scholarly research, in 60 man-hours instead of a former 24 man-years. Where, through the ravages of time, a few words have been lost from a

Dead Sea scoll, this machine can analyse the size of the gap and the sense of the passage, and by comparing with parallel passages elsewhere can suggest, with a high degree of reliability, what the missing words are. By analysing stylistic peculiarities, the Birkbeck College machine under the guidance of Rev. A. Q. Morton has produced strong evidence that only four out of the Epistles traditionally ascribed to St. Paul are actually his work. It is curious that literary applications of computers should have such a strong theological bias. But one notable exception is the claim of Professor Knorozov in Russia to have deciphered by computer techniques some 40 per cent of the three surviving manuscripts in the lost language of the Maya civilisation—a claim which is, however, disputed by some experts.

The problem of filing information in such a way that it can be retrieved when wanted is one that threatens to overwhelm the world of science and scholarship. The volume of published papers reporting chemical researches doubles every eight and a half years. Each year *Chemical Abstracts* prints classified summaries of about 130,000 of them. Searching among all these for the information one requires is becoming so time-consuming as often to be not worth the effort; the chemist may feel sure that a piece of information he requires is already available, and yet may find it easier to repeat the research than to discover the original report. It is now generally agreed that the efficiency of scientific research is seriously reduced by these difficulties. Indeed a sample survey (coupled, admittedly, with some inspired guessing) has recently suggested that more than 20 per cent of research involves unintentional duplication through failure to track down references, and that this costs Britain somewhere between £6 and £12 million a year. The only hope seems to lie in handing over the job of indexing and retrieval to computers.

As a first step the periodical *Chemical Titles* is now being produced by a computer. Fed with the titles of published papers, the names of their authors and bibliographical details, the machine automatically produces a series of indexes. The most important of these consists of key-words from the titles ('peptides', 'cations', 'pentadienone') arranged in alphabetical order and presented with their contexts—so that the subject matter can be more fully identified—and with references. The computer prints out all this in the exact form in which it will be published, ready to be photographed and printed by offset photolitho. It does about 72 million operations in 25 minutes. As a result, these indexes reach the user within a fortnight, whereas the information in abstracting journals produced by former methods is months (and sometimes years) out of date.

This is only a small first step, and research is in progress in many centres towards developing more advanced systems, in which, for example, the computer will scan the text of an article and, by counting the frequency with which certain classes of words appear, will decide the subject classification to which it should be assigned. The machine would thus store up a gradually increasing fund of information about publications relevant to this or that subject. It could then supply on demand all the references it holds to some particular topic. Or it could be instructed to print out at regular intervals all new publications within the field of interest of a particular research worker, who could then content himself with reading only what the machine recommends. Or, of course, complete classified lists of all the material in the computer's memory could be printed from time to time. Systems of this type are only in the experimental stage, but appear to be very promising.

As the volume of published material grows, the problem of translating works from one language to another becomes more acute. The number of sufficiently skilled translators—particularly from Russian into the Western languages—is far too small to satisfy the demand. And so, since the early 1950s a great deal has been done in investigating the possibility of translation by computer. But progress is slow. It has proved not too difficult to arrange demonstrations in which a machine does fairly well in translating texts within a narrow field of subject matter for which it has been specially prepared. Or, without limiting the subject matter, computers have done translations of the type that might be produced by a person of mediocre intelligence, working with the aid of a dictionary and a few of the more obvious rules of syntax; but the result is usually almost as difficult to understand as the original foreign text. It will probably be some years before computers can reliably produce translations that are good enough to be generally useful, and perhaps quite a lot longer before they can do so at a cost that would compete with human translators.

Teaching machines—in which a small specialised computer examines the student's answer to a question (given, for example, by pressing the appropriate button), and then either takes him on to the next step, or sets him a revision programme from which he will learn to correct his mistake—are beginning to play a useful role in the educational world. Wisely used, they do not replace the teacher, but take over some of the more mechanical parts of his work, and so increase the time available for more creative teaching. But a curious situation has arisen. The programming of such machines involves very thorough research into learning processes, and the results of this work may be more important than the machines themselves. When the learning problem is understood, it becomes possible to design a text-book which sets the student a problem and directs him, according to his answer, to turn to this page or that, thus ensuring that he is always led to study the points on which he has shown weakness. And naturally the text-book is much cheaper than the machine. This situation, in which research concerning how a computer could be used to solve a problem leads to better methods that do not use the computer, is not at all uncommon. Business firms, contemplating the installation of a computer for clerical work or planning, are forced to stream-line and systematise their procedures; and sometimes the result is so great an improvement in efficiency that the computer is not required after all. But, of course, the instances in which a computer is needed far outnumber those in which it is not.

There are only a few examples of what computers can now, or will soon be able to do. And it must be emphasised again that their role as tools for the advancement of fundamental science will probably have more far-reaching effects than all their other applications taken together. To quote one example, the spectacular advances of the last few years in unravelling the fantastically complicated structures of the proteins and nucleic acids which are the basis of living matter would have been quite impossible without computer aid. When we consider that this knowledge may contain the key to the conquest of many genetic diseases and of diseases like cancer in which the chemistry of the cell has gone wrong, and when we realise that this is just one scientific problem that could not be tackled without a computer, we can perhaps begin to appreciate the vast possibilities they open up.

The Future of Computers

As we said for nuclear energy, so we must say again: this is only the beginning. The computers themselves and the methods of using them are still developing at breakneck speed. The use of tunnel diodes (page 309) may raise their speed by a further factor of a hundred. The high-speed memory capacity[11] of the machine —which is now one of the major limiting factors—may be much increased by working at very low temperatures where the electrical resistance of metals entirely disappears (page 311). Early in 1964 the Radio Corporation of America claimed to have produced such a store which can memorise the equivalent of about 5,000 decimal digits on a piece of material 2 inches square and a ten-thousandth of an inch thick.

The computer's memory works at present on what is known as the 'address' system. That is to say, in order to recall a particular piece of information when required, the programme must specify a number that identifies the particular pigeon-hole in which the information is stored. The process is like that of obtaining one's coat from a cloakroom by presenting a numbered ticket. If the ticket is lost, one gets the attendant to search by giving such clues as: 'It is a raincoat; light brown; beltless; rather dirty at the collar. I handed it in just before seven, while you were having an argument with a man who sported a ginger moustache.' And with this information the attendant finds the coat—not by knowing where it is, but by knowing that it is *associated* with

[11] One distinguishes between the 'high-speed store', from which information can be extracted at the maximum speed at which other parts of the computer can work, and the 'backing store', from which data can only be drawn more slowly. The latter can be virtually unlimited in capacity, but considerations of both cost and space put severe restrictions on the former. If a piece of information is such that it is possible to predict well in advance (which may mean a thousandth of a second) when it will be needed, then it can be kept in the backing store and transferred to the high-speed store shortly before it is required. But any information that must be available on demand, without advance notice, has to be in the high-speed store—otherwise the whole calculation will be retarded when it is called for. Thus the size of the high-speed store really determines the capacity of the computer as a whole.

the properties like 'light brown' and 'dirty round the collar'. The human mind, when problem solving, uses its memory in a way that is much closer to this method than to the numbered ticket system. An *Associative Memory System* (as it is called) is less precise than an address system, but much more flexible; it lies at the root of the more creative aspects of thinking, when the mind searches associations to discover something that might be relevant to the problem in hand. Already computer stores can be arranged to reproduce some very simple cases of finding information by association—they could solve the problem of the lost cloakroom ticket if it were worth the trouble. And we have the prospect that associative stores will in the future greatly increase the complexity of problems that computers can tackle, bringing them closer to human ways of thinking.

At present the computer is really a very stupid sort of machine. It achieves spectacular results because of its high speed and its capacity for handling large quantities of information, but it is a high-speed large-capacity idiot. To use it we must know exactly how the problem is to be solved and must specify the method in every detail. The computer has no power to learn from experience and improve its own procedure as it goes along. Yet we can already see our way dimly towards improved machines that will be able to learn as they work. Let us consider, by way of illustration, the programming of a computer to play the game of draughts[12] against a human opponent. One could teach it the rules of the game, give it a few elementary notions on strategy, and instruct it to analyse the consequences of all possible lines of play for a few moves ahead (only a few, or the number of positions to be considered would become prohibitive) and to choose the line which gives maximum gains of pieces and minimum losses. The machine then certainly plays draughts—rather badly. But Arthur L. Samuels of the I.B.M. Research Laboratories in New York has shown that it is possible to programme the computer, not merely to play as well as he has taught it, but to

[12] Setting computers to play games has been a favourite method of those who have been exploring their potentialities. A game reproduces some of the features of real life, but in much simplified conditions; and investigations of the powers of machines to play games has often been a useful step towards improving their ability to do real work. The analogy with the role of games in educating the human youngster is of some interest.

learn by experience to play better. It can use its experience in two main ways. First, it can memorise the analyses that it makes of forward positions and use these to extend its forward analyses to greater numbers of moves in future. By this means it chiefly improves its opening and end games. And second, given a list of possible criteria for evaluating the strength of a position, it can use its experience of many games to decide how much weight to give to each particular criterion. Programmed in this way the computer learned to play 'a rather good game' (as Samuels put it). In fact it soon became good enough to beat its teacher.

Experiments on these lines (for there have been others) show that computers can, in principle, be programmed to improve by experience. But they still have a long way to go. The draughts-playing machine never learns to play as well as the best human players. For learning by the second method Samuels had to supply it with a list of possible criteria to choose from—the machine had no powers of thinking up new ideas for itself (though the use of an associative memory might conceivably give it that ability). And in any case the situation in draughts is a very simple one compared with what might be of practical importance in real life. With methods that are foreseeable at present computers cannot go much beyond this point—even the game of chess proves to be too complicated for them to play better than an intelligent beginner. Yet there is every reason to hope that the headlong progress of today will lead fairly quickly to computers which will be intelligent in the sense that they can usefully learn from experience.

And so we are only at the start of the computer age. In the not very distant future we may have computerised information systems that store all the knowledge of the world's libraries, and can produce any piece of it on request, not only when we can say exactly what we want, but also (using associative stores) when we can say rather vaguely the *sort of thing* we want (for example, 'any facts or any speculations by others that might help me to understand why literary researches by computers have concentrated on theological questions', page 244). We may have other machines, fed with up-to-the-minute data on all that is going on in industry, agriculture and commerce, continually analysing and collating this information, and ready at a moment's notice to provide the essence of any part of it in order that some economic decision can be taken on a fully rational basis. At present computers which have been instructed in the little we know about how weather systems develop are giving modest help to forecasters. In future we may tell our meteorological computer what we know, feed it continually with new information on temperatures, pressures and the like, and leave it to discover trends in weather development which the complexity of the data would prevent us from finding out for ourselves. Computers storing all the medical information about the population (assuming greatly improved health services, so that the medical state of every individual is thoroughly known) could give us far greater powers in the control and prevention of disease. Already there are demonstration machines that can obey instructions given verbally, provided one speaks carefully and sticks to a vocabulary of a dozen words or so. In future a computer may 'listen' to the speeches at an international conference and almost instanteously 'speak' the translations in other languages. And in all this we have again done no more than predict that computers will enable us to do efficiently and speedily things that we already do clumsily and slowly. But surely, when we really come to understand them, they will also help us to do things that at present we cannot even imagine.

Already computers are relieving us of much of the drudgery of routine brain work. And soon this sort of mental hack-work will be entirely taken over by electronic slaves. Whether computers do (or will in future) 'think' is probably a meaningless question. But certainly they can do for us a very great deal of the work that *we* do by thinking, and will be able to do much more. We can imagine the time coming when the scientist or scholar at work on a piece of creative thinking has the input and output connections of a computer at his elbow. Some new idea requires a lot of mental hack-work to test and develop it. But instead of devoting his brain-power for the next few weeks or months to this low-grade drudgery, he speaks to his computer. By virtue of its superior speed, the computer gets through this hack-work in a few seconds (presumably consulting as necessary the information machine of page 249) and tells him the result—and he can get on with the next creative step in his work.

All this does not mean that we shall be encouraged to become mentally lazy. On the contrary—as the speculation of the previous paragraph should suggest—one has to think much harder to provide the problems that are to keep the computer going. Its function is not to reduce the amount of our thinking, but to relieve us of the simpler types of mental work and so leave us free for more creative thought, while at the same time greatly increasing the effectiveness of the whole process. But we have carried long-distance speculation far enough, and had better return to the world of the present and immediate past.

CHAPTER 14

AUTOMATION COMES OF AGE

THE trend towards automatic machinery, which we noted as one of the most interesting features of the twenties and thirties (pages 158-61), was nevertheless restricted in that period to fields in which, for one reason or another, the problems of control and automatic manipulation are comparatively simple. Wartime needs, like that for keeping an anti-aircraft gun trained on its target, led to rapid developments in automatic control mechanisms, while radar work produced great progress in the electronic devices that are essential to all but the simplest automatic control. By the end of the war, as a result, the technical means were available for applying automatic methods over far wider fields. Automatic control and manipulation became one of the dominant industrial trends, for which a new name had to be created—*Automation.*

By automation we do not merely mean very elaborate mechanisation. Mechanisation does away with human labour, but a human operator is required to control the machine in its every action. In automation the machine is equipped with automatic control devices, which enable it to 'observe' (as it were) the results of its work and take 'decisions' as to what to do next—so that it can perform long and complicated sequences of tasks of its own accord. It no longer needs an operator; human intervention is required only to design and build it and keep it in good working order.

Transfer Automation

In making some mass-produced article by the continuous flow production methods emerging towards the end of the 'thirties (Chapter 8), the practice was to pass an unending series of work pieces along a great line of machines. Each machine did one job —milled a face, drilled a few holes, or the like—until at the end of the line the finished component emerged. Each machine had its own operator. But the skill had been built into the machine, and the operator's work was in principle entirely automatic—moving the work from conveyor to machine and back, clamping and unclamping, switching on and off, all according to an unvarying routine. Virtually his only responsibility was to ensure that each of these actions was completed before he initiated the next. It should not be too difficult to do without these human automata—to arrange that the movement of the work from machine to machine, the switching on and off, and all the rest, should be done automatically. And that is the principle of *Transfer Automation* (though naturally the practice is more complicated), the simplest type of automation and the most widely used till now.

The first transfer machines, for making cylinder blocks for cars, were built by Morris Motors of England in 1924. But, relying on mechanical controls, they proved unreliable and had to be abandoned. In 1939 a fitter at a Russian tractor plant linked five lathes by means of automatic conveyors to create a simple transfer line for machining parts of tractor tracks. But serious development began only after the war, when transfer machines became common in the car industry, particularly in the U.S.A., for machining parts like cylinder blocks and cylinder heads. Such a machine would at first be the equivalent of ten or twenty individual machines, and would usually require only one or two operators. It did only a part of the process and was set in line with other transfer machines or individual machines. In the early fifties American automobile firms began to link several such machines end to end, with automatic loading and unloading devices between them, to make transfer lines up to a quarter of a mile long, which would complete the job entirely automatically.

This trend reached a climax in 1954, when the main car factories, preparing for the following year's model, installed dozens of elaborate transfer lines of this integrated type. One example, 350 feet long, did 555 operations on cylinder blocks at 104 stations, producing 100 blocks an hour. All machining operations and inspections were automatic. Tool wear was measured automatically, and when a tool needed replacement the section of the line concerned automatically stopped (the rest continuing to work with the aid of storage bunkers). The only direct labour was one loader to place the blocks in position at the first station, and there were two tool-setters, besides maintenance staff. Early transfer lines were confined (with very minor exceptions) to machining operations like milling, drilling and tapping, in which the work remains stationary while the tool moves. Jobs which involve turning or grinding, in which the workpiece rotates, require more subtle arrangements to do the clamping and transferring. So far as America is concerned, serious development towards automating them began about 1952. And by 1954 Pontiac had installed an advanced line for manufacturing car pistons. Starting with rough castings, it undertook all the varied machining operations (turning, grooving, grinding, and so on), tin-plated the pistons and did the necessary inspections—all automatically.

So far as this particular line of development is concerned—for we are now speaking only of transfer automation in the making of metal components—American progress seems at present to have slowed down. Few radical advances have been made, though the number of automatic lines continues to grow. This retardation may be connected with economic problems that resulted from the marked intensification of automation in 1954, which we shall discuss later.

In Britain progress has been slower. Transfer machines began to have a notable impact by the middle fifties. And in the following years, though the total amount of automation has remained much less than in America, some more ambitious projects have been undertaken. The Churchill Gear Company, by the economical method of linking twenty-five standard machines together by means of special transfer and loading devices, created in 1958 a completely automatic line for machining lay-shafts of gear-boxes, each of which has four gear-wheels cut on it. With automatic inspection throughout, and arrangements for stopping any machine that is producing too many rejects, the shafts are produced at about one a minute. A Vauxhall automatic press line about the same time was saving 150,000 man-hours a year. A Fisher and Ludlow stretch-pressing line of 1963 produces 800 car door panels per hour under the control of one man at a console and saves 1s. 3d. per door on materials alone, compared with conventional pressing methods.

Contrasts in Policy

In America and Britain (and the capitalist countries in general) transfer automation has proceeded in a step-by-step fashion. Individual firms concentrated first on getting maximum immediate gain from the widespread use of simple transfer machines. When these possibilities were near exhaustion, they moved on to more elaborate lines like that of page 254. And at every stage the tendency has been to leave the exploration of a more advanced type of automation until as much as possible had been gained from the use of the more elementary types. The Soviet line of development has been quite different. After constructing only a few simple transfer machines immediately after the war, the Russians undertook a great leap forward in 1950, with a line for making car pistons, which very dramatically revealed what transfer automation in a well developed form could do.[1] This remarkable machine does *all* the processes required to turn ingots of aluminium into fully finished pistons, wrapped and packed. It melts the metal, casts and anneals it, tests the castings for hardness and sends rejects back to the furnace for re-melting. Then it undertakes all the very varied machining operations needed to turn the casting into a completed piston. These include not only the simple work-fixed jobs of milling and drilling, but also several operations of turning, grooving and centreless grinding, which are much more difficult to automate. Nearly every type of metal-cutting operation is required. After that the pistons are cleaned and tin-plated, inspected for accuracy, and then wrapped and packed.

Producing 3,500 pistons in a 24-hour day, the original plant needed nine men to care for it, including five maintenance workers and a supervisor, but later versions have reduced the staff to eight, while increasing the production rate. They give about a ten-fold increase in the productivity of labour, and, after allowing for overheads, the cost of production is reduced to a half or a third.

This line, it will be seen, was already much nearer to the fully automatic factory than the best American examples of four years later. It did everything that the Pontiac line (page 254) was to

[1] For a fuller account of this plant, see A. Erivansky, *A Soviet Automatic Plant* (Moscow, Foreign Languages Publishing House, 1955), or pp. 45 to 50 of *Automation and Social Progress* (London, Lawrence and Wishart, 1957) by the present author, which also gives detailed descriptions of many automated machines that cannot be repeated here.

do, and undertook besides all the metallurgical operations at the beginning and the packing at the end. As against the step-by-step progress of the West, the Soviet Union had suddenly jumped from a few tentative examples of the simplest automation to a degree of complexity that was to be unrivalled for a decade. The contrast is even more striking when one remembers that the piston plant must have been planned in 1947 or 1948, at a time when transfer machines were known only theoretically in Britain and were just beginning to be seriously developed in America. The Soviet view, in fact, was that the short-term gains to be had from the simpler types of automation were comparatively unimportant to the economy as a whole, however much they might improve the figures for particular factories—especially as they did not at that time have the capital resources necessary for exploiting automation on a large scale. The important thing, it was felt, was to prepare for a programme of really advanced automation a decade or so in the future. Therefore the first task was to acquire 'know-how' over as wide a field as possible. And the project of making car pistons automatically was chosen because successful completion of it would involve discovering how to automate practically every type of process involved in engineering production (except, obviously, pressing and stamping processes).

The same policy led to an automatic shop for ball- and roller-bearing manufacture, which started work at the end of 1955, and which again was far more complex than anything that had been attempted elsewhere. This plant does automatically every step in the production of the bearings, except the manufacture of the balls themselves.[2] Starting with either bar stock or forged blanks, it does all the turning and grooving operations on the races, subjects them to a complicated heat treatment, demagnetises them, grinds and polishes them, and inspects the results. It then assembles races, balls and cages to make complete bearings, does a final inspection, greases the bearings, wraps them and

[2] For the production of the balls, the Russians had by 1957 succeeded in making practical an advanced method which had been tried in England before 1914 and subsequently in Sweden and Germany—namely that of rolling them in spirally grooved rollers. Compared with the traditional forging and stamping methods, this has the advantages of giving a continuous (and therefore easily automated) process, of producing a better geometrical shape, and of leaving less burr to be removed by further treatment.

packs them. With a staff consisting almost entirely of maintenance workers and supervisors, it produces about 1,750,000 bearings a year. The productivity of labour is increased more than two and a half times.[3]

With the know-how from these ambitious schemes at his disposal, the Soviet engineer was well equipped for applying automation in a wide variety of contexts. And so, the last few years have witnessed a flowering of automation in that country, as the following examples will illustrate. A plant for making tractor gudgeon pins, which came into full operation in 1953, cuts the blanks, turns the pins, chamfers and grinds them and inspects the results, after which they are polished, plated, washed, dried, inspected again, greased, wrapped and packed—all automatically—at the rate of 300 an hour. A line controlled from a single console produces 10,000 gears a month in ten sizes from about 3 inches to 12½ inches in diameter. One making splined shafts of complex design, as parts for machine tools, is manned by three operators; with two-shift working, it turns out 260,000 shafts a year in thirteen sizes (Plate XXXIV). Several lines are in use for making transmission chains for combine harvesters. They cut the links from steel strip, shape them and assemble them into chains, which are then heat-treated and packed. Four operators replace a previous twenty, and the cost of production is cut by 60 per cent.

Even the making of machine tools is moving in the direction of automation. At the Krasnoi Proletarii works in Moscow small universal lathes are mass-produced on a flow-line (conveyor) system. And various parts of the process—the making of gears and of spindles, for example—are gradually being taken over by transfer lines. In fact, the method of production is comparable to that of a car factory around 1950; but nowhere else in the world has the manufacture of machine tools reached a comparable level. Production of these lathes had reached 12,000 a year by 1956—which is getting on towards the British figure for machine tools of all types. And the price works out at about half that of a comparable British model.

It is probably too early yet to draw definite conclusions, but on

[3] This figure refers to the overall productivity of all personnel employed. Productivity increases are usually quoted in terms of machine operators only, and since these almost disappear in automation, the figure given is much higher.

the evidence so far available it seems that the Soviet policy of concentrating attention at first on solving the problems of automation in a few difficult cases is the one that gives better results in the long run. It meant that in the fifties the U.S.S.R. had to be content with much less automation than the leading capitalist countries. But it also meant that the engineers quickly learned methods by which they have in the last few years been building automated lines at a continually accelerating rate—two or three hundred a year as we approach the mid-sixties. It seems that within less than a decade the U.S.S.R. will have more transfer automation, quantitatively, than any other country, and that this will be qualitatively at a higher level of completeness and integration than that reached elsewhere. The widespread use of automation has become the central point in the Soviet plans for increasing industrial efficiency and applying it to raise the standard of living.

The transfer line of the future will probably not be specially built for its particular purpose, as most of those already described have been. It will be constructed instead mainly out of standardised unit machines and standard transfer links, which can be assembled together in many ways to make lines for different purposes—just as the non-automated line is assembled from a few standard types of machines and their 'standardised operators'. In this way the capital cost will be greatly reduced, and as a result transfer methods will become available in industries whose scale of production is too modest to justify the expense of specially constructed machinery. Developments on these lines have been taking place in the West—notably at the Renault factory in France.[4] But a competitive industrial system greatly restricts possibilities of standardisation. National planning allows standardisation to be carried much farther, and has enabled Soviet work since about 1955 to go a long way towards producing a complete range of units from which transfer lines can be built.

Programme-control Automation

Let us now turn to another type of automation, in which the leading role has been played by the West. Transfer automation

[4] **And compare the lay-shaft line of page 254.**

—even when lines are built from standard units—can only be used in mass-production industries. When small quantities are needed—perhaps only a single piece of a given design—the work would normally be done on a versatile machine, capable of a variety of movements, under the control of a skilled craftsman, who must be able to take instructions (usually in the form of drawings) and operate the controls in the appropriate manner. The essence of *Programme-control Automation* is that the machine is equipped with a control mechanism (which is essentially a small and specialised computer) that enables it to read the instructions for itself and operate accordingly. The instructions will usually consist of a table of dimensions (measurements) which are presented to the control device by means of punched or magnetic tape. The control system can read and obey these commands almost instantaneously, whereas the former craftsman probably spent more time studying the plans than operating the machine. This means a very great saving in time and a corresponding improvement in the economy of using the capital tied up in the machine. Even an early version of this type of automation, applied to a milling machine, reduced the time for cutting a complicated cam from three *weeks* to four *hours*. And only a few minutes are required to change from one job to a completely different one, so that a programme-controlled machine can be very versatile.

The main developments in this line were carried out in Britain and the U.S.A., and it was about 1956 that programme-controlled machines began to be generally available. In this case the socialist countries have on the whole been content to follow a year or two behind the capitalist ones.

Programme-controlled milling machines have proved effective for very large-scale work such as the shaping of aircraft wing skins up to 10 feet wide and 40 feet long; and equally for very delicate and complicated jobs like the making of wave guides, where in one case a previous 150 hours of work was reduced to four. Programme-controlled flame-cutting machines, in use in England and Norway, can cut ship's plates 12 feet by 40 feet and 3 inches thick, economically and to a high degree of accuracy (Plate XXXV). Programme-control has also been applied to drilling, turning and forging. And these are only the early examples of a technique whose potentialities are still largely unexplored. A hint of one possible line of further development is contained in a prototype 'all purpose' machine produced by a British firm in 1964, which can be programmed for jobs involving drilling, milling, boring, reaming or tapping.

The general principle of programme control has applications far outside the field of engineering. An example is an American device of 1964, which produces animated cartoon films (for instructional or similar purposes) from a programme presented as a deck of punched cards. Obeying the programme instructions, a computer produces a sequence of cathode-ray tube displays, which are photographed to make the film.

Computers and Automation

When the progress of transfer or programme-controlled automation is surveyed, one thing becomes clear. We cannot hope by these methods alone to progress much beyond the automatic production of single components or of rather simple assemblies (as in the Moscow bearing factory). If we aim at eventually reaching the automatic factory, in which complete washing machines, refrigerators or even cars, are made without the help of human operators, then we shall need automation of a more complex type. All the individual transfer lines or automated machines will have to be made to work together as a single harmonious unity. But we have already seen (pages 238-41) that computers are capable of planning the production process as a whole. It seems natural, therefore, to consider the possibility of building a factory in which all the individual jobs are done by automated machinery, while the entire process is supervised by a computer, which continually receives telemetered progress reports from the machines, analyses these and transmits orders for speeding up, slowing down or changing from one line of work to another.

An early example (1961) of this new trend is a line for making carbon resistors (for use in electronic apparatus) in a North Carolina factory of the Western Electric Company. This is basically a twelve-station transfer line (Plate XXXVI), which coats a ceramic core with carbon, inspects the result, sputters gold contacts on the ends (at a station which is itself a thirty-six-station rotary transfer machine), fits caps with leads attached, cuts a spiral groove in the carbon coating to bring the resistance to the specified value, inspects again, fits a plastic capsule over the core and cures and seals it, tests the capsule for leakage, prints the specification and production details on the resistor, carries out a final inspection, and packs the product. But the production problem was special in two ways, each of which was such as to require computer control of the whole line.

First, the line was required to produce a large variety of resistors, with four different standard wattages and a virtually unlimited number of resistance values. As batches with these different parameters follow each other along the line, the computer has to make sure that each successive machine is appropriately adjusted to the requirements of the batch that is passing through it.

Second, and more important, several of the processes need very delicate adjustment. They cannot be simply pre-set to produce the required results. Their performance constantly tends to deviate from specification and must be continually readjusted. So the computer has to receive a stream of information from the inspection stations about the quality of work being produced, analyse this, and issue instructions to the control mechanisms at the various stations. For example, the second inspection station measures the resistance of the pieces coming from the spiral-cutting station and sends the results to the computer, which does a quality control analysis, detects any tendency to wander away from specification and appropriately adjusts the controls of the spiral-cutting machinery. But this is not enough. For the heating involved in curing and sealing the capsules alters the resistance value. So the measurements of the final inspection station are again analysed by the computer and used to adjust the workings of the second inspection station in such a way that the resistance, *after* alteration by the heating, will be the required one.

So here the computer *both* plans the production process in such a way that varied products move smoothly along the line, *and* carries out an extremely refined piece of quality control, which—if it could be done at all in purely human terms—would otherwise require a small army of inspectors and a great flow of instructions passing back and forth to tell operators to adjust this or that control. The production rate is about 1,200 an hour.

This is still very far from a computer-controlled automatic factory—it is only a line for making one component. But it does signpost the road to the automatic factory of the future. How soon this can become a reality depends very largely on the complexity of the product. The simplest product of all, in many ways, is electricity, and the automatic control of its generation and transmission has made steady progress since the first automatic sub-station of 1914 and the first automatic hydro-electric station of 1917. The completely automatic operation of individual power stations now presents few difficulties and is actually in operation in some cases. The control of a complete grid, arranging to use its many generating plants in the most economical way as the pattern of demand varies, is a highly responsible task which computers are beginning to take over. Already cases exist where a computer is in full charge of a network involving two or three dozen generators. And Britain is embarking on an experimental scheme, involving at the start thirty-one generators totalling 1½ million kW., which is expected to lead on to completely integrated computer control of the whole grid by 1975 or 1980.

Next in simplicity come processes involving liquids and gases, as in oil-refining and many chemical plants. In this field, electronic control of individual parts of the process has been common for years. But operators, usually working in a centralised control room in front of large panels of dials and switches, have had the task of co-ordinating the whole and attempting to do so in such a way as to get maximum efficiency. Computers are beginning to take over this work. The object in these cases is not to save labour costs (which are usually very small already) but to improve the quality of the product and reduce the waste that comes from operating below optimum conditions. In Calvert City, Kentucky, a plant making vinyl chloride (for use in resin production) and another making acrylo-nitrile (for synthetic rubber) have been controlled by computer since about 1959. In an Imperial Chemical Industries factory for soda-ash (anhydrous sodium carbonate) at Fleetwood, Lancashire, a computer takes the place of nearly a hundred individual control devices, and six more I.C.I. plants are to be similarly equipped. A distillation unit in a Belfast oil-refinery, which opened in 1964, is designed for normal control by operators, but equipped with a computer system running in parallel, which will be used to investigate the possibilities of obtaining optimum working in this way and the saving that can result. The U.S.S.R. does not appear to have advanced far in this sphere as yet, but computer control systems are in use at a few factories, including a synthetic rubber plant at Yefremov.

Computers in Steel Making

Coming now to those much more intractable things, solids, we may consider the steel industry. Many parts of iron and steel production have been automated for some years. And in a few cases substantial sections of the process have had computer control. This applies to several rolling mills in America, where the computer is fed with information on the composition of the alloy and the size and gauge of the sheet or coil to be produced, and then takes charge of the whole rolling process. Another case is a blooming mill with a capacity of 6 million tons a year, built in 1962 by the Urals Heavy Machinery Works, in which a computer with the help of television and remote control reduced the staff to a handful of men.

But we reach a completely new level of integration with the Spencer Steel Works of Richard, Thomas and Baldwin (the only major state-controlled steel undertaking in Britain at the time of writing), which began to produce its first pig-iron in June 1962 and is scheduled to be working at full capacity about the end of 1964. It is a huge establishment, costing £141 million to build, covering about 1,700 acres of land, and destined to produce 3 million tons of steel a year in the form of cold-reduced sheets and coils, hot-rolled strip and light steel plates. Its individual parts are highly automated. For instance, the charging cycle of the blast furnaces is entirely automatic, with one operator controlling the selection, weighing, charging and distribution throughout the furnace of the raw materials. Again its hot strip mill, 500 yards long and yielding 1¼ million tons a year of hot-rolled coiled strip, will be under fully automatic control throughout, from the re-heat furnace to the coilers—which, incidentally, have to pick up strip moving at 37 m.p.h. and wrap it in a few seconds into coils up to a mile in length and weighing 27 tons.

The individual processes, then, will be highly automated, but what is really interesting about this plant is that, when completed, the whole production process will be under the control of nine computers. Six of these will look after individual processes—some are already in action. Two of them will plan the flow of work from one process to another in order to fulfil current orders at maximum efficiency. And the ninth will take over advance planning for the whole plant.[5]

Of course, this is still far from an automatic steel works. Despite the automation of many sections and the use of computers to supervise the whole, it still depends on human intervention at many points. Yet it foreshadows the time when a steel works, or any other comparable unit, will be so completely automatic that manpower will be used only for maintenance and for making the high level policy decisions which the computer will translate into detailed instructions that will control the working of fully automatic machines and conveyors.

The savings to be got by computer control are probably of the order of a few per cent of the total cost of production. But this is achieved in return for a very modest addition to capital expenditure. Early in 1964 an American firm supplying such equipment gave some figures for nine installations. The *annual* saving that resulted ranged from 46 to 500 per cent of the cost of the computer, with an average figure of 150 per cent. It is not surprising, then, that the use of computers to control production processes is spreading rapidly. By mid-1964 there were estimated to be about 440 of them throughout the world, of which about 200 were in the U.S.A. and Canada and a little over twenty in Britain. But far more subtle and complex systems are already used in military installations—for the control of aircraft or missile systems, and in warships. The frigate H.M.S. *Aurora* has at her heart a Poseidon computer, probably the largest in Britain (not even excepting *Atlas*). Using information received by radio com-

[5] A similar system on a smaller scale is already in action at the Park Gate steelworks near Rotherham. One computer plans up to three weeks ahead, on the basis of customers' orders and information supplied by the second computer about the state of production. The second using orders issued by the first, produces detailed instructions for the treatment of each ingot (though it does not control the machines directly). A third computer arranges for the billets to be cut automatically into lengths in such a way as to minimise wastage.

munication, radar, sonar and 'intelligence', this computer solves the various problems about intercepting aircraft and missiles, makes recommendations about the action to be taken against the enemy, and passes such information on to other vessels. Development of Poseidon cost about £2½ million. Electronic equipment of one sort or another accounts for at least 10 per cent of the cost of a modern warship, and the figure rises to some 50 per cent in the latest American nuclear submarines or British frigates of the Leander class. Electronic devices, including more advanced versions of *Aurora*'s equipment, accounted for about half of the £31 million spent on the modernisation of the aircraft carrier H.M.S. *Eagle*, which was completed in 1964. If control systems of comparable refinement and complexity were applied to peaceful purposes, the industrial scene could be entirely transformed.

Automation throughout Industry

We have so far confined our attention to a very few industries, but in fact there is hardly a sphere of production where automation is not applicable. Consider, for example, the assembly of logs into rafts for floating down river to the sawmills. On some Soviet rivers this is done by what amounts to a huge transfer line built across the water in pontoon-bridge style. The logs are picked up, graded by length, tied into bundles and labelled for quantity and quality, and then towed away for assembly into big rafts. In the Swedish timber industry, the sorting of logs by size for the sawmills is done automatically. There, too, a factory for making sulphite wood pulp for paper manufacture is controlled by one man, who looks after a sequence of seventy phases of manufacture, producing 70,000 tons a year.

In Moscow that very difficult metal tantalum is being turned into welded tubes by a completely automatic process, which first forges the ingots into slabs, then butt-welds these to form a strip, which is trimmed, bent to shape by rollers and welded to form the final tube. A fully automatic British mill takes only 82 seconds to transform a copper bar, 4½ feet long and weighing 265 pounds, into a rod 1,300 feet long and ¼ inch in diameter; it can produce 400 tons of copper rods a day in diameters from ¼ to $\frac{9}{16}$ inch.

Computer-controlled type-setting machines in the U.S.A. take care of such problems as spacing, adjusting the length of the line, and hyphenating words that must be split (doing so according to agreed conventions as to where the hyphen should be placed). The 'copy' is typed on a typewriter which simultaneously prepares a punched tape; corrections and editing instructions can then be put on a further tape, and the computer combines the two in setting type at a rate of up to 12,000 lines an hour. Similar machines, though apparently less well developed, are reported from the U.S.S.R. As the typist, using another recent American device, produces a document, it is simultaneously recorded on tape. She then makes corrections by typing over the original. The tape follows her, substituting the corrected version for the old one, and finally it is 'played back' to produce a fully corrected copy. With the addition of a second tape station, a letter can be mass-produced as a circular, with appropriate names and addresses added, and if necessary with alterations in the text for particular addressees.

Automatic devices for aiding the sorting of letters are in use in many post offices, and one of the latest (in West Germany) actually reads coded addresses and sorts accordingly at 40,000 letters an hour. A British process for making sheet glass, details of which are still secret, floats a film of molten glass on the surface of a tank of molten tin, from which it is taken off in a continuous strip and passed to an automatic cutting plant and automatic warehouse; by eliminating grinding and polishing it cuts capital cost by half, and the number of workers is reduced from thirty-five to twenty-five.

A programme-controlled device for testing electronic circuits (again British) can check each of 600 terminations against every other, testing for correctness of connections, resistance, continuity and insulation—a total of about 180,000 checks done in 5 or 6 hours, against the 165 days that would be needed for manual testing. The printed circuit technique has changed assembling of circuitry from something that is hardly conceivable except in terms of nimble fingers into something eminently automatable. The printing of the circuits and the fixing of components to them has in many cases become completely automatic. In 1962 a Liverpool factory broke new ground with a programme-controlled circuit-assembling machine which, according to instructions given by tape, sorts out and tests the required components, drills appropriately placed holes in the printed circuit panel and affixes the components; working at ten times the speed of manual assemblers, it is operated by one unskilled girl; it will produce about 7,000 circuits in a year, in 400 different types, using sixty different components. The fabrication of electronic components themselves has also become highly automatic—as with the resistor plant described earlier or an American line that unaided assembles 1,800 transistors an hour.

Automation in Transport

Automatic railway marshalling yards have become fairly common. Wagons roll down from a hump, are switched hither and thither automatically according to a paper-tape programme and brought gently to a stop at the right point by devices that weigh them, measure speeds and distances to be travelled and apply brakes accordingly. The driverless train has become a reality, at least on urban and suburban lines. An experimental version was demonstrated on the London Underground in 1963, and full-scale trials began in April 1964. In Moscow successful tests were completed early in 1962, and by May the first automatic train had carried a million passengers, since when three driverless[6] trains have become part of the normal service with another five due to be introduced in January 1965. The computer which controls the train stores permanent information about gradients, distances between signals, speed restrictions and the like, and is fed from the wheels with data about the position and speed of the train from moment to moment and the signal situation. On this basis it calculates how to use power and brakes in the most economical way to keep up with the timetable, and manipulates the controls accordingly.[7]

Automation in ships is fast bringing them to the point where a vessel may be completely controlled by one officer on the bridge, who can rely most of the time on automatic navigation devices, and can signal his requirements for changes of speed direct to the engines. In the engine-room there will only be maintenance

[6] During the development phase a stand-by driver is still carried as a precaution.

[7] An experimental main-line automatic train was under test between Moscow and Klin in late 1964.

staff, since automatic devices will translate the bridge's orders into movements of the controls, taking care of all those precautions about doing things in the right order and without undue haste that would normally be the responsibility of engineers. And in one case at least, automation is beginning to take a hand in maintenance. For the Shell Oil Company has under development a system by which instruments monitor the performance of ships during normal voyages and radio the information to a central computer, which detects incipient faults and organises maintenance action—thus avoiding the costly business of taking ships out of service periodically for testing.

In the air, automatic pilots have been in use for many years, radar navigational devices are largely automatic, and automatic systems of blind landing are in an advanced state of development. And, with the rapid increase in traffic density, it seems that soon the work of the control tower must be handed over to a computer—for human controllers are too slow.

Automation in Agriculture and Mining

It was commonly believed even ten years ago that conditions in two basic industries—agriculture and mining—are too complex and variable to permit automation. This view is rapidly being proved wrong. Automatic tractors—under radio guidance or starting from a single furrow previously ploughed round the periphery of a field—are in use in America and Russia; indeed they are even in moderate quantity production. The U.S.S.R. uses harvesters that feel their way along the side of the uncut grain, automatically adjusting their speed to the thickness and humidity of the crop, and which stop and call for help if anything goes wrong. In the University of Reading experimental work is well advanced towards the creation of a system by which tractors can be equipped to undertake complex tasks—moving from farmyard to field, completing the assigned programme of work automatically, and returning of their own accord to base—with even the possibility of making automatic decisions about the best order in which to undertake several tasks in the prevailing weather conditions. Dairy farms, in advanced cases, have become factories in which the feeding and cleaning is done automatically, and the cows are taken by conveyor to the milkmaid, who has nothing to do but attach the milking cups to their teats. And in view of the progress of our knowledge of the chemistry of life, the day may not be far off when we shall produce at least some of our food (as we already produce many of our textiles) in chemical plants that can be fully automated.

In coal-mining, cutter-loaders—that is, machines that cut the coal by one of several methods, pick it up and deposit it on a conveyor—were tried before the war[8] and began to make serious progress after it. Various types of powered roof supports gradually came to replace the old props. The work of the mine thus became mechanised, rather than manual, in all its main aspects, and by the late fifties the stage had been reached at which serious experiments towards automation could begin. In Britain, U.S.A. and U.S.S.R. there are faces—experimental, but in an advanced state of development—where coal is being cut, loaded and conveyed, and all the cutting and conveying machinery and the roof supports are being moved forward as the face advances, under the control of one man sitting at a console. So successful have the British experiments been that it is planned to set up similar faces during 1965 in every coalfield (except Kent), and it is hoped that within ten years half the country's coal will be mined automatically by remote control (Plates XXXVII and XXXVIII).

This is essentially a development of the old longwall system, which began as a manual method, was then extensively mechanised using machines worked by teams of miners, and finally in these experiments is being automated. But if experience in other industries is any guide, the best way forward may not be by automating the traditional methods, but rather by discovering quite new methods that are designed for automation from the start. An example of experiments on these lines is the British Collins Miner (primarily for use in thin seams) which bores a series of tunnels at right angles to the roadway. It automatically advances about a hundred yards into the seam, carrying its extensible conveyor behind it, and then returns to the roadway, moves sideways and cuts another tunnel parallel to the first. It is entirely controlled by one man at a console.

[8] The U.S.S.R. claims to have been the first country to experiment with cutter-loaders—in 1932—but there, as elsewhere, the practical development belongs to the post-war period.

The hydraulic mining method of the U.S.S.R. (page 171) is obviously suitable for automation, and an experimental automated pit is due to start work in 1964. Miners will go underground only for maintenance work. The water will carry the coal by pipeline to a power station 6 miles away. Shaft sinking has also been automated in Russia since 1959, with a machine that will dig the shaft at about a yard an hour under the control of a single operator (Plate XXXIX). And machines are under development there for automatically driving roadways under the guidance of a control mechanism resembling the autopilot of a plane.

Automation, Productivity and the Standard of Living

This survey will serve to indicate that in the not very distant future virtually the whole of production will be automated in one way or another. What will be the consequences? The most obvious effect of automation is that it raises the productivity of labour and reduces the cost of production. Productivity increases (for direct labour on the job) are often of the order of five, ten or twenty times, occasionally much more. Production costs are typically reduced to a half or a third. This clearly is the material basis for a rapid rise in the standard of living—for higher wages, cheaper goods and shorter working hours. Indeed it is not difficult to calculate that, if there were no extraneous inhibiting factors—no vested interests, no perversion for private profit, no fears about markets, no waste of potential capital on armaments—then the application of automation and other advanced techinques could *double* the standard of living in something like *ten years*.

In America, where automation has been most widely used, there has been an increase in wages and a reduction in the working week, but to a very much smaller extent than the productivity increases would justify. From 1956 to 1963 real hourly earnings in manufacturing industry rose about 10 per cent[9] against an 18 per cent increase in productivity. Though some trade unions negotiated agreements for a shorter working week, average actual hours worked were the same in 1962 as in 1956—40·4 hours a week. Some consumer durables—a field where automation has wide

[9] This corresponds to doubling the standard of living in fifty years, not ten. But the discrepancy is not surprising, since the 'extraneous inhibiting factors' of the previous paragraph have been very much to the fore.

application—have fallen in price,[10] even though the general price trend has been sharply upwards. But the most striking effect of automation's productivity increases in America has been of a very different nature.

Automation and Employment

Automation can only raise the standard of living if the increase in productivity is used to bring about a proportional increase in production. And that, in a capitalist economy, means that the market must expand in step with productivity. If it does not do so, the automation can only lead to an increase in unemployment. We have seen (pages 139 and 183-4) how the economic structure of capitalism tends to lead to restriction of the market and consequent unemployment. In the early days, it was commonly said that automation would not aggravate these difficulties—the cheapening of the product, through greater productive efficiency, would ensure that markets expanded sufficiently to maintain full employment. But experience in America—the only capitalist society with enough automation to show striking effects[11]—has clearly demonstrated the falsity of this view.

Up to 1954 American car firms had experimented with automation. In re-tooling for their 1955 models, they all simultaneously took the decision to go in for it on a large scale. Each of them installed dozens of elaborate transfer lines like those described on pages 253-4—an enormous capital expenditure. Each of them then calculated that in order to pay for this investment it would have to increase its share of the market. Between them they were going to capture something like 115 per cent of the market!

In the event, 1955 was a record year for American car production—almost 8 million cars turned out, against a previous best of 6,600,000. But at the end of the year 750,000 of these cars were unsold. And by April 1956 the unsold total had reached a million, with sales still well below previous averages.

[10] However the fall has been due at least as much to the rapid growth of discount trading, cutting out middleman profits, as to automation. The quotation from Norton Leonard on page 183-4 explains why, in many cases (and outstandingly in the case of cars), the introduction of automation has *not* led to a fall in prices.

[11] For a 'minor key' version in Britain of the story we are about to tell of America, see the author's *Automation and Social Progress.*

There could only be one result—wholesale cutting down of production, wholesale dismissals of workers. Unemployment in the industry rose to 200,000—a quarter of the total labour force. This was the effect of automation in an economy which could not properly plan the relations between productivity and market expansion. And the industry has never fully recovered from that disaster. Productivity increases have kept ahead of market expansions, so that unemployment has become chronic. The number of workers fell from 730,000 in 1955 to 550,000 in 1962. The chief automobile centres face almost continuous unemployment problems. Spring is the time when the industry traditionally prospers, and yet in spring 1961 Detroit had 207,000 unemployed, or 14·4 per cent, while the following spring Cleveland, Ohio, had one in fifteen out of work.

The car industry was the first to adopt automation in a radical way. But much the same story was repeated elsewhere in the American economy. As mechanisation and automation came into bituminous coal mining, employment dropped from 400,000 in 1947 to 135,000 in 1963. From 1953 to 1961 the electrical industry increased its output by 21 per cent, but decreased employment by 10 per cent. The steel industry had about the same production in 1959 as in 1952, but with 127,000 fewer workers, a drop of 23 per cent. The introduction of computers has seldom led to actual dismissals of clerical workers, since the normal policy has been to stop recruitment and rely on natural wastage to reduce staff. But opportunities in this field are becoming restricted. The gain in 'white collar' employment was only 0·9 per cent in 1963, compared with 2·8 per cent a year on the average during the fifties. If the trend continues, unemployment among clerical workers will also become serious.

The American economy continued to have its booms and slumps, but at every boom the hard core of unemployment was higher than in the last. In 1953—a boom year—there were 1·9 million unemployed, or less than 3 per cent. Three booms later in 1963, the number of unemployed was 4·2 million or 5·7 per cent.[12] And now it is generally admitted by business men, official

[12] These are official figures, but the Association for Economic Studies claimed that the real unemployment rate was 8·6 per cent. The picture is made much worse by the fact that automation has tended to abolish

Government committees, economists and trade union leaders that the cause of this steady increase in unemployment *is* automation —or rather the failure of the economy to expand at the rate that the proper use of automation demands. An official of the Department of Labour testified to a Senate Sub-Committee in 1963 that automation is wiping out 200,000 jobs a year in manufacturing industry alone—but the President of a large firm making automated equipment, U.S. Industries Incorporated, described this figure as a 'gross underestimate'. It has been calculated that in order merely to keep pace with growing productivity and prevent unemployment from growing worse (but without in any way improving it), the U.S. economy would have to expand by 5 per cent each year, whereas it has only averaged 2½ per cent over the past decade. Thus, unless something quite unexpected happens, automation with its increasing productivity will go on driving people out of work till by 1970 something like 10 per cent of workers will be unemployed on the official scale, representing perhaps 15 per cent in reality. No wonder, then, that the trade union leader Mr. George Meany has spoken of automation, not as a blessing, but as 'a real curse on our society. If continued at the present pace it can lead to a national catastrophe.'

All this has another side, too, If men and women are unemployed, then wealth that they could be producing is not being produced. From 1956 to 1963 America's factories never worked at even 90 per cent of their capacity, and the figure twice dropped below 80 per cent. If a tenth or a fifth of the plant is not being used, the potential benefits of automation are being thrown away. Naturally this reduces the incentive for further technical improvement—if a manufacturer cannot sell all that he can produce with present equipment, why should he undertake the risk and expense of installing yet better machinery? And so there has been a tendency to go slowly and cautiously with automation (compare page 254). American industry automates as much as it dare within the limits of the economy, but what it does is much

reasonably well paid jobs in manufacturing, while those who found other work usually had to be content with poorly paid jobs in services. In addition more than 2 million were working part-time, not by choice, but because full-time jobs were not available.

less than what is possible and much less than what would be desirable in a society that planned to use automation for the maximum benefit of its people.

We saw in Chapter 9 (pages 163-4) that this sort of trouble does not occur in a planned socialist economy. Expansion is so rapid (with rates approaching 10 per cent a year, against the 5 per cent that America needs to prevent unemployment from worsening, and the 2½ per cent actually achieved) that new jobs are immediately available for those displaced by automation. And when the time comes—though it will be many years yet—when rapid increases in production are no longer needed, then a planned economy can smoothly arrange to transfer workers to service industries and to shorten the working hours all round.

Automation and Skill Changes

In the pre-automation era, mass-production methods constantly tended to replace skilled workers by unskilled or semi-skilled, both through the minute division of labour and through building the skill into the machines. In particular it created a whole new army of repetition workers—who had hardly existed before—whose functions were to repeat over and over again some very simple sequence of manual operations. Automation reverses this trend. Automation has little use for unskilled and semi-skilled workers; in particular it has *no* use for people doing repetition jobs[13]—for a repetition job is one that, almost by definition, can easily be automated. But automated production needs large numbers of skilled craftsmen—maintenance engineers, electricians and electronic engineers, tool-makers and the like—whose role is to keep the automatic machinery in good working order. And apart from the higher proportion of skilled craftsmen that automation requires, it makes enormous demands for greater numbers of technicians and technologists, design engineers and production engineers, draughtsmen and research workers—for all the more highly qualified, professional and semi-professional ranks.

Now this trend is surely to be welcomed. Repetition work is an

[13] Naturally in the conditions of partial automation that are still common, repetition workers remain—for example, in loading automatic lines. But in full automation, like the piston plant of page 255 or the resistor line of pages 260-1, only skilled personnel are required.

insult to the people who have to do it. It treats them as less than human. We need not be surprised if it sometimes turns them into something less than human. When a man has to spend eight hours a day at work in which he has nothing to think about, nothing to exercise his mental powers on, it is not surprising if he becomes incapable of exercising those powers in his leisure time, but must spend it in uncreative passivity, or even in senseless and destructive activity. Automation offers the prospect of giving every man and woman a job that is interesting and worth doing in itself, a job requiring initiative and creative thought. And surely that is as desirable an object as providing a higher standard of material living. In fact, when the standard of living reaches that of, say, the professional classes of today, a worthwhile and interesting job becomes *more* important than further increases in luxury. We can begin to visualise a not very distant future in which we shall all live in plenty of material comfort, we shall all work some twenty hours a week, we shall all do a job that is worthwhile in itself—and consequently we shall all spend our ample leisure in an equally creative way, making music or pottery, doing scientific research, what you will. By offering us material plenty, ample leisure and intelligent constructive work for everybody, automation opens up wonderful new prospects for the expansion of the creative energies of mankind.

But naturally this wonderful future is not there just for the asking. It has to be worked for. Maintenance electricians and production engineers do not grow on trees. A very extensive and very powerful educational system is needed to produce them. No country in the world has at present enough skilled and technically qualified people to carry through a really thorough programme of automation. Radical changes in educational systems will be required—both for the initial education of far greater numbers of highly qualified people, and for the continual re-education of those already at work in new and higher skills. The latter may ultimately become the dominant factor, since technology is now changing so fast that we can no longer be content with educating young people once and for all in some skill that they will use throughout their lives, but must rather think in terms of the continued re-education of most people every few years to cope with new technological tasks as they arise. A portent of the future is that over a quarter of all the people in the U.S.S.R. are students in one capacity or another, most of these being engaged in further education while at work. In fact it has become generally recognised in the last few years that the educational provision of the West is woefully inadequate, and that the socialist countries have made far bigger strides towards the sort of education that is needed to make full use of automation, or indeed of modern technology in general. However, what led the Western world to appreciate this point was not so much the story of automation, as the spectacular part played by the U.S.S.R. in ushering in the Age of Space.

CHAPTER 15

THE CONQUEST OF SPACE

As these lines are being written, the Space Age is less than seven years old. But the rockets that were to usher it in have a much longer history. Rockets are usually thought to have originated in China, perhaps in the eleventh century, though the evidence is by no means decisive. They were apparently used as war weapons in China, Islam and Europe during the thirteenth century. From that time on they developed, mainly as fireworks, sometimes for military purposes, until an unexpected event of 1760 suddenly gave them prominence. In that year an Indian Prince, Hydar Ali, equipped a body of 1,200 special troops with rockets having a range of about a mile, and with them severely defeated a British colonial army in the battle of Guntur. His son expanded the rocket corps and several times beat British troops. Interest in rockets as weapons was revived, and by 1805 Sir William Congreve had produced his much improved military rocket, with a range of up to 3,000 yards, which was to contribute to the defeat of Napoleon. But the enthusiasm for rockets did not last. They could not compete with the improvements that rifling brought to gunnery, and no great progress took place during the nineteenth century.

Pioneers of Modern Rocketry

From Greek times onwards, and especially after the rise of modern science in the seventeenth century, men had dreamed of journeying to the Moon or the planets. But the first to set space travel on the scientific path was Konstantin Tsiolkovsky, a poor Russian schoolmaster. After many years of study, he published in 1903 a paper which analysed the problem in great detail and with remarkable foresight. Among other things, he showed the superiority of liquid fuels over solid ones, and worked out the fundamental formula connecting the speed attained by a rocket with the speed of the gases coming from its nozzles, its weight and its fuel load. His work was to have no effect for twenty years.

In 1919 the American, R. H. Goddard, published a study of rockets as a means of reaching high altitudes for research purposes, and made some incidental points about space exploration. He began experiments with powder rockets, but after coming across the work of Tsiolkovsky turned to liquid fuels. His first liquid-fuelled rocket was launched on 16 March 1926 and travelled a distance of 183 feet! (Plate XLVII). Goddard continued his researches and the American Interplanetary Society did further experiments. But this work attracted little support and virtually no official recognition, so that American rocket research did not begin seriously till after the Second World War.

The new Soviet state showed more interest in Tsiolkovsky's ideas, and the first Russian liquid-fuelled rocket, with a thrust of 20 kilograms, took off in 1933 and reached a height of 6 miles (Plate XL). In a book of 1929, Tsiolkovsky had made clear the essential role of multi-stage rockets[1] in attaining the high speeds needed for space flight. And as a result Soviet workers ten years later were the first to produce a two-stage rocket. The sustained Soviet interest in the subject led to the tactical Katyusha rocket—striking contrast with the V-2 terror weapon—which played a notable role in, for example, the defence of Stalingrad and Kharkov.

Meanwhile a book on space flight, published in 1923 by Hermann Oberth, had led to the foundation four years later of the German Society for Space-Travel. The Society began practical experiments, which—largely owing to lack of funds—had little success. But it was through the work of Oberth and his followers that rockets were to have their first really spectacular impact on the world. For when the Nazis came to power the Society broke up, some of its members emigrating, while the others were transferred to military research. In particular Wernher von Braun, who had joined the Society in 1930, became in 1937 Technical Director at the Peenemunde Rocket Centre, and under his leadership the intended vehicle of exploration was transformed into the

[1] The idea of the multi-stage rocket had been suggested several times from 1650 onwards, but it was Tsiolkovsky who first reached a true appreciation of its importance.

V-2 weapon of mass destruction. The first experimental V-2 was fired in 1942, and in 1944 began the long-range bombardment of London and other cities—with rockets capable of reaching a height of 130 miles or so.

The Space Age Begins

It did not need much insight to see that the V-2 required only a little more development to become either the launcher of space vehicles or an Intercontinental Ballistic Missile. The Americans took great pains to capture over a hundred of these rockets and to bring with them most of the leading German rocket scientists—including, of course, von Braun. And the most successful American rocket vehicles have been those developed from V-2 under von Braun's leadership.[2] The Russians also got hold of some German experts, extracted what knowledge they could from them to supplement their own, stronger and more continuous, work on rocketry, and sent them home.

Then on 4 October 1957 the world reacted with amazement to the news that *Sputnik I*, weighing 184 lb., was in orbit. There should have been no surprise, for Soviet intentions had been announced months in advance; but illusions about 'Russian technological backwardness' had misled the Western countries into ignoring these statements. The launching on 3 November of *Sputnik II*, weighing 2,000 lb. and with a payload of half a ton, further increased the wonder. For the U.S.A. had been thinking in terms of satellites weighing a few pounds, and launched in more easily attained orbits at that. In an effort not to be beaten, the U.S.A. (after several failures) succeeded in putting in orbit *Explorer I* (31 lb.) on 31 January 1958, *Vanguard I* (3¼ lb.) on 17 March, and *Explorer III* (31 lb.) nine days later. Then came *Sputnik III* on 15 May, weighing 2,925 lb. and carrying 2,130 lb. of instruments.

Having completed this initial programme of three Earth satellites, the Russians turned to other fields of space exploration. In most of these they have maintained—up till 1964—a clear lead over the Americans. But there are important exceptions. In the early years the U.S.A. was more successful than the U.S.S.R. in

[2] The *Observer* (20 March 1960) reported that eighty-nine German members in von Braun's team were working on the *Saturn* rocket.

carrying out scientific research with the aid of space vehicles. To do so, within the limitations imposed by their tiny payloads, they achieved marvels of micro-miniaturisation of scientific apparatus and radio circuitry. The difference between the two countries has not, however, been so great as has been popularly supposed, and the programme of *Cosmos* satellites (50 of them between March 1962 and October 1964) is fast closing the gap. Latterly, indeed, the Soviet effort in this field has far exceeded the American, though it is too early yet to judge if success commensurate with the effort is being attained.

The U.S.A. has led, too, in the matter of practical applications of space technology—a field which has so far been steadily ignored by the U.S.S.R. Thus American satellites[3] have demonstrated the possibility of a world-wide system of radio communication (including live television) using orbiting relay stations. The most promising method (used for the *Syncoms*) seems to be to place the satellite in an orbit at such a height that it moves round the Earth once a day, and thus from a terrestrial point of view appears to remain stationary. Plans are in hand for putting such a stationary satellite (*Early Bird*) over the Atlantic in 1965, to provide 240 two-way telephone channels or one television channel between America and Europe.[4] And it is hoped that by 1967 a world-wide system of communications via satellites will be in action. It is curious that, although the experimental work has been done entirely at public expense, the commercial system is to be run by a privately-owned corporation (COMSAT).

Again, American work has demonstrated that space photographs of cloud cover can be of great value to the weather-forecaster, and in particular can help in predicting the paths of hurricanes. The *Tiros* series[5] was the most consistently successful American space effort. The equipment carried has proved to be very reliable—*Tiros VI* at the time of writing has been operating without trouble for over two years. And the first *Nimbus*, launched on 28 August 1964, embodied many improvements (but broke down after only a month). The *Tiros* satellites had pointed

[3] Particularly *Telstar I* (10.7.62), *Relay I* (13.12.62), *Telstar II* (7.5.63), *Syncom II* (26.7.63), *Relay II* (21.1.64), and *Syncom III* (19.8.64).

[4] *Early Bird* was successfully launched on 6 April 1965.

[5] From *Tiros I* (1.4.60), to *Tiros VIII* (21.12.63), with only one total failure.

in a fixed direction in space, and so could only survey 20 to 25 per cent of the Earth's surface each day; but *Nimbus* pointed its cameras always towards the Earth, allowing them to take 2,000 photographs covering the whole surface of the globe every 24 hours (Plate XLI). It incorporated infra-red radiometers for measuring cloud cover in the dark. Undoubtedly the *Tiros* series, *Nimbus*, and their successors will help to produce great advances in the science of meteorology.

Yet at this early stage of a new venture, the mastery of the technique of space exploration is surely more important than immediate practical results. And here the pioneering has been done almost—though not quite—entirely by the U.S.S.R. After the establishment of Earth satellites, the obvious next step was the exploration of the Moon and its neighbourhood. The three *Luniks* of 1959 were all successful. The first (2 January) passed within 4,000 miles of the Moon. The second (13 September) hit it. And both sent back much information about conditions in the Moon's neighbourhood—proving, for example, that it has not got a magnetic field. *Lunik III* (4 October) performed a very complicated manœuvre that took it round the far side of the Moon, which it photographed many times, and then back towards Earth again to transmit its pictures by radio (Plate XLII). And so one quite nearby piece of the universe, which had hitherto been a closed book, was brought within the scope of human knowledge. A fourth *Lunik*, launched on 2 April 1963, passed with 5,300 miles of the Moon, but since little has been said about results, one may infer that it was not a complete success.[6]

American efforts to explore the Moon began on 17 August 1958 with a rocket that blew up 77 seconds after launching. Between then and January 1964 eleven more attempts were made. Some failed completely. Some were near misses. *Ranger VI*, launched 30 January 1964, hit the Moon, but with the cameras that were intended to give close-up pictures not working. And several sent back useful scientific information, though not about the Moon. But none was successful in its main tasks.

[6] American sources have alleged that in addition there have been several failures to launch lunar probes. It appears likely that the U.S.S.R. (like the U.S.A.) has yet to master fully the technique of launching probes from 'parking orbits', which is required for the more ambitious projects.

Success arrived with *Ranger VII*, launched on 28 July 1964, which hit the lunar surface only 6 miles from its target, and transmitted back to Earth 4,316 pictures taken during the last 19 minutes of its flight (Plate XLIII). These photographs enormously increase our knowledge of our nearest neighbour. Previously our best telescopes in ideal conditions allowed us to view the Moon as it would be seen by the naked eye from a height of 500 miles. *Ranger VII* obtained its last photograph from about 1,000 feet. Tiny craters, some 3 feet in diameter, are shown.[7] We now know that the level parts of the surface are not oceans of dust (as some believed) into which a space-ship would sink. The eventual landing on the Moon will be easier than it might have been.

So far as obtaining knowledge of the Moon is concerned, the Americans had at last surpassed the Soviet achievements of five years earlier. In the main they had done so by means of much more advanced cameras and transmitters than the *Luniks* had carried. But in the matter of rocketry, the achievement of *Ranger VII* is about on a level with that of *Lunik II*. The latter had a pay-load of 858 lb. (carried in a last stage vehicle of 1½ tons), while the *Ranger* weighed 806 lb.[8] And the complicated journey of *Lunik III* (with a 960-lb. pay-load) remains unique. If only it were possible to combine Soviet rocketry with American instrumentation!

The one field in which the Americans have done better than the Russians is the extremely chancy one of deep space exploration. The third attempt at a Venus probe—*Mariner II*, launched in August 1962—passed within 21,500 miles of the planet and sent back valuable scientific information about it. The Soviet shot at Venus on 12 February 1961 was successful as far as the rocketry was concerned, but radio contact was lost at 4 million miles. Their shot at Mars (1 November 1962) was again spoiled by radio failure, though it did achieve a distance record of nearly 66 million miles for radio communication.[9]

[7] *Rangers VIII* and *IX* were equally successful in February and March, 1965.

[8] However, the American shot was made by more subtle (parking orbit) techniques, using a much less powerful rocket.

[9] And there may be something in American allegations that the U.S.S.R. made perhaps four unsuccessful attempts to 'shoot' Mars and Venus, which were not publicly announced.

Further attempts to send rockets to Mars in the favourable period in November 1964 have shown that success in this line of research still depends on a good deal of luck. America's *Mariner III*, launched on the 5th, failed to jettison a protective cover and became a total loss. *Mariner IV*, intended to send back twenty-two photographs of the planet, was successfully launched on the 28th, but picked out a wrong star for fixing its orientation, and had to go through the process a second time. Even then it transferred its attention several times to a wrong star, though it appears at the end of the year that corrective action by radio has eradicated this bad habit. It also developed a wild roll at the start of a course-correction manœuvre, but this difficulty, too, was eventually surmounted. The Soviet *Zond II* followed two days later, but its power supply has only been half of that planned.[10] Whether these probes will overcome all the hazards and succeed in their missions will be known by the time this book is published.

Man in Space

However, the crucial issue in the conquest of space is manned flight. The words 'Age of Space' will only take on their full meaning when man himself is travelling freely in outer space, mastering it as he formerly mastered the surface of the Earth. Sending out satellites and probes, and receiving information from them by radio, is not very different in principle from surveying the universe by telescope—not very different in principle, except in so far as it is a prelude to man's own journeys into space. The *Ranger* programme, for example, though it certainly gives immediate results that interest astronomers, is mainly intended to provide data which will enable men to land on the Moon. And the dog in *Sputnik II* (with instruments that sent back information on its reactions to the initial accelerations and subsequent weightlessness) indicated that the U.S.S.R. even in 1957 was thinking in terms of manned space travel.

But the serious attack on this problem, only began when the initial *Sputnik* and *Lunik* programmes had been completed. It started with a series of unmanned *Vostok* space-ships, all weighing

[10] Its predecessor *Zond I* (2.4.64), aimed at 'nowhere in particular' seems to have been a preparatory experiment towards setting the techniques of deep-space exploration on a firmer basis.

(like the manned ones to follow) about 4½ tons. The first (15 May 1960) carried a dummy pilot. The cabin was not intended to return to earth, but that part of the re-entry programme which was to be tested in fact went wrong. The next (19 August) carried two dogs and landed successfully on its eighteenth orbit. The third (1 December), again carrying two dogs, took a wrong trajectory for descent and burned up in the atmosphere. The fourth and fifth (9 and 25 March 1961), once more with dogs aboard, returned safely. And so all was prepared for Gagarin's one orbit flight on 12 April 1961 (Plate XLIV), and for Titov's voyage of seventeen orbits in 25 hours on 6 August.

Meanwhile the American *Mercury* programme had begun with various preliminary tests from September 1959 onwards. A sub-orbital lob of a passengerless capsule was achieved at the third attempt on 19 December 1960, and on 16 February following a chimpanzee was successfully lobbed 155 miles up and 420 miles out to sea. Then in the summer of 1961 Shephard and Grissom were similarly lobbed to rather smaller distances and heights.

Only three attempts to orbit unmanned capsules were made before risking manned flight. On the first (25 April 1961) the booster rocket had to be blown up after 40 seconds. The second —on 13 September, that is, a month after Titov's flight—was a successful single orbit flight of a capsule with a dummy pilot. But the vehicle came down 40 miles from the nearest ship and was not picked up for 2½ hours. And there was trouble with the attitude control—that is, the control of the direction in which the capsule faces, which must be correct when the retro-rockets are fired if re-entry is to be successful. And when another ship was sent up on 29 November, with a chimpanzee aboard, it had to be brought down after two orbits instead of a planned three, because the attitude control again went wrong, while the poor animal was greatly distressed by the malfunctioning of the psychological test equipment.

Such was the eagerness to catch up with Soviet efforts that, despite these ominous faults, Colonel Glenn was launched on a three-orbit flight on 20 February 1962 (Plate XLV). As might have been expected, the attitude control again went wrong, and Glenn had to work the reserve manual system on his second and third orbits, with the result that 90 per cent of his scientific programme went unfulfilled; and in addition the telemetering system gave a false warning that the heat shield had come unlatched. When Commander Scott Carpenter followed with another three-orbit journey on 24 May, apart from trouble with over-heating of his space suit, he had again to work the attitude control manually; and because he did not do so quite accurately enough, he came down 250 miles from the landing area and had to spend three perilous hours on a life-raft waiting to be picked up. Schirra's six-orbit nine hour flight of 3 October narrowly avoided disaster at the start, when the carrier rocket fell behind in its acceleration schedule and the safety officer was within a few seconds of taking the decision to blow it up. Finally on 15 May 1963 Gordon Cooper began his journey of twenty-two orbits, lasting 34 hours. This time a fault developed in the system controlling re-entry procedure. The astronaut had to fire his retro-rockets manually and, with the appearance of further faults, had to orientate the capsule so that the heat-shield was in the correct position. He succeeded in doing all this more accurately than the automatic systems had done on the earlier flights. With Gordon Cooper's flight, the *Mercury* programme was declared complete. It had operated throughout on such small safety factors that the wonder is that disaster was avoided.

But in the previous year the U.S.S.R. had passed on to the stage of putting two astronauts close together in space—an obvious first step towards solving the problem of rendezvous. On 11 August, Nikolayev was launched on a flight of sixty-four orbits, lasting almost four days. And on the 12th he was joined by Popovich (forty-eight orbits, almost three days), whose ship went into orbit only 3 miles from the former. This implies that the timing of the second launch had to be accurate to less than a second, whereas up to that time the best American launches were minutes behind schedule, and hours of delay were more usual. The feat was repeated the following year (1963), when Bykovsky went up on 14 June and two days later was joined, again with an initial separation of about 3 miles, by Valentina Tereshkova, the first woman in space. The former was aloft for nearly five days to complete eighty-one orbits and the latter for nearly three days, forty-eight orbits.

And so by the summer of 1963, Soviet astronauts had completed 259 orbits, with apparently no more trouble than some spells of nausea and one bruised nose, while their American counterparts had done thirty-four orbits in conditions of almost continuous crisis.[11] This comparison becomes even more striking when one remembers that the *Vostok* ships landed on the ground with no special preparations to receive them and that their communication system was confined to Soviet territory, whereas the Americans had the easier task of coming down in the sea, the support of tracking stations all over the world and an extremely elaborate and expensive organisation for recovering the capsule—in the case of Gordon Cooper's flight, the recovery forces included 22 ships, 100 aircraft and 27 emergency rescue crews. The main difference was that American rockets were only capable of putting into orbit one-third of the weight of the *Vostok* ships. Equipment had therefore to be pruned to a minimum, with consequent loss of reliability.

However, in 1964 there were signs that at last the Americans had produced the larger rockets that were needed. They launched a 19-ton satellite—the largest yet—on 29 January (with a payload consisting only of a tiny tracking beacon, the rest of the weight being made up with sand). On 8 April they orbited an unmanned *Gemini* capsule (Plate XLVI)—the first step in a programme for space vehicles carrying crews of two, the first of which may be launched in the spring of 1965. This weighed 3½ tons—still less than the *Vostoks*. Finally they surpassed the *Vostoks* for weight with an 8½-ton unmanned *Apollo* space-craft,[12] which was put into orbit on 28 May. This, and a repeat performance on 18 September, form part of the programme for putting three men together in space and landing two of them on the Moon by 1970. Re-entry was not attempted in any of these test flights.[13]

[11] We did not mention many minor failures and the frequent and repeated postponements which characterised the American programme. While we cannot be sure that some similar faults did not occur in Soviet work, at least there can have been no postponements or delays in the launching of Popovich or Tereshkova.

[12] Actually two of its three sections. The part which is intended to land on the Moon was not carried in the test. This was a mock-up, simulating the eventual *Apollo* in shape and weight, but without the instrumentation.

[13] The second dummy *Gemini* capsule successfully completed the re-entry manœuvre on 19 January 1965, and on 23 March Grissom and Young achieved the first manned flight of the programme (3 orbits).

Yet before the *Gemini* and *Apollo* projects could get beyond the stage of tests with dummy capsules, the Soviet *Voskhod* ('Sunrise') carried three men on a day-long, sixteen-orbit flight on 12 October 1964. Technically this flight represented a new leap forward. Rocket power was so much increased that, besides carrying a heavier load than before, the vehicle could be provided with cabin conditions so good that space suits were not required, and with a reserve retro-rocket system. The greater safety factor thus provided justified an orbit reaching the record height of 254 miles. A new landing system, using jets to slow the ship down, was so effective that the ground where *Voskhod* landed was unmarked. And the ability to carry scientific and medical specialists, instead of relying on the part-time work of the pilot, should make it possible to speed up research, both on the physics of the upper atmosphere and on the further problems of manned space-flight.[14]

Contrasting Policies

Thus, despite the developments of 1964 and 1965 (which are not likely to mark any sudden reversal in the situation, though they do indicate that the Americans are beginning to atone for earlier misjudgements), the Soviet space programme has on balance been decisively more successful than the American. Since the adventure into space is in many ways the most novel of all the new enterprises which mankind has undertaken in the twentieth century, it is interesting to look for the reasons for this Soviet lead. The facts given on page 279 will be sufficient to dispose of the tale that the Russians gained their successes merely by using German brains and experience. It is more to the point that the U.S.S.R. has had a continuous tradition of rocket research and development from the thirties onwards and right through and beyond the war, whereas in America (despite the efforts of Goddard and a few others) little was done towards developing really powerful rockets until after the war. However, with the help of leading V-2 experts and her own much greater

[14] *Voskhod II,* launched on 18 March 1965, was aloft for 26 hours and 17 orbits, during the second of which Alexei Leonov became the first man to 'float' freely in space. It raised the altitude record to 307 miles. But, for the first time on a Soviet space ship, faults in the attitude control compelled the use of a manual landing system.

resources, America ought easily to have outdistanced the Soviet Union, if other and more powerful influences had not been at work to frustrate her efforts.

The most obvious characteristic of the American space programme has been what has been called a 'proliferation of projects'.[15] Apart from military adventures, which we shall discuss later, there has been no clarity in the U.S.A. as to whether the target to be aimed at is the mastery of the technology of space, or scientific research (on dozens of lines) with whatever space technology happened to be available, or the early practical application of space vehicles, or the achievement of manned space flight.

By contrast the most cursory glance at a list of Soviet launchings reveals a clear, simple policy based on the primary importance of mastering the technology of putting vehicles safely in space and then, as soon as it could be reliably done, of putting men into space. *Sputnik I* was almost entirely a demonstration of the possibility of putting a satellite into orbit; it carried only a small amount of research instrumentation, most of which was concerned with monitoring its own performance. The second and third *Sputniks* did more research, but were still primarily tests of the ability to orbit very heavy vehicles and communicate with them. That programme completed, attention was next concentrated for a whole year on mastering the technique of sending rockets to or round the Moon. That having in turn been done, the next two years (1960–1) were devoted (apart from one abortive Venus probe) to establishing the technique of manned orbital flight. And only at this stage, when they had all the basic technology of space at their finger tips, did the Soviet space workers turn seriously to the question of exploiting this technology for purposes of scientific research. But, having decided to do so, they have pursued their research policy steadily and thoroughly, launching their *Cosmos* satellites at the rate of about one every third week, and during 1964 accelerating this programme till eight were launched in August alone.[16] On 30 January 1964 they introduced the new

[15] Nigel Calder, *New Scientist,* 31.7.58, p. 522.

[16] On August 18, three of them were launched into similar orbits by a single rocket. On the 28th, two were launched by one rocket, and a third separately.

technique of putting the two *Electron* satellites simultaneously into very different orbits for a comparative study of radiation conditions at various distances from the Earth.[17] The main object of this research programme still seems to be the acquiring of the knowledge that will be needed if man is to venture safely beyond the Earth-hugging orbits to which space flight has so far been confined. The three-man space-ship (page 287) begins a new phase in which the development of manned flight and the pursuit of scientific research can be more closely combined. And the manœuvrable satellites, *Polyots I* and *II* (1 November 1963 and 12 April 1964), which altered their orbits several times on command, are presumably early steps towards solving the problem of rendezvous in space, and so of building a large space-ship out of several small ones in order to undertake more ambitious manned flights.

The contrast between the two programmes may be illustrated by the statistics for successful launchings in the year ended 17 September 1961.[18] In that period the U.S.A. sent up eight satellites whose main purpose was apparently scientific research or the improvement of launching techniques, one communications satellite, two weather satellites, one satellite for the detection of rocket launchings (by their infra-red radiation) and two others to gather data for this project, one military reconnaisance satellite, two satellites for navigational purposes, nine satellites ejecting a capsule intended to be brought back to Earth again, and one failed Moon probe; one chimpanzee and two men were shot up in space lobs and one dummy spacecraft orbited. In the same period, the U.S.S.R. launched one heavy Sputnik, one partially successful Venus probe, three space craft containing dogs and two containing men. Thus, while the Soviet effort has been concentrated on a few well planned targets, the American programme has been spread over a great variety of largely independent projects, straining resources of brain-power and equipment to the utmost and therefore giving a poor return for the

[17] Another, very similar, pair of *Electrons* was launched on 11 July 1964.

[18] These statistics are based on a list given in the *New Scientist*, 5.10.61, p. 31. The American catalogue may be incomplete because of the habit of the Armed Forces of launching satellites that are not publicly announced.

effort. There is more than a passing resemblance here to the contrasts between the policies of the two countries in regard to transfer automation (pages 255-8).

Military Misuses of Space

The American list in the previous paragraph mentions four satellites whose purpose is explicitly military. In addition, as we shall see, the capsule recovery programme and the navigational satellites are also military in objective, the eight satellites which were listed as scientific include LOFTI (page 297) whose purpose may really be military, and the communications and weather satellites cannot be completely dissociated from espionage projects. Thus at least fifteen (and possibly nineteen) out of thirty-one successful launchings in that period had military purposes. And therein lies another of the reasons for the poor American record. It is frequently assumed that prowess in creating guided missiles and success in the conquest of space go together. There is some connection, of course, since it was the V-2 weapon that brought rocketry almost to the verge of space launchings, and since the further development of rockets after 1945 would have been less speedy were it not for the promptings of the Cold War. But already when rockets have reached the power necessary for the first space satellites, the two paths begin to diverge. The rocket that best suits the military staff for carrying warheads half-way round the world is much too small to be an efficient space launcher.

In the early post-war years it appeared that nuclear warheads for guided missiles would be rather heavy, and accordingly both powers began preliminary work on fairly powerful rockets. When it came to be realised that H-bomb warheads could be made much lighter than had been anticipated, the U.S.S.R. carried on with large scale rockets for space projects, while the Americans concentrated on smaller ones for weapons. Thus work on the *Atlas* rocket was suspended in 1951. At this stage space research was regarded very much as a side issue—a game that some scientists might be permitted to play with a few of the missile rockets. The early American space shots—with their small satellites and high failure rates—had to be made with rocket combinations built out of the essentially military *Jupiter* and *Thor*, which were very inefficient and costly for this purpose. The first moderate successes did not come until the delayed *Atlas* project at last reached maturity—with Glenn's flight in 1962. Even this, however, was really only a stop-gap effort, an over-sized Intercontinental Ballistic Missile adapted for peaceful purposes. The *Saturn* rocket (Plate XLVII), which was in the long run to put America in the picture, was a descendant of V-2, created by von Braun and his team. It was conceived in April 1957, but von Braun was working for the Army, whose chiefs openly declared their lack of interest in it, as being too large for their purpose. They starved it of funds and in autumn 1959 nearly killed it outright. It was saved by transferring the work from the Army to the recently created National Aeronautics and Space Administration. But as a result of these delays it was not ready for its first test flights till late 1961, and achieved a successful test launch only in mid-1962. And so it was not till 1964 that *Saturn* orbited its 19-ton satellite and its dummy *Apollo* space-craft (page 286), and at last put American capacity for lifting big loads into space somewhat ahead of where the Russians had been in the middle of 1960.[19]

That the United States regards outer space very largely as a new field for warlike activities is made clear by repeated statements of military and political leaders. Testifying before a Congressional Subcommittee in 1962, the Vice-Chief of Staff of the Air Force said: 'It is hard for us now to visualise complete weapon systems in space, but we know that we are going to have them and are going to need them.'[20] And Lieut.-General James Ferguson, also of the Air Force, said: 'Should the survivability of Earth-based systems become marginal, deploying systems in deep space may be the only means of providing dispersal and remote location to ensure survivability. For example, the survivability of present command and control systems—for both offensive and defensive missions—will become marginal as bomb yields increase.'[21] The Democratic leader in the House of Representatives reacted to the news of *Lunik I* by declaring that it accentuated the need 'to overtake and surpass the Soviet Union regardless of costs. We must not have a Pearl Harbour in outer

[19] But the triple *Cosmos* launch of 18.6.64, and the *Vokshod* space-ships show that Soviet rocketry has still kept ahead.

[20] Quoted *New Scientist*, 6.9.62, p. 496.

[21] Quoted ibid.

space.'[22] President Kennedy's view was that 'We cannot possibly permit any country whose intentions towards us may be hostile to dominate space.'[23] And later he reacted to suggestions, emanating from Russia via Sir Bernard Lovell, that the effort to land a man on the Moon should not be treated as a race, by saying that the proposed American Moon-landing by 1970 would demonstrate 'the capacity to dominate space,' which 'is essential to the United States as a leading free world power'.[24] His successor Lyndon B. Johnson, during his Vice-Presidency, stated that 'We must push on with all determination into space, so as to win it for peace before some other nation conquers it for war and destruction.'[25] And, as a foretaste of the attitude of one who might later have become President, Senator Barry Goldwater said in 1962, 'We must decide to dominate in space as we have dominated in the air.'[26]

With such attitudes in leading circles, it is far from surprising that a major part—and perhaps *the* major part—of the United States effort has been diverted to military ends, to the detriment of their work towards the real conquest of space *for* mankind. The *Midas* satellites were intended to detect launchings of missiles by sensing the infra-red radiation from their exhausts. The two which were orbited in 1960 and 1961 revealed inadequacies in the original programme, which was therefore reduced and re-orientated in 1963—at which time it was stated that about half of the £150 million spent on it would be wasted, even from the military point of view. For comparison with this, and with a few other figures of military expenditure that we shall be able to give below, it may be noted that the entire cost of all nine launchings in the *Ranger* programme (page 282) is estimated at £93 million. The diversion of resources and effort is clearly on a far from negligible scale. The announcement of 1963 went on to say that work would continue on another approach to the same goal; and presumably the two Air Force satellites of 1963, which were claimed to have successfully detected missile launchings, were modifications of *Midas*. The *Samos* satellites are

[22] *Daily Telegraph*, 5.1.59.

[23] Quoted by Jay Holmes, *The Race for the Moon* (Gollancz, 1962), p. 20.

[24] *New Scientist*, 1.8.63, p. 241.

[25] Holmes, op. cit., p. 20.

[26] *The Times*, 22.8.62.

intended for reconnaisance of the Soviet Union. Apart from *Samos II* (13 January 1961), which received much publicity, the programme costing over £100 million a year has been carried on 'behind a heavy security curtain (even the name *Samos* is now classified, and may not be mentioned in public by anyone remotely connected with the project)'.[27] Apparently about eight satellites had been launched up to autumn 1962, and presumably many of the subsequent secret launches are of *Samos*.

Another programme (nicknamed 'Ferret') whose existence was unintentionally revealed by a commercial advertisement in December 1962, is aimed at eavesdropping on Soviet radio and radar. The *Vela Hotel* satellites, of which two were sent up on one launcher on 17 October 1963 and another two on 17 July 1964, are intended to detect nuclear tests carried out up to several hundred million miles away in space—though there has been no revelation about who is expected to execute these tests.

The 'Saint' programme, of which very little has been publicly revealed, was an Air Force attempt to develop manœuvrable satellites which could inspect unknown satellites in orbit and decide their nature and purpose. Later versions were intended to be capable of locking themselves on to their targets and boosting them to escape velocity. The programme was closed down in 1962, and its experiments are to be carried on in the two-man *Gemini* space-ships (page 286). For this purpose a device called a Remote Manœuvring Unit is under development; weighing 125 lb., it is to be released and controlled from a manned space-ship and used to examine any satellite that is regarded as suspect. President Johnson announced in August 1964 that his country had two weapon systems, in place and operationally ready, for intercepting and destroying satellites in orbit. These, however, are ground-based systems, developments of anti-missile missiles.

The largest and most spectacular American series in the early years of space was the *Discoverer* programme for recovering a 300-lb. capsule from a satellite.[28] This was widely publicised as a

[27] Dr. F. Pirani, *New Scientist*, 6.9.62, p. 494.

[28] From 28.2.59 to 17.9.61, thirty-one launches were made; ten failed to orbit. In eleven cases the capsule was lost; in two it was recovered from the sea; in six it was caught by a plane (as intended). And two *Discoverers* carried no capsule, but instead gathered scientific data for the *Midas* project.

development on the way to solving the re-entry problem for manned space flight. But it gradually became clear that the purpose was quite different. Television and radio techniques are not capable of sending back to Earth enough detail from the photographs which a spy satellite could take. The capsules of the *Discoverers* were meant to bring back the photographs themselves —so that this largest of early American programmes was once more a diversion of resources from true space exploration to military ends. It is generally believed that the *Discoverer* techniques have been used to recover material from *Samos* satellites (pages 292-3). After this, it is not surprising that many commentators have suspected that the weather satellites are not entirely innocent. Certainly the meteorological value of *Tiros* and *Nimbus* for peaceful purposes has been clearly demonstrated (pages 280-1), and this programme forms one of the greatest American contributions to the constructive use of space techniques. But, apart from the fact that weather information is itself of major military importance, the techniques of photography and data transmission used by the meteorogical satellites are closely related to those required for espionage.[29]

The U.S. Navy's *Transit* system of navigational satellites is intended for such purposes as helping a submarine to fix its position accurately from time to time (as a check on its inertial navigation system) and thus to improve the accuracy of aiming Polaris missiles. Possible civil uses, it is said, will be investigated, but it seems that existing methods are quite adequate for civilian purposes. Beginning in March 1960, the experimental part of the programme had achieved five successful launches by November 1961. It was then believed that a fully operational system should be in use towards the end of the following year. After an unsuccessful *Transit* in December 1962, further launches have been kept secret, except for accidental 'leaks'—as when a failed launching in what is presumed to be this series scattered 2¼ lb. of plutonium from its nuclear power pack (page 227) around the stratosphere in April 1964, thus adding yet another quota to the

[29] The fact that weather satellites (or communications satellites—see page 280) are launched by the National Aeronautics and Space Administration is unfortunately no guarantee of an entirely peaceful purpose, since the U-2 spy-plane which was shot down over the U.S.S.R. in 1960 bore the insignia of NASA.

radiation peril of our time and giving a forewarning of bigger dangers that might follow.

Geodesy—the science that seeks to determine the exact size and shape of the Earth—would seem far removed from the field of war. But to aim an Intercontinental Ballistic Missile accurately one must know the exact relation between launching pad and target. Accordingly the three branches of the Armed Forces and the National Aeronautics and Space Administration combined in a geodetic project, which launched the satellite ANNA 1-B on 31 October 1962. This was originally to have been a secret programme, but public pressure resulted in the results being made available for scientific purposes. However, the Army mapping satellite SECOR, which was carried aloft on the back of an Air Force satellite (itself of a secret nature) in January 1964, appears to be a further attempt to pursue geodetic military work in secret.

Dyna-Soar (perhaps appropriately named, though it became extinct before it came to life) was intended to be a cross between a delta-winged aircraft and a manned satellite. It was to be launched by rocket into low orbit, but to return to Earth as a glider. And the aim from the start was to create a space bomber, or possibly a fighter for shooting down satellites. Active work began about 1958, and by early 1963 parts were being made. But already rumour was saying that it was a failure, and by the end of the year the project had been completely abandoned—after something like £150 million had been wasted.

The long-distance space ships of the future will presumably be powered by nuclear rockets. The effort and resources (£70 million spread over ten years) that might have gone to developing these were devoted instead by the Atomic Energy Commission to an attempt to develop a low-flying missile driven by a ram-jet powered by a nuclear reactor. The project was dropped in July 1964.

Space Bombs and Needles

The ventures so far described have not actually done damage (apart from the diversion of effort from more worthy causes)—they have only threatened. This does not apply, however, to the explosion of the American *Starfish* hydrogen bomb at high altitude in July 1962. There have been other high altitude explosions, both before and since, and carried out by both the U.S.A. and the U.S.S.R.; but these can to some extent be defended on the grounds that they were small and conducted at such heights that they could do no serious damage, and that they did yield valuable scientific information (though one questions if that was their main purpose). But *Starfish* was a 1·4 megaton bomb,[30] and was exploded at a height of about 250 miles. Scientists—other than those whose job was to justify the experiment—predicted that it could seriously alter the Earth's environment, and nearly unanimously called for the abandonment of the project. Events proved them right. The explosion created a new belt of intense radiation close to the Earth, which will take some ten years to die away (and which might affect the weather). This makes much more difficult the task of investigating the natural belts of radiation surrounding the Earth, which must be thoroughly explored before space travel can safely reach out towards the Moon. It interferes with the work of radio astronomers. It partially disabled several scientific satellites, including Great Britain's (American launched) *Ariel*, whose rate of transmitting data was reduced by 60 or 70 per cent. And it has increased the radiation risks of pushing manned space flight beyond the very modest heights so far attempted—already it doubled the radiation to which Nikolayev and Popovich were exposed, compared with Gagarin and Titov the year before. And, despite claims in America that this was a magnificent experiment, an official report by twelve leading British scientists to the Minister of Science had to say firmly that the explosion 'appears to have been planned purely for military reasons'. The main purpose seems to have been to investigate the possibility of using the intense radiation produced by the bomb to black out an enemy's radio communications.

How, then, does one ensure one's own communications in the circumstances? This seems to have been the main point of another experiment, which again brought world-wide protests from scientists—namely the West Ford project for putting a belt of tiny needles round the world to act as a reflector for radio waves. After an abortive attempt in October 1961 (the needles failed to disperse) a second shot on 9 May 1963 put 400 million needles in

[30] That is, equivalent in power to 1,400,000 tons of T.N.T.

a belt encircling the Earth at a height of 2,000 miles. The results seem to have satisfied the American authorities. But they confirmed the fears of the scientists that, though this belt was too thin to have serious effects, any attempt to extend the experiment into a working system would seriously interfere with both optical and radio astronomy. As Sir Bernard Lovell said, 'The damage lies not with this experiment alone but with the attitude of mind that makes it possible without international agreements and safeguards.'[31] There are also Defence Department projects for active repeater communications satellites, but these may not be carried out till it is known whether civil systems will also serve military purposes. And satellites like LOFTI (22 February 1961) for measuring very low frequency signals seem to be aimed at solving the problem of radio communication with submarines.

Much more ambitious plans are on foot. The *Ithacus* rocket, designed by the Douglas (aircraft) Company, though not yet constructed, is intended to deliver 60 tons of stores or 600 paratroops to any part of the world in half an hour. When Defence Secretary Robert McNamara reported the abandonment of the *Dyna-Soar* programme on 10 December 1963, he also announced an Air Force project for a Manned Orbiting Laboratory, to be in use by 1967 or 1968. Its purpose is to investigate a variety of possible military uses of space. The Defence Departments are also to use the *Gemini* programme for experiments on soldiers in space. The object of these studies is presumably to lead on to projects, which have already been discussed in general terms, for manned orbital bombers and for orbiting command posts which, in a time of universal destruction, could at least ensure the survival of the military staff (just as flying command posts are intended to do today).[32] And apart from all these projects on which some information has been revealed, the American Navy and Air Force regularly launch satellites—at least twenty of them in 1963—which are either completely unannounced or merely announced as having been launched but with no statement on their purpose. The enormous diversion of effort that has been described in the last few pages clearly constitutes one of the main reasons for the comparative lack of success of American space exploration.

[31] *The Times*, 14.5.63.
[32] Compare the statement of James Ferguson quoted on page 291.

In the conditions of our time it is, of course, unlikely that the U.S.S.R. has not also concerned herself with the military possibilities of space. She was the first, by some fifteen months, to launch an Intercontinental Ballistic Missile—in August 1957. But, according to official American estimates, she had less than 200 of these in early 1964, as against nearly 1,000 in the U.S.A. The U.S.S.R. claims to be ahead in the development of anti-missile missiles. But in the realm of space itself, rather than of rocketry, there is no significant evidence that the U.S.S.R. is indulging in much military activity, and a good deal of evidence to the contrary. Espionage cameras *could* have been incorporated in the *Vostok* space ships or the *Cosmos* satellites, and indeed Mr. William Benton, U.S. delegate to UNESCO, asserted[33] that Premier Khrushchev had told him that Russia possessed photographs of military installations taken from space—a report that was neither confirmed nor denied. Unannounced launchings would be possible, but they would be detected; and even if one assumes that every American claim to have discovered an unannounced Soviet satellite is accurate and refers to a warlike project,[34] the number would still fall far short of any serious military space programme. Nothing comparable to the *Starfish* bomb or the West Ford belt of needles could be concealed, even from the civilian scientific world. The aggressive quotations of pages 291-2 cannot be paralleled from the U.S.S.R. And in summary, the simple and straightforward programme outlined on pages 288-9 leaves no room for any major diversion of effort from the conquest of space to the possible use of space for the conquest of the Earth.

The analysis of the last few pages can be summed up in terms of the following table, which shows the numbers of space craft successfully launched up to 1963.[35]

[33] *The Times*, 30.5.64.

[34] In fact the Americans have usually alleged them to be parking-orbit satellites for failed lunar or deep space probes.

[35] The American statistics are from a table given by Sir Bernard Lovell in the *New Scientist*, 9.7.64, p. 80. The exact number for any particular entry will depend on just what items one decides to count as successful. For example, in the 'Scientific' row for 1958, the present author would have given America credit for two intended lunar probes that failed in their main object, but gave useful scientific results, so that the figure would be 6 instead of 4. But the general trend will not be affected by these details. The Soviet statistics are the author's compilation.

	1957	1958	1959	1960	1961	1962	1963	Total
U.S.A.								
Scientific[36]	–	4	5	2	5	10	4	30
Manned flights[37]	–	–	–	–	2	3	1	6
Applications	–	1	–	3	2	6	5	17
Military	–	–	6	12	21	38	45	122
U.S.S.R.								
Scientific[36]	2	1	3	–	2	13	14	35
Manned flights[37]	–	–	–	3	4	2	2	11

The most striking fact revealed by the table is that the number of American military space craft considerably exceeds the total number of all other ventures, both American and Russian; and that this is true also of every individual year since 1960. Furthermore this military effort is steadily growing, whereas American work in other directions remains at a fairly constant level (at least as far as numbers are concerned). The table also shows the over-eagerness of the Americans to find profitable applications of space vehicles before their ability to launch them was securely established.

The simplicity of the Soviet programme clearly emerges—two years devoted to the first three *Sputniks*, one year for the *Luniks*, and then a year in which everything else was dropped in order to prepare the way for manned orbits. And only from 1962 on, when the basic problems of putting vehicles reliably in orbit had been mastered, did the Soviet programme turn seriously to scientific research—in which field their effort has since considerably exceeded the American.[38] The stage of looking for practical applications has, so far as the Russians are concerned, still to come. One may guess that it will start as soon as they feel that the expanding scientific programme has yielded enough knowledge to give it a firm basis.[39]

[36] Including cases where the main object was the testing of launching techniques, improvement of communication equipment, etc.

[37] Including unmanned versions of space ships launched in preparation for manned programmes.

[38] The number of Soviet satellite launches—most of them scientific—doubled between 1963 and 1964.

[39] It started with a communications satellite—*Molniya* ('Lightning')—on 23 April 1965. In fact the range of possible applications, in present conditions, is very limited. Reconnaissance satellites might help in locust control. Suggestions have been made for using satellites to speed rescues after

One thing that the table does not make clear is that recently the American programme has tended to copy the Russian in the matter of concentrating energy on a few worthwhile projects instead of scattering it wastefully. The military side continues to swallow up an increasing proportion of resources; but leaving that apart, something like 80 per cent of the money available for civilian purposes was by 1964 allocated to the programme for landing men on the Moon and research connected with it. The Americans have already corrected some of their earlier errors (like ignoring the big rockets which the military did not need). And having recently learned in the hard way that concentration of effort is the paying method, it may well turn out that they will be able, with the aid of the bigger resources at their disposal, to catch up with the Russians in space. But if they are to do so, they will also have to find ways of overcoming other hindrances that have beset their work. One of these hindrances is the tendency to look on space as a race-track where prestige is the prize.

Space and Prestige

Naturally the U.S.S.R. has not neglected to acquire as much credit as possible from her successes. But there is little in the Soviet story to suggest that the search for prestige has been a main motive. Indeed the quiet refusal to join in a Moon-race suggests the opposite. By contrast the U.S.A. was prepared to devote valuable weight in its little satellite of 19 December 1958 to the essentially propaganda job of broadcasting a Christmas message from President Eisenhower. The search for prestige has constantly led the Americans into pushing ahead with panic haste on ill-prepared and hazardous programmes—like the *Mercury* flights, which attracted much publicity, but added little to man's mastery of space. And when President Kennedy announced, in his State of the Union Message in May 1961, his

shipwreck or forced landing: signals from an emergency beacon would be transmitted by satellites to land stations which could pin-point its position. Apart from applications already mentioned, that is about all. Ultimately, one must presume, the conquest of space will bring great practical benefits, just as the conquest of the forests or of the oceans did in the past. But these possibilities can only emerge when much more knowledge is available—and perhaps only when the Moon and the planets have been mastered—so that it is probably wiser to concentrate for many years on research, and let applications follow in due course.

plan to land a man on the Moon by 1970, he was not basing his declaration on an evaluation of what had already been done (for Glenn's flight was still nine months in the future), nor on a scientifically sober choice of target date (since the radiation hazard for the lunar voyager will reach a maximum from 1968 onwards). The main motive was to avoid loss of face from Gagarin's flight of the previous month, and to regain prestige by challenging the U.S.S.R. to a Moon-race.[40]

The irony is that America seems to be engaged in a race that has only one runner. In October 1963, Premier Khrushchev made officially clear what had been unofficially known for some time, that 'At present we are not planning Moon flights'. Much more scientific preparation was necessary, he explained. Of the American plans he said: 'I wish them success. And we shall watch how they fly there, how they land . . . and, which is the main thing, how they take off and return home. We shall take their experience into consideration. We do not want to compete in sending people to the Moon without thorough preparation. It is clear that such competition would not produce any benefit, but on the contrary only harm, since this could lead to the loss of human lives.'[41] This insistence that every step in space exploration must be well prepared has been the main source of Soviet strength, whereas the American sensitivity on questions of prestige has time and again led them into hasty, ill-considered projects, which have in the long run paid poor dividends. One hopes that the rush to the Moon is not another such.[42]

[40] A committee of the American Association for the Advancement of Science (the most representative body of American scientists), reporting on the last day of 1964, stated categorically that the *Apollo* project (page 286) arose from a purely political decision, unrelated to scientific considerations. The report was concerned with the dangers to science in general arising from political and military pressures, and it made similar comments on the *Starfish* and West Ford adventures (pages 295-7).

[41] *Soviet News*, 28.1.63, p. 54.

[42] Yet another motive, unconnected with the main issue, has been suggested for the American space effort. The chronic unemployment of a capitalist economy can be combatted (at least for a time) by employing people on any type of work, the results of which do not ultimately produce either consumer goods or further investment. Digging holes in the ground and filling them up again would do, if any Government could face the ridicule involved. Arms expenditure is another way, but cannot expand indefinitely. It has frequently been suggested that space exploration is increasingly playing this role in the U.S. economy. The National Aeronautics

Organising a Space Programme

The competitive and individualistic structure of American society also proved to be ill-adapted for carrying out so vast a task as space exploration. When the foolishness of running the programme as a sort of celestial darts competition between Army, Navy and Air Force had become apparent, the National Aeronautics and Space Administration was formed on 1 October 1958. But it was another year before the Army was compelled to hand over to NASA its 5,000-strong space research team, led by von Braun. The Air Force and Navy space research establishments remained independent, and lack of co-ordination between these and NASA, with great duplication of effort, has been a constant source of inefficiency.

But this is only a beginning of the complication. NASA contracts 90 per cent of its work to private industry. Some 4,000 companies were involved in the *Mercury* (manned flight) programme. The result has been waste, profiteering and muddle. And worse! Either from the temptation which the profit motive gives to skimp and save costs, or because top quality engineers and scientists were spread too thinly among so many competing concerns, the standard of work produced by the contractors has proved to be dangerously low. NASA reports[43] on the *Mercury* programme listed instances of mismanagement and bad workmanship costing more than £35 million. The reserve space craft for Cooper's flight (the last of the series) was found to have 720 faults. Glenn's escape mechanism had defective wiring. Batteries for Schirra's vehicle leaked. There was an average of ten equipment failures for each of the six flights. In the circumstances, it is remarkable that all the astronauts returned safely.

Details of the organisation of the Soviet space effort have not

and Space Administration early in 1964 was directly or indirectly responsible for the employment of 74,000 scientists and engineers—4·9 per cent of all scientists and engineers in the country. An unknown, but presumably larger, number were employed on military space research. A levelling off of space expenditure in 1964 led to unemployment in these categories. Figures for employment of all types on space work are harder to estimate. NASA in 1964 had about 32,000 employees, and through contracting must have given employment to a total of perhaps 250,000. To this must be added all the personnel involved on the military side, *and* also the employment created by the expenditure of those directly employed on space work.

[43] Summarised in *The Times*, 5.10.63.

been revealed. But we know enough from other fields to be sure that (human failings apart) duplication of effort has been avoided, scientists and engineers have been rationally distributed through the organisation wherever they can be most effective, and a co-ordinated and agreed policy has been operated at every stage and every level. And, of course, private enterprise was not involved. The story of space exploration has, in fact, been the clearest demonstration yet of the superiority of a socialist economy in carrying out the large-scale co-operative enterprises that the technology of our time demands. It was also, as we mentioned on page 276, the events of the early Space Years that drew the world's attention to the superiority of the system of technical and scientific education in the socialist countries. If we add what has already been said about the advantages of a simple planned policy over a great variety of loosely co-ordinated projects, and about the search for prestige, the diversion of effort to military ends, over- eagerness for early applications, and the lack of organisation in a private enterprise economy, we begin to understand why the U.S.S.R. was able to take the lead into the Space Age, in spite of the greater resources at America's command.

The Coming Conquest of Space

Let us look into the future. The space we have started to explore is vast, almost beyond imagination. To get an idea of it, let us consider a scale model in which the Earth is represented by a globe 6 inches in diameter. The distance across the Solar System on that scale is about 90 miles. The *Luniks* and *Rangers* have shown that we can reliably send instruments the mere 16 feet to the Moon. Beyond that, we still depend on a great deal of luck, but *Mariner II* sent back information about Venus from a distance of some 750 yards, and our record so far is the signals from the Soviet Mars probe at 1,400 yards. As to manned flight, the three-man team of October 1964 circled this 6-inch globe a mere fifth of an inch above its surface! Obviously we have a long way to go before we can master the exploration of even the Solar System.

Yet it seems clear that space journeys throughout the Solar System can be achieved by the development of techniques of rocketry we already know, or perhaps using nuclear-powered rockets, ion rockets or photon rockets which we can visualise theoretically now and may put into practice soon.[44] But we cannot yet say how long it will take—whether a Moon-landing will be achieved by 1970 as the Americans hope, or (more likely) within the following decade; whether men will visit Mars and Venus this century or next. Having studied the persistence with which this little creature man has made the Earth his own, we can hardly doubt but that he will in due course also make the Solar System his own. No part of it would be habitable in its natural state. But similiarly few parts of the Earth's surface would have been habitable to the primitive men with whom this book began. Just as our ancestors developed techniques which enable us to live almost anywhere on Earth, so our descendants will develop the new techniques that will allow them to live beyond the Earth. And within a few centuries there may well be human colonies on Mars and Venus or on the satellites of bigger planets—perhaps even colonies living in open space. We must resist the temptation to speculate on the new opportunities and new problems that will face them.

One thing, however, is certain. They will not, within the confines of the Solar System, meet any other intelligent life. But then the Solar System is, as it were, only our own back-yard in space. Our Sun is just a typical member of a family of about 100,000 million stars which we call the Galaxy—a conglomeration of stars in the form of a disc, bulging a bit at the middle, and something like 6,000 million miles across *even on our reduced scale*! Of course our own Galaxy is just one of millions upon millions of other galaxies, which stretch out to distances a hundred thousand times as great again, and probably much more. But let us be

[44] Ion rocket engines would give a very small thrust, but over very long periods, so that ultimately very high speeds could be reached. In 1964 the U.S.A. tested two experimental engines in realistic conditions, by attaching them to a normal chemical rocket, which was lobbed up above the atmosphere. One of them worked perfectly for half an hour, though the other developed a fault. Another small experimental ion engine (powered by the SNAP nuclear reactor mentioned in a footnote on page 227) was carried aboard a satellite launched on 3 April 1965. Plasma engines, working on a similar principle were used to control the orientation of *Zond II*. Photon rockets would carry even further the property of small thrust over long periods. But practical developments are probably farther ahead. American reactors for powering nuclear rockets were successfully tested on the ground during 1964.

content with out own Galaxy—the city of stars in which our Solar System is just one house and garden. Though we are very far yet from any positive knowledge on the subject, theoretical considerations suggest that a very large number of these stars should have planets providing environments rather like that of the Earth—600 million of them according to a recent sober estimate[45]—and very probably intelligent life will have evolved there.

What are our chances of visiting[46] these distant planets and getting to know their inhabitants? This is a very much tougher proposition than anything we have considered so far. For the distance to even the nearest star has gone up by a factor of thousands or tens of thousands compared with distances inside the Solar system. Even on our reduced scale, with the Earth 6 inches in diameter, this nearest star would be 300,000 miles away —and so far we've lifted Gargarin and his followers a fifth of an inch towards this journey! If we got our rocket away at 25,000 miles an hour (on the real scale this time) after overcoming the gravity of the Earth and then of the Sun—which would be a very tall order by present standards—it would still take 100,000 years to reach this nearest star, which is hardly a practical proposition.

But let us not give up hope. This calculation was made on the assumption that we should be using rockets which, like our present ones, could only have their engines running for a few minutes, and must coast for the rest of the journey. If we could create space ships whose engines would run continuously for years on end, then they would be steadily accelerating all the time; and even with very modest engine power, they would reach such enormous speeds that journeys to other stars would become quite feasible. Such rockets are quite impossible at present. And even if we assume perfectly efficient use of the best energy source we know—namely the building up of hydrogen into helium in a fusion process—and even if we could arrange to re-fuel continuously on the journey by picking up the hydrogen that is scattered between the stars, they would still be quite impossible.[47] But it

[45] S. H. Dole, *Habitable Planets for Man* (Blaisdell Publishing Company, 1964).

[46] Or receiving visits from them?

[47] Perhaps thermo-nuclear powered photon rockets might run for a few months or a year or two. But they certainly could not undertake the

would only require another step comparable in magnitude to the step from chemical to nuclear energy that has been taken in the last few decades—and with that, these continuously accelerating rockets would be on the cards. In view of the headlong advance of science nowadays, it would be foolish to deny the possibility of such a discovery within a few decades or centuries. And so the prospects of journeys with continuously accelerating rockets are worth considering.

Let us, then, imagine a journey made in a rocket which has a steady acceleration of 1*g*—that is, the same acceleration as a stone falling near ground level. Travelling in such a ship would be comfortable, for one would feel all the time as if ordinary gravity were pulling one towards the tail. For half the outward journey the rocket accelerates; it is then turned round so that the motors act in reverse, decelerating it to a stop at the target point and then accelerating it back towards the Earth; at the half-way mark the rocket is again reversed and decelerates to land at its starting point. With such a vehicle this journey of about 25 million million miles (that is its real distance) to the nearest star and back would take only about seven years and three months—not much worse than a voyage round the world in the time of the first Elizabeth.

But now comes a curious point. That seven and a quarter years is the time taken for the return journey *as measured by the traveller*. But the people that he left behind on Earth will say that it took him nearly twelve years. Time is not the universal thing, the same for all, that it seems to be in everyday experience. It only appears so to us because we have never had the experience of moving very fast. Time is something that, as it were, each individual carries with him; and when people travel at very high speeds in relation to one another, their individual times will get out of step. In this case the traveller will have reached nine-tenths of the speed of light, and as a result he will have aged less than his friends at home.

Let us consider a much longer journey—right across the Galaxy, coming to a stop on the far side. Even this enormous

journeys we are about to describe. The production of energy by the total annihilation of matter would do still better, but we have at present not the slightest inkling of how to bring this about (except in the tiniest quantities from the annihilation of particle pairs).

voyage would only take twenty-two years of the traveller's life. But he need hardly bother to consider making the return trip of forty-four years, for his friends at base will have been dead for 120,000 years when he returns. With this continuously accelerating rocket, if and when it can be built, virtually no part of the universe would be barred. A trip to the farthest galaxies that our radio telescopes can detect would take only forty-five or fifty years (of the traveller's time). And every time one *multiplies* the distance[48] to be travelled by ten, one only *adds* four years seven months to the journey time.

All this may seem utterly fantastic. But if the primitive man with whom this book began could be told of the things that happen nowadays, would they seem any less fantastic to him? In this crucial era when man has completed (to all intents and purposes) his conquest of the Earth, and has just begun his conquest of the space beyond it, we may expect to meet many things that are new and strange. But let us return to the Earth and the present.

[48] Distance here is as it would be measured by us on Earth. To the traveller the journey would be a very much shorter one. We are *not* making him move faster than light!

CHAPTER 16

. . . AND ALL THE REST

MANY of the big achievements that we have been describing would have been virtually impossible without a very small component—the transistor. And as time passes, this little transistor might well prove to be far more important than the radio sets, computers and rocket control systems in which we have been using it—just as the gearing in Hero's hodometer (page 35) or in the water-raising wheel (page 38) proved to be far more important than either of those machines; just as the thermionic valve turned out to be much more significant than the radio for which it was invented. The little parts that we use to make our big schemes work may seem to posterity to be far more important than any use that we have put them to. And similarly, the techniques that we have developed for fabricating the turbine blades in jet-propelled planes or the miniature circuits in computers may eventually prove to be so widely applicable that their original use will be looked on as of antiquarian interest only. It is nevertheless a regrettable fact that we must confine ourselves to a brief glance at such matters.

Transistors and Semi-Conductors

The transistor was invented in 1948 by John Bardeen and Walter H. Brattain, working under the direction of William Shockley in the Bell Telephone Laboratories, but difficulties over producing materials of sufficient purity held back its practical application until 1953, when the method of 'zone refining' was invented. Because of its smallness and lightness, its low power consumption, its freedom from warming-up delays, its robustness and various other characteristics, it has rapidly displaced the old thermionic valve from most of its applications. It is, in fact, the product of a line of research of very respectable antiquity—the science of semi-conductors[1]—and many readers will remember one of its early ancestors, the crystal and cat's-whisker detector of early radio, which was invented in 1906 and was still in common use in the twenties. A junior first cousin of the transistor is the tunnel diode, invented in 1958 by Esaki of Japan. It uses only a hundredth of the power of a transistor and can switch from one state to another in less than a thousandth of a millionth of a second. As we have already mentioned it offers the possibility of making computers a hundred times faster even than those of today.

By suitable treatment semi-conductors may be turned, not only into diodes and transistors, but also into other circuit elements, such as resistors and capacitators. Hence arises the idea that a single crystal of a semi-conductor, by treating different parts in different ways, could be made into a complete electronic circuit—a technique called 'solid circuit micro-miniaturisation'. The smallness obtainable in this way is almost incredible. The wafers shown in Plate XLVIII are 0·05 inches square and 0·006 inches thick, yet each contains the equivalent of 28 components—22 transistors and 6 resistors. They are logic circuits for use in computers or missile guidance. A hearing aid amplifier has been demonstrated, so small that ten could be squeezed into the volume of a match-head. The U.S. Air Force has an experimental computer weighing 10 ounces and occupying 6·3 cubic inches, which can do the same work as a conventional computer containing 8,500 components.

Semi-conducting devices are also playing an increasing role in the handling of electric power. Efficient generation, transmission[2] and distribution of electricity require alternating current, but very many applications—making aluminium, chlorine, hydrogen and other substances by electrolysis, electroplating, electric railways, steel rolling-mills, and so on—make use of direct current. In fact about half the world's electricity is used as direct current, which must be obtained by conversion from the alternating current supply. Until recently the bulk of the conversion was done either by what amounts to using an alternating current

[1] Materials with electrical properties intermediate between those of conductors (like the metals) and insulators (like glass or rubber). The most important semi-conductors at present are germanium and silicon.

[2] Except in the circumstances discussed on page 214, which need direct current transmission.

motor to drive a direct current generator, or by means of huge thermionic valves called 'mercury arc rectifiers'—and high power losses are involved in both methods. Semi-conductor rectifiers which could be useful in limited circumstances were developed in the twenties and thirties. In the early 1950s, in parallel with the evolution of the transistor, American workers developed the germanium power rectifier and then the superior silicon power rectifier, which are much more adaptable. Recent versions can handle largish currents at up to 5,000 or 10,000 volts. Compared with the previous methods these offer a great reduction in size, higher efficiency and lower cost, and they are rapidly taking over most jobs of providing direct current for the consumer. Presumably they will ultimately be developed on a scale that will allow them to replace the enormous mercury arc rectifiers that are at present used to feed direct current power lines (page 214). A further advance is the thyristor—in effect a combination of a rectifier with an infinitely variable power control—which should have a wide field of application, for example, wherever variable speed electric motors are involved. Suitably arranged thyristors can also do the job of converting direct to alternating current.

Some other Recent Developments

Among the newest tools that science has put at the technologist's command is the laser.[3] Its immediate predecessor, the maser,[4] was created simultaneously in 1953 by teams in the U.S.A. and the U.S.S.R., while the first laser appeared in America in 1960. This one worked in short pulses only, but the following year saw the birth of the continuous laser. Because the laser produces what is called 'coherent' light, the beam has very little spread—a half-inch beam would still only be a foot across at a distance of a mile. This means that enormous intensities can be produced, equivalent to the brightness of an ordinary lamp of some millions of watts. Investigation of practical applications has hardly begun, but enough has been done to indicate great possibilities in the drilling of very fine holes for engineering purposes,

[3] Abbreviated from the initials of 'light amplification by stimulated emission of radiation'. No comprehensible explanation of what that means can be given in the space available.

[4] 'Micro-wave amplification. . . .'

in very fine welding work on micro-miniaturisation, and for extremely precise localised heat-treatment of materials. The same properties make the laser a promising tool for the surgeon, as clinical trials have already indicated. Laser range-finders, on a principle akin to radar, are capable of measuring distances up to 5 miles with an accuracy of 5 or 10 yards. Another property of coherent light implies that laser beams could provide very efficient communications systems; if the knotty problem of putting the signals into the beam at one end and extracting them at the other can be satisfactorily solved, then a single beam could provide enough channels for all the inhabitants of the world to talk to each other in pairs. Unfortunately, as with so many advances of our time, a great deal of attention is being paid to possible uses in war. Laser guns to blind enemy troops are being actively investigated in America.[5] And, though calculations would seem to suggest that laser 'death rays' are mere science fiction, nevertheless a Congressional committee gave them consideration in a report recommending the appropriation of £2,284 million for military research in the fiscal year 1964–5.[6]

As far back as 1911 Kamerling Onnes of Leiden discovered the phenomenon of superconductivity—the complete disappearance of all electrical resistance in some metals at temperatures near to absolute zero. Unfortunately the resistance returned as soon as one tried to use sizeable currents or work in the presence of a moderate magnetic field. And so little attention was paid to possible applications until J. E. Kunzler and his co-workers at the Bell Telephone Laboratories discovered in 1961 that a compound of niobium and tin would remain superconducting even when carrying a heavy current in a strong magnetic field. Several even better compounds and alloys have since been worked out. It is too early yet to say what applications of these discoveries will prove to be practicable, but many possibilities are being actively investigated. Superconductors could be used to reduce greatly the losses arising from resistance in electricity generators, transformers and underground transmission lines, but it is not yet possible to say whether the savings would outweigh the cost of refrigeration. Very strong magnetic fields produced by currents

[5] *New Scientist*, 9.4.64, p. 69.
[6] *The Times*, 18.4.64.

in superconductors may be the key to practical thermo-nuclear power, or may alternatively prove to be more effective than heavy shielding for protecting space men from dangerous radiations. The possibility of better memory systems in computers was mentioned on page 247. We cannot speculate further, but merely take the opportunity to inform the reader that he would be well advised to keep an eye on 'cryogenics' (as this branch of science is called) in the next few years.

This inordinately long description of the technological progress of a mere nineteen years must some time draw to a close—though we have left unmentioned dozens or hundreds of inventions and developments that in any earlier period would have deserved at least a paragraph apiece. Such is this accelerated progress of our time that we cannot hope to catalogue even its main technological successes, as we have done for previous eras. We can do no more than mention that vertical-take-off-and-landing aircraft, using jet thrust for lift as well as propulsion, seem to be nearing success, though so far they have been developed in a purely military context; that supersonic flight is already established in the military sphere and looks like reaching civil aircraft in the next few years; and that the hovercraft, riding its self-produced air-cushion, which made its bow in 1959, may well become a main means of transport in future.[7]

And finally, since all our advances for many years to come are likely to depend on our ability to shape metals as we wish, let us remind ourselves that instead of being confined to casting, forging or pressing them, or cutting them with sharp edges, we can now shape them in many other ways. The shock waves produced by a chemical explosion or by a powerful electric spark force metal sheets into forming dies more efficiently than do conventional presses. Powerful magnetic fields acting directly on ferrous metals can do the same. Electro-chemical techniques (electro-plating in reverse, as it were) can remove metal in a highly controlled way

[7] But again it is so typical of our time that 'particularly in the United States, considerable emphasis has been placed upon the military uses of hovercraft, and the realisation that such vehicles have military advantages is growing rapidly'. (Kenneth Hall, *New Scientist*, 9.1.64, p. 77.) It was announced in August 1964 that hovercraft will be used by British troops in Malaya, and in the following month that Britain is to develop an ocean-going hovercraft warship.

to give results equivalent to milling, drilling, turning, and so on. Concentrated electron beams, like those of a television set but thousands of times more powerful, vaporise the metal instead of cutting or abrading it. A jet of chlorine gas directed on a heated metal surface reacts with it to produce chlorides, which vaporise and leave a clean cut. The destructive action of ultra-sound vibrations gives yet another method of cutting. The use of the laser has already been mentioned, and several other methods could be added. The well established metal-cutting machine tools will, of course, continue to be used for most purposes. But the new methods are sure to replace them for certain types of very fine or very accurate work, and especially for shaping hard alloys which make ordinary machinery prohibitively slow and expensive.

Some Economic Considerations

'And all the rest' was the title of this chapter. But that promise cannot be literally fulfilled. Mechanisation, electronics and nucleonics are advancing in so many different directions that the technological history of our time could not be described within the pages of a single book—even if an author with the requisite knowledge could be found. This many-sided progress consists partly in radical innovations (some of which we have been discussing) and partly in the improvement and wider and more efficient use of already existing techniques (of which we looked at two examples in Chapter 11). What really matters is the totality of all technological advance, both the creation of the new and the development of the old. And to gain some understanding of this totality, we are forced to abandon the hope of describing it, and resort to the colder, but more comprehensive, methods of studying statistics.

Between 1952 and 1962, world industrial production increased by about 87 per cent—that is, by an average of 6·5 per cent a year. For comparison, the annual rate of increase averaged just under 4 per cent from 1860 to 1913; and (excluding the U.S.S.R.) 2·5 per cent from 1920 to 1938 (dropping to a mere 0·3 per cent between 1929 and 1938). In other words, industrial production has in recent years been advancing very much more rapidly than at any time in the past. On the one hand, this is an indicator of the increased rate at which technology in general is progressing in our time. On the other, it shows how speedily this technology is increasing the wealth at our disposal.

Yet progress is certainly nothing like as fast as it should have been. Unemployment, under-utilisation of existing plant, reluctance to introduce new methods, and many other influences, have combined to keep the rate of progress well below the optimum. This point is brought out clearly when we compare the rates at which production has been expanding in various countries, as in the following table of indices of the volume of industrial production:[8]

Year	All capitalist countries	U.S.A.	U.K.	All socialist countries	U.S.S.R.
1950	100	100	100	100	100
1951	111	109	103	119	116
1952	113	112	101	136	130
1953	120	122	106	155	145
1954	120	115	113	175	165
1955	134	129	119	194	185
1956	140	134	119	216	205
1957	145	135	122	234	226
1958	141	125	120	273	249
1959	155	141	127	320	280
1960	164	146	135	357	304
1961	–	147	137	–	332
1962	182	158	138	–	364
1963	192	166	143	432	394
Average annual increase (per cent)	*5·2*	*4·0*	*2·8*	*11·9*	*11·1*

The progress achieved by the socialist countries, or by the U.S.S.R. in particular, is presumably not the best possible. But it does demonstrate that the rate of industrial advance on a world scale was less than half of what would have been possible. The capitalist economies, because of their trade cycles, their unemploy-

[8] Taking 1950 = 100 as base. Since the indices had to be calculated by putting together data from several sources, the figures may in some years be a point or two in error; but this will not affect the general trend. Some of the figures for 1963 are provisional.

ment, and various other features that we have discussed, expanded at much less than the optimum rate. And since they still constitute two-thirds of the world economy, they dragged down the average for the whole.

This brings us back to a point that was mentioned on page 208—that the relative merits of the capitalist and socialist systems must eventually be decided by peaceful economic competition. And it becomes clear that the socialist world is doing much better than—more than twice as well as—the capitalist. This has been no simple story of uninterrupted triumph. The Budapest rising of 1956 produced a severe set-back in the Hungarian economy. Serious mistakes in planning greatly reduced Czechoslovakia's rate of advance in 1962 and 1963, and recovery will not be completed before 1965 at the earliest. Underestimation of the importance of the chemical industry has caused considerable difficulties in the U.S.S.R., and a crash programme of investment in chemical plant has had to be instituted.[9] But by and large, the socialist countries have been advancing much more rapidly than those of the capitalist world. In her very best years (1954–5 and 1958–9) the U.S.A. attained increases comparable to the Soviet average, but the recurrent recessions pulled the American average down to 4 per cent a year, against 11·1 per cent for the U.S.S.R. Britain's industry made a spurt during 1963, and expanded about 10 per cent during the year; but in 1964 growth again came to a standstill.

The use of indices with a common base year in our table conceals the fact that the socialist countries are still well below the capitalist ones in the actual volume of industrial output. In 1953 Soviet industrial production was only a third of American; by 1958 it had reached 56 per cent; and in 1963 it was some 65 per cent. Allowing for the differences in population, this means that in 1963 Soviet production *per head* stood at about 55 per cent of the American level. And calculation show that if present trends

[9] In addition, the progress of agriculture in the socialist countries as a whole has not been satisfactory. The rate of expansion of agricultural production (expressed as a percentage of the existing level) has been considerably higher than in the capitalist world, but it has not been high enough to satisfy needs or to give a balanced economy. It remains to be seen whether recent measures—for example, the U.S.S.R's increased investment in factories supplying fertilisers and other materials to farms—will be sufficient to set matters right.

continue, Soviet *per capita* production will overtake that of America by about 1970, and ten years later will have reached twice the American level.

Another, and in some ways a better, measure of all-round technological progress is to be found in the productivity of labour. In recent times labour productivity has been increasing by about a quarter in ten years in Britain and by rather less than a half in the U.S.A., whereas in the U.S.S.R. it has almost doubled, and in Poland and East Germany it has risen by almost 125 per cent. There are great difficulties in comparing different countries in respect of productivity. The more optimistic Soviet writers claim that by 1956 Soviet productivity had reached some 40 or 50 per cent of the American level (and was therefore ahead of Britain and other countries of Western Europe). More cautious estimates put the date for reaching this level at about 1962. And according to which view one takes, Soviet productivity will reach the American level (and well over twice the British) about 1970 or about 1974–5. In 1917 the technical level of Soviet industry was on a par with that of India. Even in 1950, despite many very advanced factories, the *average* level had only reached that of Greece. But by 1965 it was higher than in Britain.

Thus it is clear that the general advance of technology—both the creation of the new and the development of the old, as we put it before—is going on considerably faster in the socialist world than it is under capitalism. Within a decade or so, unless some dramatic change takes place, the economic leadership of the world will pass from the countries that went ahead in the eighteenth and nineteenth centuries and will be taken over by the more advanced parts of the socialist world. Nevertheless, the crucial point to be emphasised—the point that characterises the age we live in—is that *in the world as a whole* technological progress is going on a great deal faster than it has ever done in the past. What this implies for the future will be one of the main themes of the concluding chapter.

CHAPTER 17

PAST, PRESENT AND FUTURE

HISTORY, it has been said, is the science of the future. In other words, if we want to control our future and direct it towards desirable ends, our main hope must be to study the past in order to learn what we can about how society develops, and apply to our time the lessons thus gained.

Men do not make history entirely as they wish it. Perhaps this is most obvious in the field of technology itself. Merely wanting to fly yielded no practical results until during the nineteenth century men came to understand the laws of nature that govern the possibility of flight. Once that understanding had come, the task was not too difficult. And just as there are laws of nature that must be understood if we want to conquer our environment through technology, so also there are laws of social change that must be understood if we wish to control the history of the future and make it develop along lines that we regard as desirable. Mere wanting does not decide how things will go. Few, if any, wanted the First World War; but it came. The Romans did not want their Empire to decline; but it did.

On the other hand we are not just playthings of blind forces of history. Men can choose to do this thing or that. When they fail to create the history they want, that is because they have failed to foresee the consequences of the choices they have to make—they have failed to understand the laws affecting historical development which ensure that one choice will produce such-and-such results, and another choice will have a different set of effects. The great need, then, is to understand the laws governing social change, in the same way as we understand the laws of aerodynamics;[1] and to use the former to shape the future of mankind, just as we have used the latter to enable him to fly.

[1] Since society is a great deal more complicated than the air, we cannot hope to state social laws with the precision that we are used to in aerodynamics. But we must do what we can.

The Motive Forces of History

If we are to gain an understanding of the laws that govern social change, we have to follow the same method that has led in the past few centuries to the mastery of so many laws of the physical world—we have to examine the facts, make generalisations from them, and check these generalisations, so far as we can, against other facts. And the chief source of relevant facts is history. It is in that sense, then, that history is the science of the future. By studying it we can hope to learn the laws of social development, and then we can apply our knowledge to shape the future—not by *wishing* that it shall go in such-and-such a way, but by *knowing* which course of action now will lead in the direction we desire.

Surely the most obvious lesson that one can learn from history is the emptiness of the word 'impossible'. There may be some things that are literally impossible, but history teaches us that our guesses about impossibilities are usually wrong. Aristotle, whose mental powers were perhaps as great as any ever possessed by a man, committed himself to saying that 'There is only one condition on which we can imagine managers not needing subordinates, and masters not needing slaves. This condition would be that each instrument would do its own work, at the word of command or by intelligent anticipation.' He meant it to be understood that such self-acting machines could not possibly exist, and that therefore the abolition of slavery was impossible. Yet machines that work 'at the word of command or by intelligent anticipation' are precisely the automation of Chapter 14. And this automation bids fair to abolish not only slavery in Aristotle's sense, but also wage-slavery and all the other forms of bondage that have been imposed by the necessity to work to wring a living out of nature. Almost every achievement that has been described in this book was regarded a little earlier as impossible (except by those who hoped for magical answers to their wishes). In fact, the word 'impossible' has a meaning only when we attach to it a phrase that begins with 'unless': talking to people a thousand miles away is impossible, *unless* one masters the laws of electricity; the abolition of war is impossible, *unless*—just what? The question to be asked is never '*Can* we do this desirable thing?', but always '*How* can we do it? What are the conditions for achieving it?'

And this brings us back to the need for understanding the laws of historical change. It is these that determine the conditions for altering society and directing the history of the future in the way that we desire.

The story that has been told in these pages makes it very clear that technological development is a powerful force that moulds the shape of history, not merely in the simple sense that it tends to raise the standard of living (at least for some), but also in the more profound sense that new technologies have from time to time altered the whole character of society. It was the invention of agriculture and the subsequent flow of inventions like metallurgy and the harnessing of animals and wheeled transport that transformed the simple life of primitive communism into civilisation with all its complexities and with its class-divisions. The dependence of the early civilisations on bronze and irrigation ensured that the barrier between the classes should be virtually absolute, but the new technology of iron broke through the rigidity of these states and led (in favourable conditions) to more democratic societies like that of Greece. The medieval development of power-driven machinery abolished the dependence of high-level civilisation on slavery and led on to feudal society in which the craftsman in his Guild organisation held a position of greater respect than ever before.[2] The still further progress of heavy machinery, and of the expanding commerce that went with it, in turn made feudal society obsolete and compelled its replacement by capitalism.

How important is technology, compared with other factors, in directing the course of historical change? Obviously, in a book that mostly neglects the study of these other factors, we do not have the evidence for settling that question—which is hotly disputed today. Let it simply be said that there is one view (and the author shares it) according to which technological development is the greatest single factor in promoting and directing social change. Religions, philosophies, political theories, or kings and their foreign policies, have had little effect on history (accord-

[2] It has not been possible, because of limitations of space, to say all that could be said about the role of technology in determining the general nature of European feudalism—the way, for example, in which the heavy plough, with its requirement of a team of eight oxen, was instrumental in shaping the manorial system.

ing to this view), except in so far as they worked in harmony with the technological drives of their times. Whether the reader agrees wholeheartedly with this thesis or not, he can hardly avoid concluding, on the evidence presented, that technological progress is one of the main causal factors which from time to time change one type of society into an entirely different one.

But this is no one-sided relationship. For the successive types of social organisation have also had their profound effects on the progress of technology—sometimes speeding it up, sometimes slowing it down, turning its main lines of advance in this direction or in that. The rigid class-divisions of the Bronze Age civilisations brought progress virtually to a standstill. The less rigid social forms of the Iron Age allowed advance to begin again. A few centuries later, slavery and endemic warfare created conditions in which inventive genius ran largely to making mechanical toys or instruments of destruction, and the labour-saving machinery that had now become technically possible remained almost undeveloped. Next the higher status of manual work in feudal Europe brought about a renewed wave of inventiveness. And in its turn, capitalism provided new ways of organising industry that encouraged technical progress to an extent that no society had ever done before.

Shall we, then, use our study of history to choose that social system which best encourages technological advance and directs it into the most beneficial channels? And having made our choice, shall we aim to mould our society along those lines in future? Unfortunately the relation between technology and society is not so simple. Every society has had its progressive phase in which it encouraged invention and the development of new techniques; and every society has had its later phase in which it tended to resist the introduction of the new.

Primitive communism served very well for the first million years of slow, but steady progress. It allowed the critical step of the invention of agriculture to be taken, and after that such major advances as metallurgy, the plough and the harnessing of animals. But once these techniques had been developed to a certain level, primitive communism proved incapable of organising the use of the new technology and concentrating resources and manpower in the way that was needed to get the best out of them. To enable the new technology to transform barbarism into civilisation, primitive communism had to give way to the class-divided societies outlined on pages 14-5. The extremeness of class-division in this new type of society, its ability to take from the producer all the surplus that he created above what was needed to keep him barely alive, provided the means for rapidly constructing the material basis of civilisation—its towns, its irrigation systems, and even its (to us useless) pyramids. But once this immediate task of making the best use of the existing techniques had been completed, that same rigidity of class-division proved to be a fetter which brought further progress almost to a standstill. The more 'democratic' Iron Age societies provided the conditions in which technological advance could get going again—but only up to a certain level; for slavery, which was the source of prosperity, was also the main thing that prevented the full development of techniques like the use of animal-power and water-wheels. So the slave states had to be replaced by medieval feudalism, in which the greater freedom and higher status of the master craftsman encouraged a wealth of technical innovations, including the first steps towards the general use of power-driven machinery. But towards the end of the Middle Ages, this machinery grew too large for the industrial organisation that had created it; the master craftsmen and their powerful Guilds became an impediment to further progress. At this level of development the capitalist organisation of industry was needed. And capitalism, when at last it replaced feudalism, provided the social organisation for using heavy machinery on a much wider basis and for developing the commercial framework within which it could be efficiently employed. Yet in the twentieth century, this same capitalism, modified in some respects, but essentially unchanged, has proved to have features which drastically reduced the pace of progress.

The point that clearly emerges from this story is that at each particular level of technological development certain social conditions must be satisfied if the technology is to advance yet farther. And as a result, amid all the variety of history one basic pattern is repeated time and again. Each form of society is at first well adapted to encourage technological advance. In these conditions, the technological level rises more or less rapidly, and eventually reaches a point at which yet further progress requires a different form of social organisation. Then progress is slowed down—until the required social change is made.

Before we pursue further this line of thought, let us note that it has been derived from studying only one line of social evolution —that which led to the development of the European culture which was eventually to spread over the whole world. In different conditions elsewhere, other forms of society developed. Though these cannot be discussed here, the author knows of no case in which the pattern of historical change was essentially different from those that we have considered—except in one very important respect: each one of these other paths of development led eventually to a position in which the society was incapable of transforming itself in the way required for further progress; it then remained static or went into decline. China, for example, developed ahead of Europe in the medieval period, but reached a point at which society settled down to a fixed pattern and progress ceased.

What was special about the evolution from Egypt and Mesopotamia, through Greece and Rome and the European Middle Ages to the modern world? Why have these societies always been capable of taking a further step forward at the crucial points where others failed? The question has not yet been satisfactorily answered. Perhaps an explanation could be worked out along the following lines. The place of origin of agriculture may, or may not, have been determined by geographical conditions and climatic changes. Bronze Age civilisation necessarily arose nearby, and could reach a high level only in situations where irrigation gave high productivity—only Mesopotamia, Egypt and the Indus Valley were possible.[3] Iron technology could not develop within the stagnant Bronze Age civilisations. It had to come from barbarians—but from barbarians whose propinquity to the civilised areas gave them the second-hand benefit of the most advanced technologies in existence, as well as the incentive to emulate the wealth of the civilisations. The Caucasian centre in

[3] The civilisations that developed—much later—from the independent origin of agriculture in Central and South America lacked suitable river valleys, as well as good animals for domestication. They never reached even the level of Mesopotamia in 3000 B.C., and they perished after a few hundred years.

which iron technology actually arose was one of the very few sites that satisfy this condition. The 'democratising' effects of iron—the essential requirement for further progress—could be fully developed only in a region that satisfied three conditions. It must be (1) near the original centre from which the use of iron was diffusing, (2) sufficiently near the Bronze Age civilisations to be able to learn from them and exploit their wealth by trade, piracy and war, and (3) well placed for maritime trade. Only Greece and the Aegean satisfy these conditions.[4] Thus, as a result of the combination of geographical and historical conditions, the line of evolution that began with the introduction of agriculture necessarily led to a form of society in Greece which was not paralleled in any of the other regions to which civilisation spread. While the details would need much clarification, it is not difficult to believe that this would lead on to the uniqueness of European feudalism and thence of capitalism—each in its turn more flexible and progressive than any previous society.[5]

We can now return to the generalisation we had begun to make on pages 321-2. There is a recurrent pattern amid all the variety of historical development. It is repeatedly exemplified (as we saw on pages 320-1) in the main line of evolution from the coming of agriculture to the modern world. Outside this main line of evolution, the same pattern is also found, except that in all other cases a situation was eventually reached in which a particular social structure became so rigidly established that further change became impossible. This typical pattern of development can be summarised on the following lines:

The type of society needed to promote technological progress depends on the level of technology that has already been reached

[4] Pheonicia, on the extreme eastern coast of the Mediterranean, provided conditions almost as favourable, and its people did begin to develop along similar lines, only to be overwhelmed eventually by Greece and Rome.

[5] On the other hand, V. Gordon Childe in his last book (*The Prehistory of European Society*, Penguin Books, 1958), made out a strong case for a thesis that barbarian Europe, as a result of distinctive geographical-historical conditions, had even by 1500 B.C. developed a unique form of society, which 'foreshadowed the peculiarities of European polity in Antiquity, the Middle Ages and Modern Times'. (p. 172). In this view, even the Greek and Roman developments of Chapter 3 were a diversion, and it is in barbarian Europe that one must seek the roots of the Middle Ages.

—the society needed to create civilisation from the inventions of the barbarians is quite different from that required to create an industrial civilisation from the inventions of medieval workers. At a certain stage, the organisation and institutions of a youthful society are well adapted to encourage further progress of the technology it then possesses. As that progress continues, the technological level gradually rises. Eventually it reaches a point at which a different form of social organisation is required to facilitate further advance. But the society has its privileged classes—its Pharaohs and nobles and priests, or its slave-owners, or its feudal lords and powerful craft Guilds, or its rich capitalists. These classes stand to lose by the required social transformation —for their power and wealth will be transferred to others—and they have in their hands the power to resist change.[6] Thus while technology advances and comes to require new social conditions for yet further advance, society tends to remain static or at best to make slow and inadequate concessions to change. The discrepancy between the social conditions required for progress and those that actually exist becomes greater and greater, until at last a breaking point is reached and the society is transformed more or less rapidly into one which *is* well adapted to use and to further the technology of its time.[7] And then the cycle begins again, but at a higher level. To put all this more briefly:

Each society in youth encourages the advance of technology, but as the technological level rises, the society fails to keep pace with it, until there comes the breaking point at which the old society is transformed into one that is again fit to push technology to greater heights.

Or even more pithily, we might simply say that: *As technology*

[6] If their resistance is permanently successful, social evolution ceases. Our 'main line' of evolution differs from the others only in that its development was such that the privileged classes never reached the position of being able permanently to resist change—so that it continued to advance, while the others stagnated or regressed.

[7] In the case of Bronze Age civilisation the old society was not simply transformed into a new one. It remained fossilised until it was overthrown by societies of a new type (the Greeks) that had grown up on its fringes. In the transition from Graeco-Roman to medieval society, overthrow from outside again played a part. But the change from feudalism to capitalism was entirely an internal affair, and presumably all further changes will be of that nature, since in the unified world of today there is no 'outside' that can affect the matter.

advances, so also must society change—otherwise there will be trouble.

This then is the chief of the laws of historical development that we referred to at the beginning of the chapter. And the question urgently thrusts itself before us: Are we today in one of those situations in which a form of society has outlived its usefulness, but is being kept in existence by vested interests? Does further progress for us depend, as so often in the past, on transforming our social structure into a quite different one? The frustrations and failures that have bulked so large in our story from Chapter 9 onwards would suggest that we are. The social, economic and political organisation that served to promote unprecedented progress from the eighteenth century onwards has in this century only too often proved a hindrance to further advance.

Two Technological Revolutions

Before considering that question further, let us try to see our era in better perspective. If one looks at the history of technology on a large scale—standing back from it, like a visitor from some distant planet where civilisation has advanced so far that he can examine our strivings with the disinterestedness of a biologist studying an inferior species—then one discovers that there have been two main Technological Revolutions in the story of mankind.[8] The first was that which began with the invention of agriculture, carried on with metallurgy, the plough, the sailing ship and all the rest, passed on to large-scale ventures like irrigation schemes and the building of cities, and then came to an end about 2500 B.C. The second began modestly in the Middle Ages and has been growing in speed and volume ever since, and is—apparently—still at a very early stage of its life, with much more to come than we have yet experienced. The changes in the three thousand years or so that came between these revolutions would seem, in comparison, quite negligible to our extra-terrestrial historian. He would concentrate his attention on these two.

Let us do likewise. Let us try to learn something about the

[8] Apart from the events that started it all—the beginnings of tool-making and the mastery of fire—which could well be said to form the greatest technological revolution of all.

Technological Revolution that we are living in by comparing it with the one that began with agriculture. The outstanding characteristic of that First Technological Revolution is that it took a world of perpetual scarcity, a world that could never produce more than barely enough to keep life going, and transformed it into a world of partial wealth, a world that could produce enough above the level of necessity to allow a few of the people in it to live in comfort and luxury. Would it not similarly be true that the characteristic of our Second Technological Revolution is that it is in the process of transforming this world of partial wealth into a world of universal plenty, a world in which *everybody* can enjoy abundance? We have today unprecedented powers for creating the goods and services that constitute riches. The statistics quoted on page 313 show that our wealth is now increasing more rapidly than ever before. Whether the growth is fast enough to produce a world of plenty in the foreseeable future, is a question that needs more consideration; and we shall return to it later. For the moment let us assume, for the purpose of discussion, that our Technological Revolution is capable of creating within a few decades a situation in which there is so much wealth that everyone can have all he wants, without having to gain his own prosperity at the cost of the poverty of others. And let us follow out the consequences of this assumption.

The First Technological Revolution, by changing universal scarcity into partial plenty, initiated two fundamental social innovations—class-division and war. These arose, as we saw in Chapter 2, because it now became worthwhile to grab, to fight and to dominate. There was not enough to provide all-round wealth, but there was enough to give riches to the ambitious. Is it conceivable that our Second Technological Revolution, by changing wealth for some into abundance for all, can reverse this change and abolish class-division and war? If all that one wants can be obtained without the trouble, then there will again be no point in gaining power over others. The domination of one class by another will cease.[9] Similarly going to war will give the victor nothing that could not be more easily gained without doing so. War also will cease.

Our argument so far is that the Technological Revolution in

[9] Except, presumably, that 'bad habits' will persist for a time.

which we are living is in the process of making it *possible* to create a world that has neither class-divisions nor war. But we can go further. When earlier technological advances came near to the point of making social changes *possible,* they also made them *necessary*—in the sense that further progress could not take place until the social transformation had happened. Class-divisions, we saw, were not merely a possibility created by the First Technological Revolution. They were also a necessity—for without them the flowering of techniques and the large-scale construction involved in civilisation would not have been possible. And indeed this is true of the other changes that have happened in between. The advances of the Middle Ages, for example, made a capitalist economy possible; but again progress was retarded until the transition to that new economy was made. And so we can ask the further question: If the Second Technological Revolution is making it *possible* to abolish class-division and warfare, is it also true that these *must* be abolished in order to ensure further uninhibited progress?

World Without War

There will be little disagreement about the absolute necessity that faces our era of abolishing war and preparation for war. The consequences of war carried out with all the aids of science and technology are too terrible to be contemplated. Nevertheless there is still a widespread belief that the Cold War and the feverish efforts it engenders act in such a way as to speed up technological advance. Certainly war has sometimes pushed technology ahead; but not always—in Ancient Greece it diverted man's energy from far more constructive efforts (pages 33-5). Certainly during the Second World War technological advance was pushed ahead at an unprecedented rate. But we have seen that this was merely because Governments were willing to take action in a war emergency to prevent abuses that they had tolerated in peace.

In our troubled time, it is certainly true that some Governments are prepared to devote vast resources to technological development for military purposes,[10] and that inventions and advances that

[10] Of the $10,900 million (about £3,900 million) spent in the U.S.A. on research and development in 1961, almost two-thirds was directly or

have peaceful and constructive possibilities quite often emerge as by-products. But, even if it were not for the simple point that the same resources devoted to peaceful ends would produce at least as much constructive advance, we have seen in Part Three a great deal of evidence that the stress on military might is hindering the progress of technology far more than helping it. The race for nuclear weapons retards the development of nuclear power. The computers and electronic control systems that might revolutionise industry are installed instead in warships or guided missiles. Emphasis on military applications is one of the main reasons why the U.S.A. has lagged in the early days of the Space Age. Anyone who reads the daily press with a critical eye discovers frequent instances of progress being retarded by concentration on warlike applications. For example, a British firm managed to develop in 1963 a video tape-recorder suitable for domestic use, stealing a march on American rivals who, with their much greater resources, had been active in the same field. Seeking an explanation, *The Times* (25 October 1963) found it chiefly in 'the concentration of effort by United States tape recording equipment manufacturers in the defence field', and went on to show how this had resulted in a one-sided over-specialisation.

In any case, if the advance of technology is to bring us to the land of plenty, it is not enough that inventions should be made. They must be applied in practice to create new industry, better agriculture and all the rest. This requires capital, and everywhere progress is being held back by the fact that too little capital is available. Yet the world spends something like £40,000 million pounds a year[11] on war and preparation for war—rather more than the combined national incomes of Asia, Africa and Central and South America; some £12 or £13 for every man, woman and child on Earth. If our Technological Revolution is in reality to lead on to a world of universal plenty, then a prime necessity

indirectly related to 'defence'. In 1961–2 Britain's total expenditure on research and development was £634 million, of which £240 million was directly for military ends.

[11] In rough figures, using units of £1,000 million, annual expenditures around 1963 and 1964 have been: U.S.A., 20; Britain, 2; the North Atlantic Treaty Organisation as a whole, 26; U.S.S.R., 5½. In early 1964 Britain was using 4·7 per cent of her working population and 7 per cent of her gross national product for 'defence'.

is to abolish war and the threat of war, so that these vast resources can be devoted to constructive development.

Towards a Classless Society?

Our second question—as to whether the disappearance of class-divisions is also a necessary step if our Technological Revolution is to lead to abundance for all—is a much more controversial one, and there will (as yet) be no general agreement on the answer. Nevertheless, the author feels entitled to state his point of view. Fundamentally the question is not concerned with the equalisation of personal incomes, but rather with the ownership and control of the factories, mines, railways, ships and other means of production. The point at issue is whether these shall be the property of the community as a whole (as they were in primitive societies and are in the socialist countries of today), or shall be owned and controlled by some privileged class (as they have been in all societies from the beginning of civilisation down to the capitalist economies that still cover two-thirds of the world). And since all other systems are now clearly out of the running, the choice reduces to one between capitalism and socialism.[12]

Which of these can make a better job of using modern technological advances to create a world of plenty? Surely the evidence that we have surveyed in Chapter 9 and Part Three suggests that the answer is socialism. It would be tedious to recapitulate the features of capitalist society which we found to be acting as brakes on progress—unemployment, vested interests and so on. We have seen that the socialist countries, though most of them started from a very backward industrial situation, have already taken over the technological leadership in several fields. And the statistical survey of pages 314-6 showed that they are doing much better than their capitalist counterparts in using science and technology to make a wealthier world.

Furthermore, capitalism seems to have reached a limit in the speed at which it can advance—for Britain in recent years shows rates of expansion only a little higher than those achieved by the

[12] Socialism need not mean a system of living identical in all respects with that of any socialist country today—every country must choose its own form. But, as used here, the word does imply the social ownership of all (or nearly all) the means of production.

capitalist world between 1920 and 1938, while the U.S.A., though certainly bettering those very lean years, can only just equal the progress that capitalism was achieving between 1860 and 1913[13] (and this in a time which is hailed there as one of unparalleled prosperity). It appears that capitalism can expand its economy no faster than it has been doing. And one can be doubtful whether even this rate can be maintained—if, for example, the rate of automation in America causes unemployment to increase in the way we discussed on pages 272-3, there must come a point, at which either the introduction of automation will be slowed down or some drastic break will occur. But, while the capitalist economies seem to be at or near their limits, the socialist countries continue to expand their industries two or three times as fast.

To summarise, then, there is a case—and the reader must judge its strength for himself—for the thesis that we *are* today in one of those periods in which the advance of technology has outstripped social development, and that in order to permit further progress to go on unhindered, it is now necessary to make big political and social changes—namely, to complete the transition from capitalism to socialism that has already taken place in a third of the world.

If this thesis be right, then every country, by taking appropriate political and economic action, could put itself in a position to advance economically as fast as the socialist countries are doing at present—and perhaps faster, for the socialist world has made many mistakes that need not be repeated. Let us see what this means in concrete terms. Between 1953 and 1962 the national income of the U.S.S.R. increased by a factor of 2·2.[14] If the national income of Britain had risen at the same speed in those years (instead of only by 66 per cent), then by 1962 the national income *per head* would have been about £140 more than it was —about £140 more for every man, woman and child in the

[13] We are simply using a comparison of the world industrial production figures of page 313 with the last line of the table on page 314.

[14] Different countries use different ways of measuring national income, so that the results are not directly comparable. The calculations that follow can therefore be regarded only as rough approximations. The errors, however, are in such a direction that an accurate calculation (if it could be done) would reinforce rather than weaken the conclusions drawn below.

country, or more than £10 a week for a family of four. Similarly, if the U.S.A. (where the increase in those years was less than 50 per cent) had advanced as fast as the Soviet Union, its national income per head by 1962 would have been about $1,200, or well over £400, more than it actually was.[15] These figures show that the question of substituting a socialist economy for a capitalist one in order to speed the rate of advance is not one that can be lightly thrust aside.

On the Way to the World of Plenty

We begin to get some idea at this point of what is meant by saying that the Second Technological Revolution is capable of bringing us rapidly to a state of universal plenty. But before we pursue this subject, let us look at a more sobering side of the picture. In India the national income per head on 1962 was about £24. If it had been growing at the Soviet rate since 1953, it would have been £36—which may be 50 per cent better, but is hardly high enough to be encouraging. Even at this speed it would be very many years before India (and all the other underdeveloped countries of which she is typical) came within sight of the land of plenty. And in the world of today, unified by the very technological advances we are considering, it is surely meaningless to consider the possibility of achieving riches in a few advanced countries, while others remain abjectly poor. The antagonisms created by the envy of the have-nots would be certain to lead to conflicts that would (at the very least) retard progress all round.

The problem of the underdeveloped countries is, of course, to find means of providing capital investments so great that they can catch up with Europe and North America within a reasonably short space of time. And evidently out of a national income of

[15] Of course only a part of this would come to the individual for personal consumption. Some of the national income contributes to his standard of living through education, roads and other Government services. Some of it is re-invested, and this leads to further improvements in the standard of living at a later date. Some of it goes to armaments and is totally lost. If the proportion of national income used for personal expenditure remained the same as it was in 1962 (so that government-provided services, investment and arms expenditure all rose proportionately), then the increase per head of personal expenditure would have been over £90 in Britain and about £270 in America.

£24 per head (for India is typical), this cannot be done. It is clear that the advanced countries must help the less fortunate with loans and gifts. And indeed they do so, but on a scale that is far too small to solve the problem. On the other hand, it has been calculated that if one-third of what the world at present spends on war and war preparations were given instead to the underdeveloped countries—in the form of new factories and equipment, scientific and technical advice, new schools and colleges and the staff to get them going, and all the other essentials of industrial civilisation—then their progress could be so speeded up that it would only be a few decades before all the world reached a standard of living comparable to that of Western Europe today. To the people of Africa, South America and Southern Asia this would indeed seem to be a world of plenty.

Meanwhile the present advanced parts of the world need not be standing still. Their gifts to their underdeveloped neighbours will not slow them down, since this will come from expenditure that is in any case wasted. Indeed some part of the remaining two-thirds of armaments spending could be used to improve the rate of progress. And it is surely obvious that the possible speed of advance is enormous by any previous standards. Nuclear energy, after its disappointing start, is on the verge of presenting us with a cheap source of unlimited power. Automation is already applicable in many industries; soon it will be able to take on virtually any productive task. And the great increases of productivity that it offers give scope for rapid increases in wealth. Computers will enable us to plan production as a whole with far higher efficiency than ever before, besides speeding the research that will lead to even more rapid progress. And so one could go on, adding the better metal-working techniques of pages 312-3 and the dozens of other developments that we have not even found space to mention.[16] All these, provided we use them wisely, can produce more and more riches for our enjoyment.

It is naturally not possible to assess accurately how fast the world could grow rich, if all the artificial restraints imposed by

[16] Space exploration will probably add little to our material wealth for some decades. At present it remains an adventure and an investment against the productive future that it must eventually bring. Present expenditure on it is a sacrifice to posterity—but could always be reduced if more resources were urgently needed to speed progress on Earth.

inadequate social organisation were removed. But many lines of approximate calculation converge to suggest that *at the very least* it would now be possible to *double* the output of wealth per head *every ten years.*[17] In that case annual output of wealth per head would be multiplied by 4 in 20 years, by 8 in 30 years, by 16 in 40 years. Would a country in which everybody was sixteen times as rich as he is in Britain[18] today be a land of plenty? The author is inclined to think so. Each individual (*not* each earner) would have an income for personal use of between £4,000 and £5,000 a year—getting on towards £20,000 a year for each family.[19] Many rich people demand things that even such an income could not buy, but surely their diamonds, mink coats and private swimming pools are not things that people really want, but status symbols used to display the fact that they are more prosperous than others. In the author's belief, this level or something like it would indeed be universal plenty. If the reader disagrees, he may choose his own figure. Would sixty-four times the present level be enough? Then it would take sixty years to achieve. If one insists on a thousand-fold increase (with personal

[17] One rough argument would run like this. Agriculture in the advanced capitalist countries, taken as a whole, already produces a superabundance of food (so that production is artifically restricted). In the socialist world food supply is coming near to sufficiency. With the help suggested above, it could reach that level in a few decades in the underdeveloped countries. So the main source of increasing wealth would be industrial production (transport and services should also be included, but must be neglected here). Industrial production per head in all advanced countries could advance at least as fast as in the U.S.S.R., where the expansion between 1956 and 1962 was equivalent to doubling the output per head in rather less than nine years. It should probably be possible to go faster (since industrial organisation in the U.S.S.R. still has many defects, since some part of present arms expenditure could be used to increase investment, and above all since the Technological Revolution is still accelerating). But for the sake of caution, we assume the somewhat more modest estimate of a doubling in ten years.

[18] Of course Americans would be still richer in the unlikely event of their taking the necessary political measures at the same time. The present underdeveloped countries could not reach these levels so soon. But if they were helped as suggested above, they would at least be less far behind.

[19] At 1962 price levels, and assuming the same proportion as in that year between personal consumption, and national income. In addition, the individual's share in the part of national income that is not spent privately would be nearly £2,500. All these monetary calculations start from *per capita* national income figures for 1962.

income per head approaching £300,000 a year!), even that would only take a century. If a million-fold is needed (in which case every individual would have more riches than all the present inhabitants of a city like Birmingham put together), even then it would require only 200 years to attain.

The difference between forty years and a century or so may be important to us as individuals. But on the grand scale of history —the million years of humanity, or the ten thousand years since the beginning of agriculture—it hardly matters. The world of plenty is at hand, in a few decades or a couple of centuries. Or rather, it *can* come in that time, provided we find a way of casting off the fetters that are preventing us from using the Technological Revolution to the full.

Such a rich world would have no use for either war or class-division. These are merely bad habits (as it were) which arose in the special situation of the last few thousand years, when the partial wealth of the world made them profitable to some. Contrary to what those who have a vested interest in the *status quo* would have us believe, the desire to dominate others is *not* an inherent human characteristic. It was not shared by the men and women of the Old Stone Age. It was not found among primitive peoples who survived unaffected by civilisation down to the early years of this century.[20] It appears to be gradually dying out in the socialist countries of today. Trying to benefit oneself at the expense of others is merely a mode of behaviour that has arisen in the exceptional conditions of the last few millenia during which mankind has been passing from the state of general poverty to that of universal wealth. When abundance is available for all, there will be no incentive to dominate others, to seek one's own good at the cost of others' loss. Habits may be slow to die out. But they do die out eventually, when they have ceased to be useful. And so, in the world of plenty of the not very distant future, these degrading rivalries will completely vanish.

But the dilemma of our time is that the customs and institutions of class-division and war are the very things that are preventing

[20] See for example the account of life among the eskimos by Vilhjalmur Stefansson, 'Lessons in Living from the Stone Age' (*Harpers Magazine*, 1939, reprinted in *A Treasury of Science*, edited by H. Shapley, S. Rapport and Helen Wright, London, 1943).

us from rapidly moving on into the Golden Age of abundance. While we still have not quite enough wealth available to give a sufficiency to all, there are those who benefit from class-division —and even, let it be said, from war. They will not voluntarily surrender their privileges. And they command the power to resist change, whether by force or by persuasion through the mass media of propaganda. These resistances have to be overcome before the world of plenty can be attained. But when it *has* been attained, class-division and war will be so obviously useless that they will never recur.

And what will life be like in this future that some of us may live to see? It is unlikely that we shall want to take our increased wealth in the form simply of more material goods and services. Rather than multiply their material riches by sixteen (let us say), people would probably prefer to have twice or four times as much, and to reduce their working week to 10 hours or 5 hours, and so have more leisure to enjoy. But indeed the distinction between work and leisure will presumably disappear. With ample power, automation and computers—and all the new developments that are to come—available to work for us, the task of providing material goods and services will occupy a small part of each person's life. The rest of his time will not be spent in aimless amusement, but people will discover how to occupy themselves together in companionship, in joyful adventure—in space exploration or scientific research, in poetry or music, or in other creative activities which we primitive people of today cannot yet visualise. Naturally ample wealth will not solve all the difficulties of the future, for people will have to learn new ways of living to make the best use of their new conditions. But the universal plenty will give men for the first time the opportunity to tackle the really important problems, instead of having to devote their energies to scraping a living from nature or quarrelling and fighting among themselves about the sharing of the little that is available.

This is the uniqueness of our time: the prospect that the really constructive and creative period of human history is about to begin—provided we learn the lessons of earlier history and do those things that must be done to bring us quickly to a state of plenty.

Perhaps we were wrong in saying above that there have been

two Technological Revolutions. Seen in broadest perspective, there has only been one—with a hesitation in the middle of it. The historical role of this Great Technological Revolution has been to transform a world of universal scarcity into a world of abundance for all. Before it began, men co-operated harmoniously to combat their poverty. During the turbulent period of the Revolution itself, they fought and struggled bitterly about who should benefit from its partial gains. But as it draws to an end, they will again work together in harmony to enjoy the benefits of their wealth.

Draws to an end? What we know of science tells us that there can be no end to discovery and hence to the extension of man's control over nature. But it is unlikely that men will want to use this power to multiply their material wealth for more than another century or so. After that they may well decide that they are rich enough, and that there are better purposes for which they can use their knowledge and their mastery over the universe. In that sense, at least, our Technological Revolution will draw to an end.

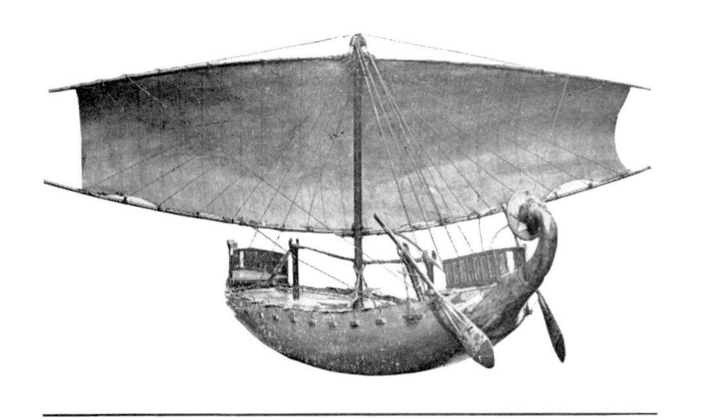

PLATE I EGYPTIAN SEA-GOING SHIPS. THE UPPER SHIP BELONGS TO THE MIDDLE OF THE THIRD MILLENIUM B.C. THE LOWER ONE, A THOUSAND YEARS LATER, SHOWS MANY DETAILED IMPROVEMENTS IN CONSTRUCTION, BUT NOTE THAT THE STEERING GEAR REMAINS FUNDAMENTALLY UNCHANGED. (pp. 9, 19, 50)

PLATE II. VASE PAINTING OF A GREEK SMITHY OF THE SIXTH CENTURY B.C. NOTE THE HINGED TONGS AND THE VARIETY OF HAMMERS. (p. 27)

PLATE III ANIMAL-DRIVEN CHAIN OF POTS—AN EXTENSION OF THE WHEEL OF POTS TO COPE WITH GREATER LIFTS. THIS MODEL OF A MODERN EGYPTIAN VERSION PROBABLY DIFFERS VERY LITTLE FROM THOSE USED IN THE SECOND CENTURY B.C. THE OX IS HARNESSED TO THE BEAM ATTACHED TO THE HORIZONTAL WHEEL; ITS CIRCULAR PATH TAKES IT OVER PART OF THE GROUND THAT HAS BEEN CUT AWAY. (p. 38)

PLATE IV DRAWING HEAVY IRON WIRE (FROM A BOOK OF 1540). THE WORKMAN SHIFTS HIS GRIP AS THE ROPE GOES SLACK, AND AS IT TIGHTENS HE TRANSMITS THE FORCE OF THE WATER-WHEEL TO DRAW ANOTHER LENGTH OF WIRE. (pp. 46, 61)

PLATE V THE DOVER CASTLE CLOCK. THIS WAS FORMERLY ASCRIBED TO THE MIDDLE OF THE FOURTEENTH CENTURY, BUT IS NOW BELIEVED TO BE OF SEVENTEENTH CENTURY CONSTRUCTION. HOWEVER, IT IS THE BEST SURVIVING EXAMPLE OF THE TYPE OF MECHANISM (PARTICULARLY THE ESCAPEMENT) WHICH WAS USED IN THE FOURTEENTH CENTURY. (p. 56)

PLATE VI POST WINDMILL AS ILLUSTRATED BY RAMELLI (1588). THIS AND PLATE VII ARE THE EARLIEST PICTURES SHOWING THE INTERNAL WORKINGS OF THE TWO TYPES OF MILL. (p. 48)

PLATE VII TURRET WINDMILL AS ILLUSTRATED BY RAMELLI. (pp. 48, 78)

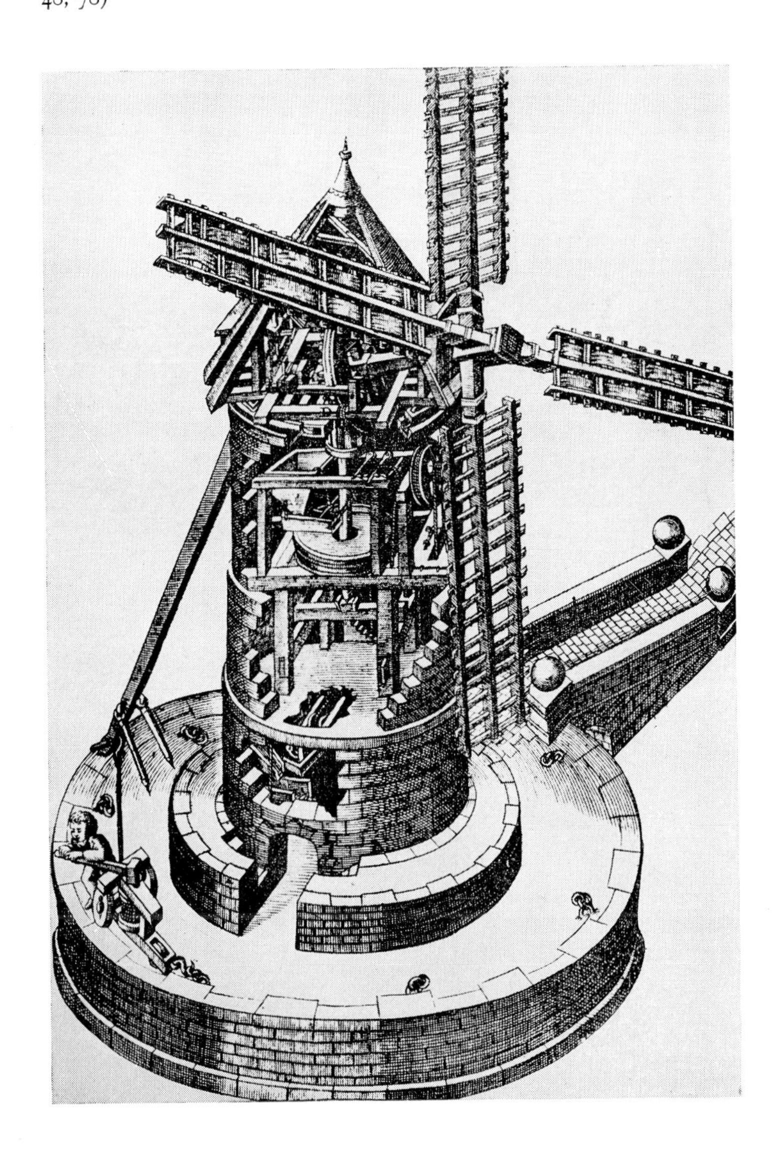

PLATE VIII A *printing shop of the sixteenth century. The workers on the extreme left are composing type from copy. The man with the dagger is making corrections. At the rear a printer inks the type, while another on the right prints a sheet.* (p. 58)

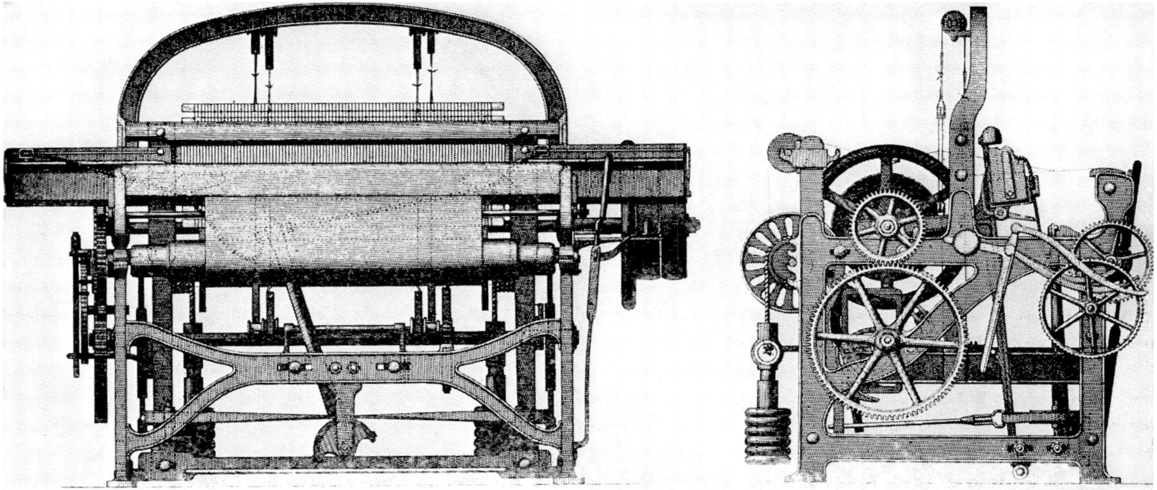

PLATE IX CARTWRIGHT'S POWER-LOOM. (p. 99)

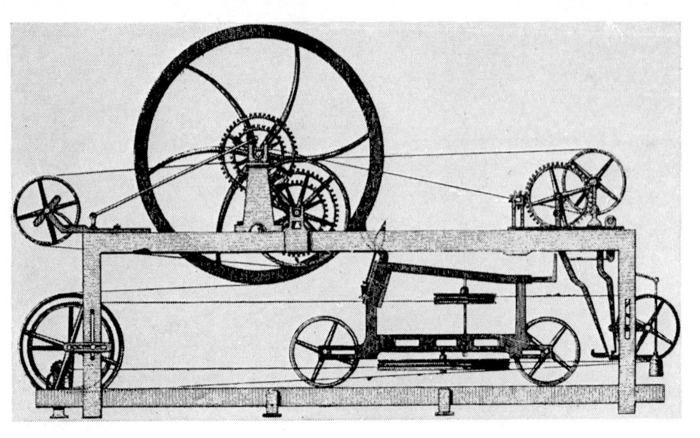

PLATE X CROMPTON'S 'MULE'. (p. 98)

PLATE XI STEPHENSON'S 'ROCKET'. (p. 117)

PLATE XII ONE OF WATT'S ROTATIVE ENGINES. IT EMPLOYS THE SEPARATE CONDENSER (AS IN FIG. 22), BUT IS DOUBLE ACTING AND WORKS EXPANSIVELY, BESIDES INCORPORATING THE 'SUN-AND-PLANET' MECHANISM WHICH ADAPTS IT TO DRIVE ROTARY MACHINERY. (p. 105)

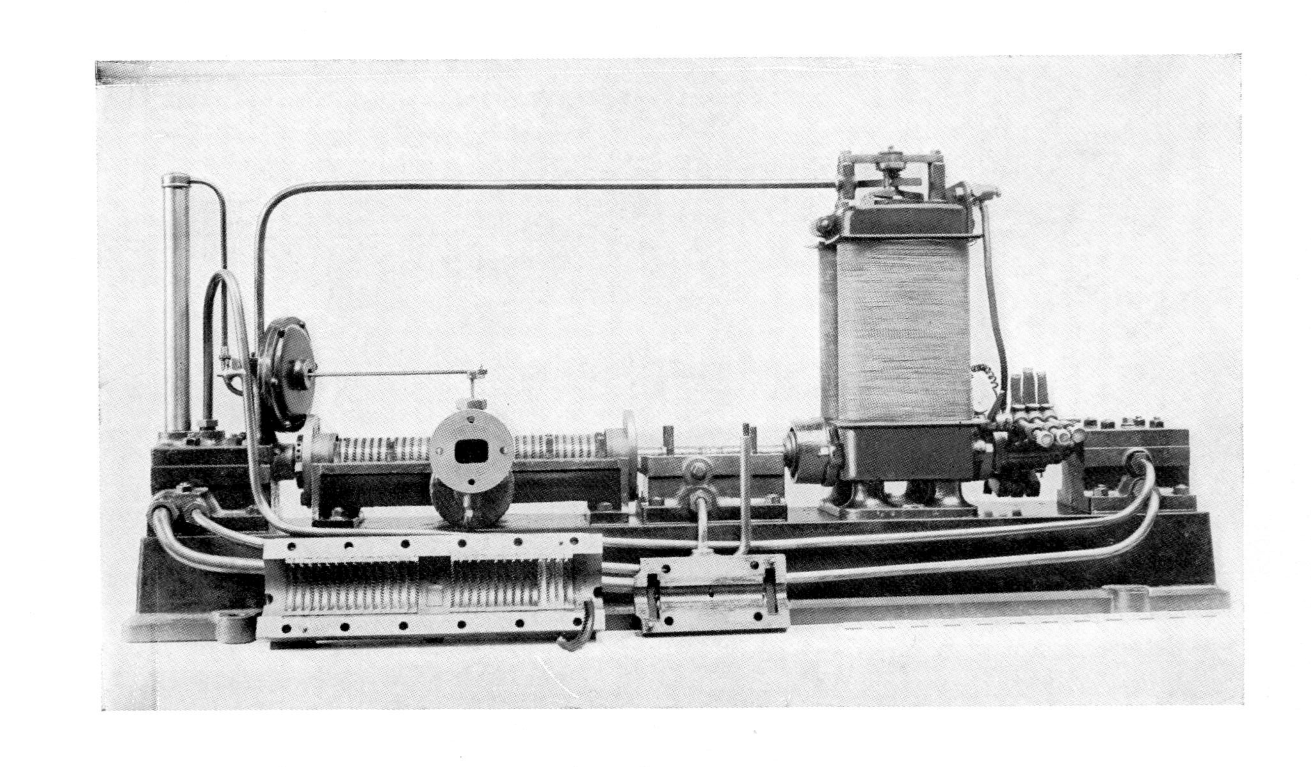

PLATE XIII PARSONS' FIRST TURBO-GENERATOR. (p. 124)

PLATE XIV. THE WRIGHT BROTHERS' FIRST FLIGHT. ORVILLE WRIGHT IS PILOTING (LYING ON THE LOWER WING): WILBUR IS ON FOOT. (p. 130)

PLATE XV MCCORMICK'S REAPING MACHINE. (p. 133)

PLATE XVI A CHAIN-TYPE COAL-CUTTER. (p. 136)

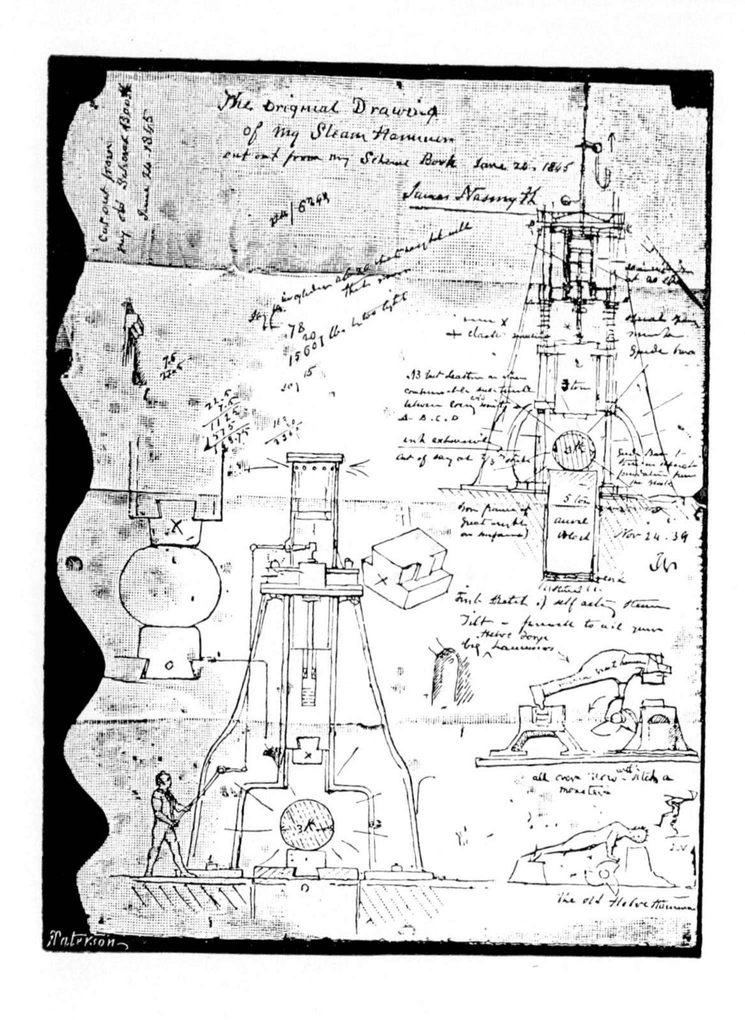

PLATE XVII NASMYTH'S OWN FIRST SKETCH FOR HIS STEAM-HAMMER, MADE ON 24 NOVEMBER 1839. (p. 144)

PLATE XVIII MODEL OF WILKINSON'S CYLINDER-BORING MACHINE. (p. 147)

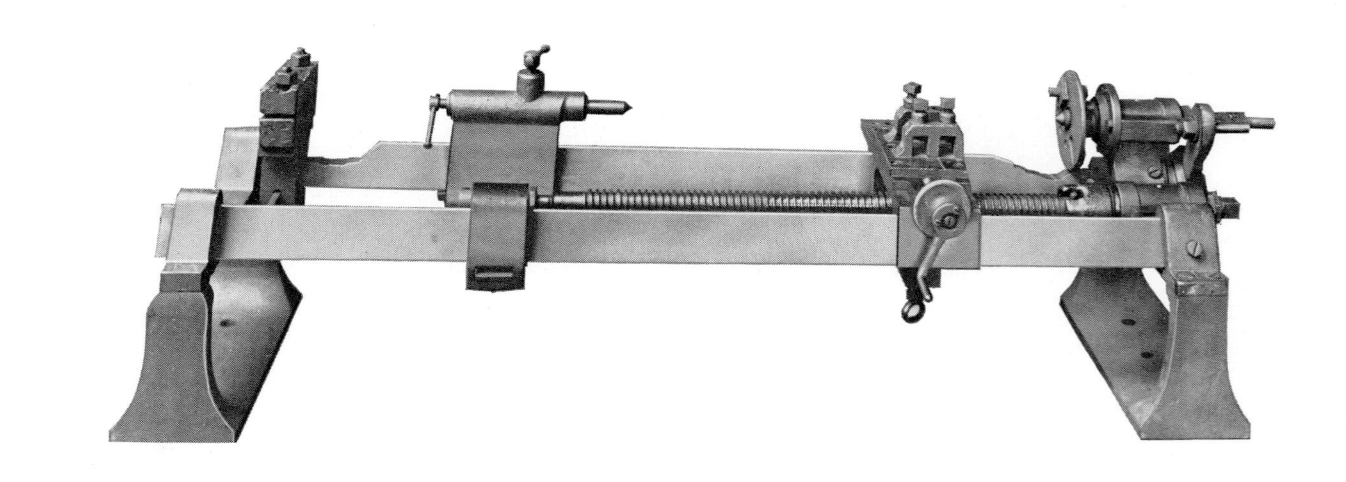

PLATE XIX MAUDSLAY'S SCREW-CUTTING LATHE OF ABOUT 1797. THE GEAR-WHEELS WHICH WOULD HAVE CONNECTED THE SPINDLES ON THE RIGHT HAVE BEEN LOST. (p. 149)

PLATE XX MAUDSLAY'S SHAPING-ENGINE, BUILT IN 1804 FOR BRUNEL AND BENTHAM'S FACTORY FOR THE MASS-PRODUCTION OF PULLEY BLOCKS. IT SHAPES THE SURFACES OF TEN BLOCKS AT A TIME. THE CONTROLS ALLOW ALL TEN BLOCKS TO BE TURNED SIMULTANEOUSLY THROUGH A RIGHT ANGLE, SO THAT FOUR FACES CAN BE WORKED SUCCESSIVELY. (p. 151)

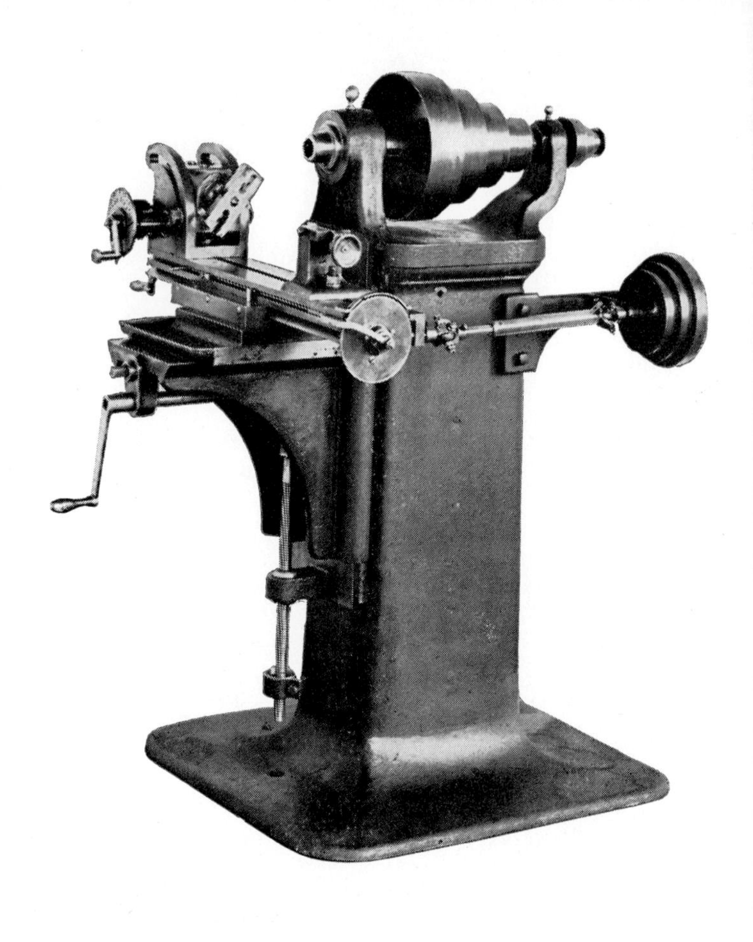

PLATE XXI THE FIRST UNIVERSAL MILLING MACHINE. (p. 153)

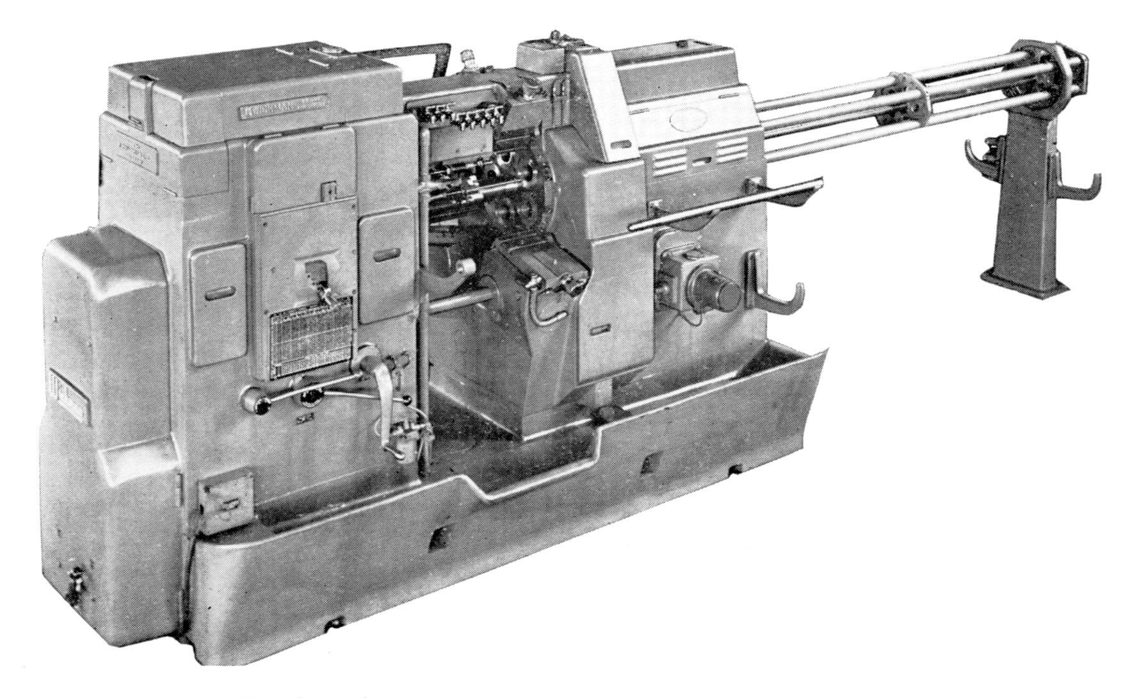

PLATE XXII AN AUTOMATIC LATHE. (p. 153)

PLATE XXIII SAMPLES OF WORK PRODUCED BY AN AUTOMATIC LATHE. (p. 153)

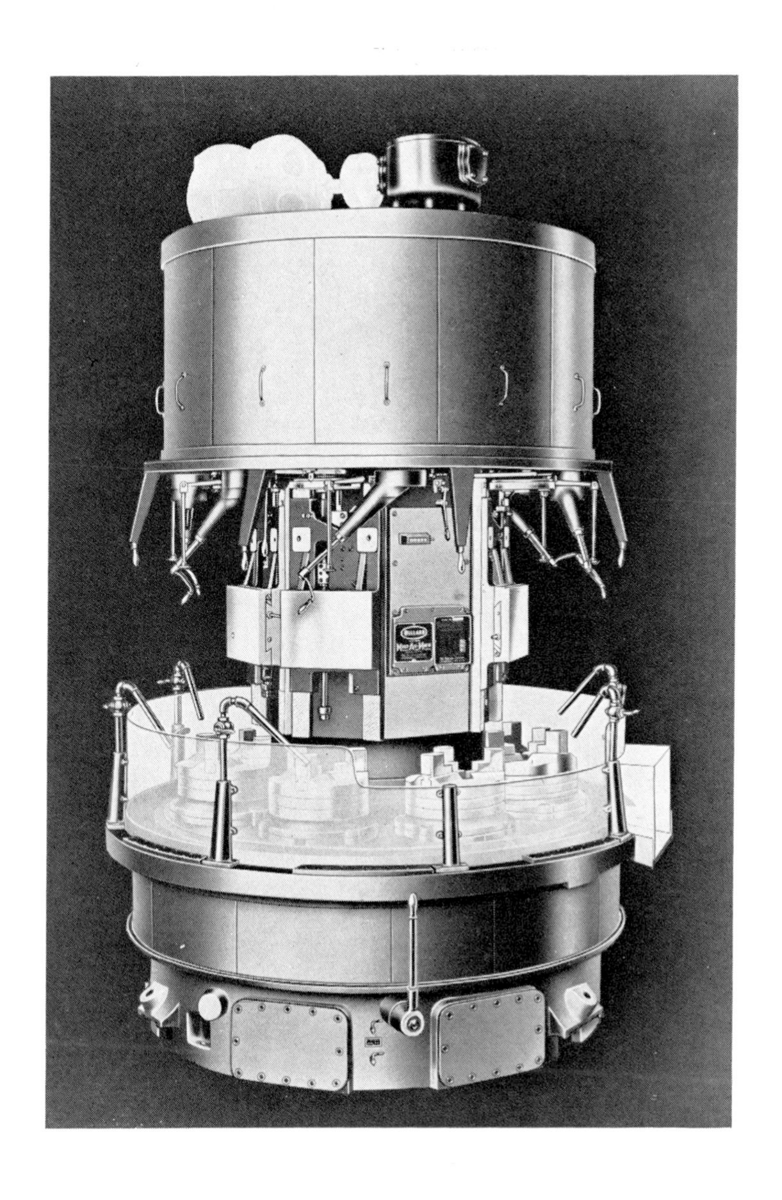

PLATE XXIV THE BULLARD 'MULT-AU-MATIC'. (p. 153)

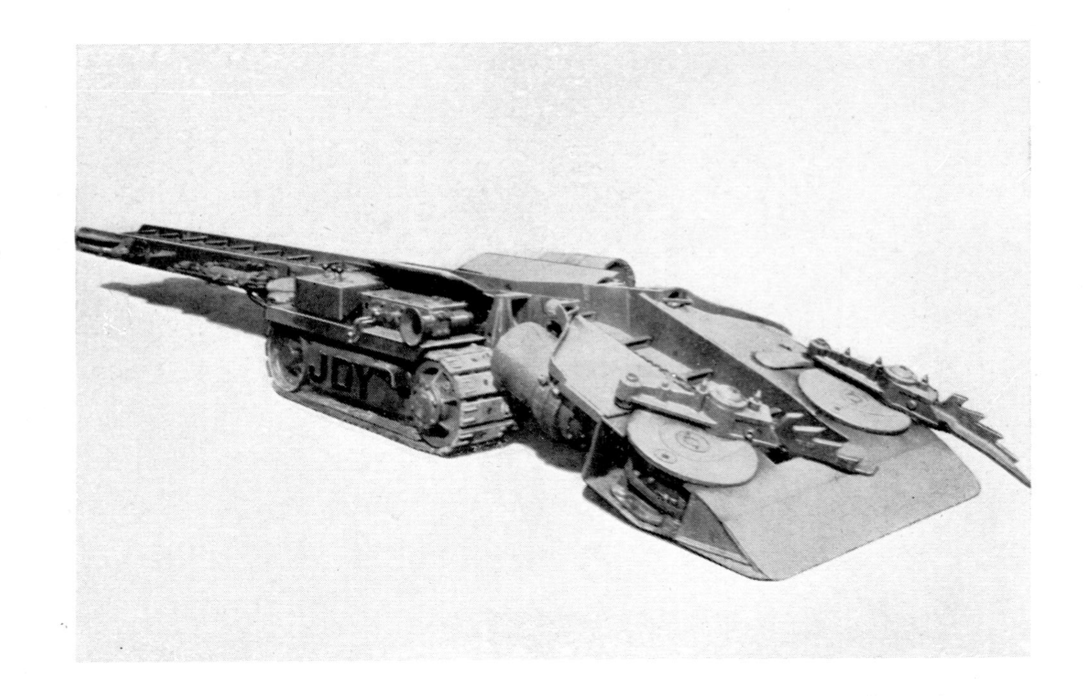

PLATE XXV A POWER LOADER FOR LOADING COAL FROM THE FLOOR ON TO A FACE CONVEYOR. (p. 171)

PLATE XXVI THE FIRST WHITTLE JET-PROPELLED PLANE. (p. 196)

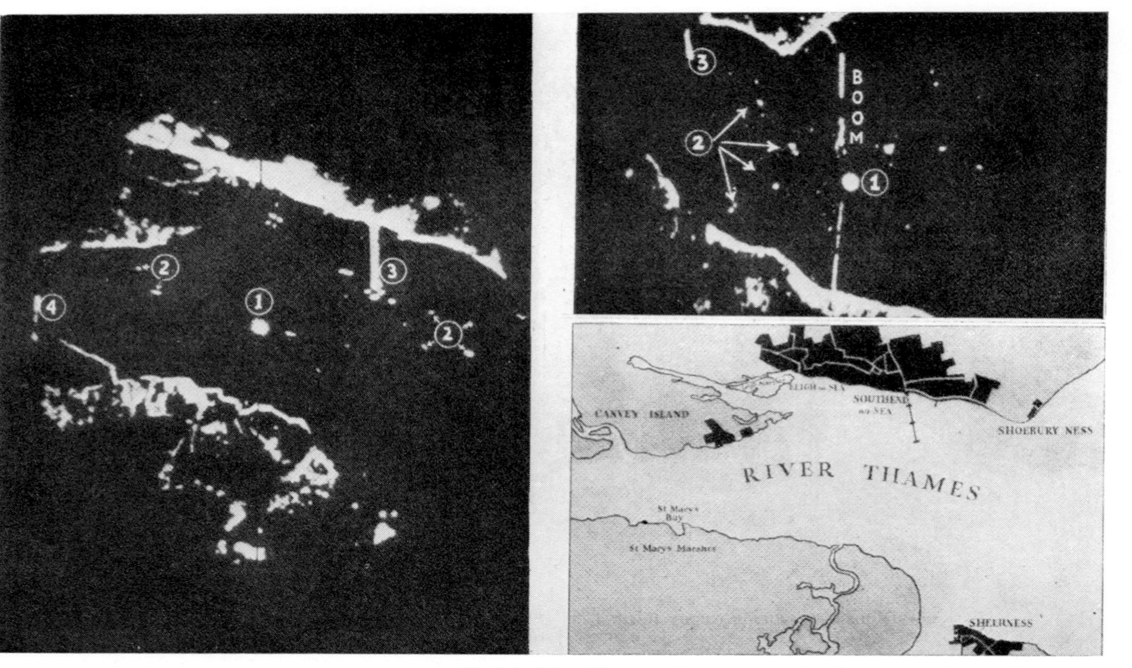

PLATE XXVII RADAR AT THE END OF THE WAR. *(Left) The Thames Estuary as displayed on the radar screen aboard ship. The points marked are: (1) the ship that 'took the picture'; (2) other ships and buoys; (3) Southend pier, with ships lying off the end; (4) oiling jetty on south bank of the river. The bright patches round the coasts indicate built-up areas. Compare the map. (Top right) The ship is passing through the boom off Southend.* (p. 197)

PLATE XXVIII AN EARLY POST-WAR GAS-TURBINE FOR USE IN A ROYAL NAVY GUN BOAT. (p. 210)

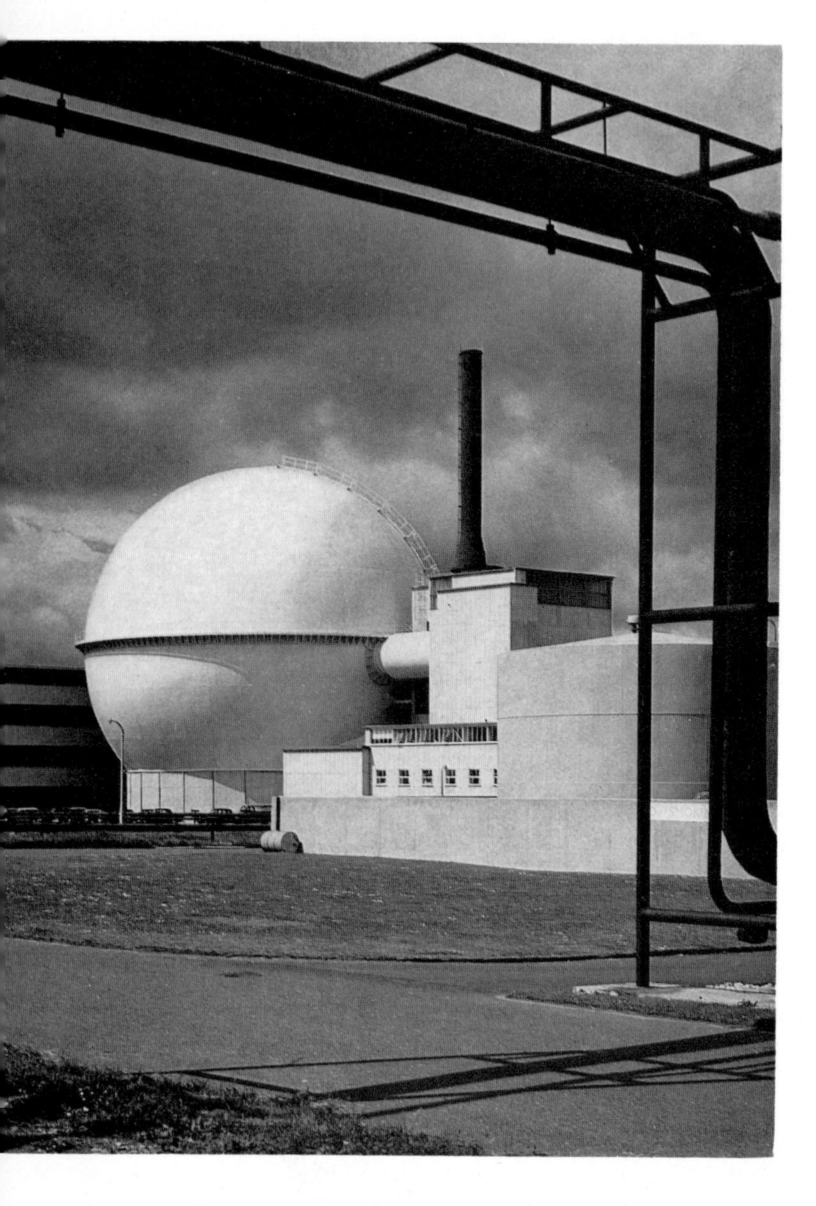

PLATE XXIX GENERAL VIEW OF THE DOUNREAY NUCLEAR POWER STATION. THE REACTOR IS INSIDE THE SPHERICAL STRUCTURE. (p. 220)

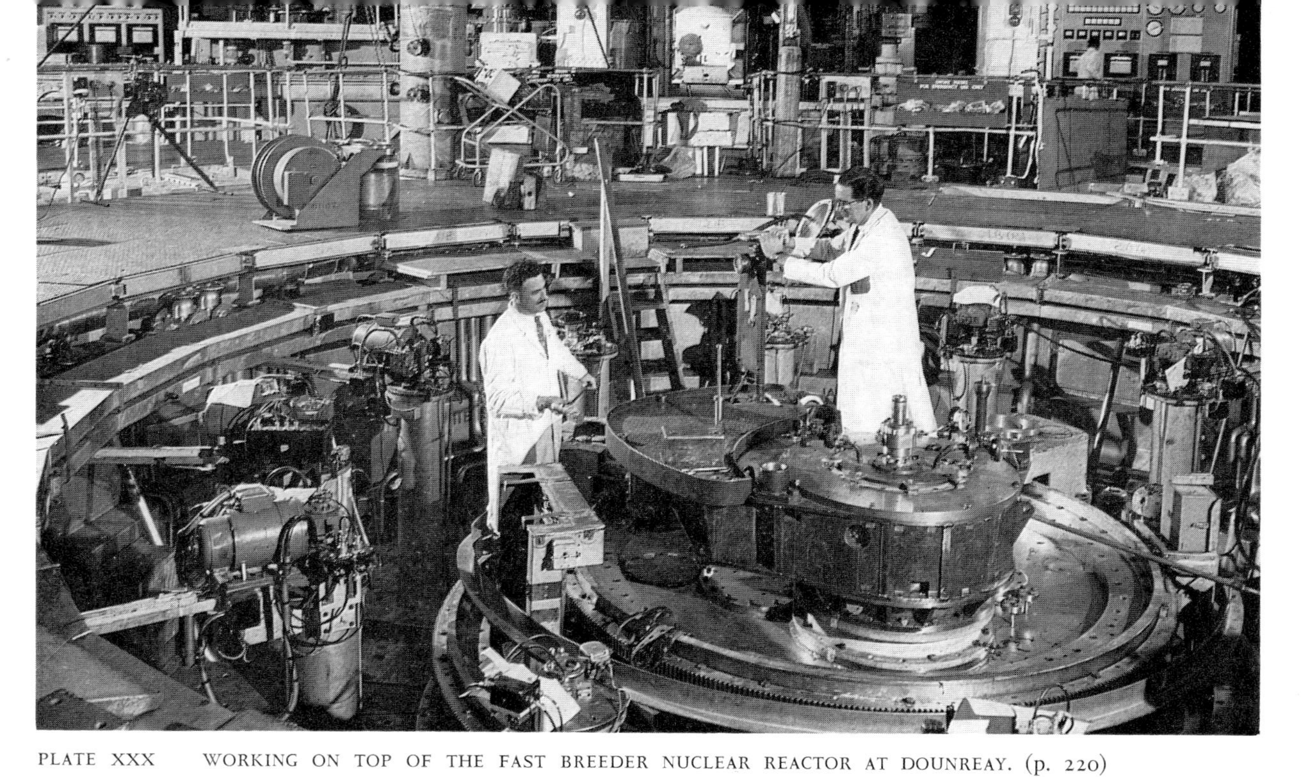

PLATE XXX WORKING ON TOP OF THE FAST BREEDER NUCLEAR REACTOR AT DOUNREAY. (p. 220)

PLATE XXXI THE SOVIET NUCLEAR-POWERED ICE-BREAKER, *Lenin.* (p. 224)

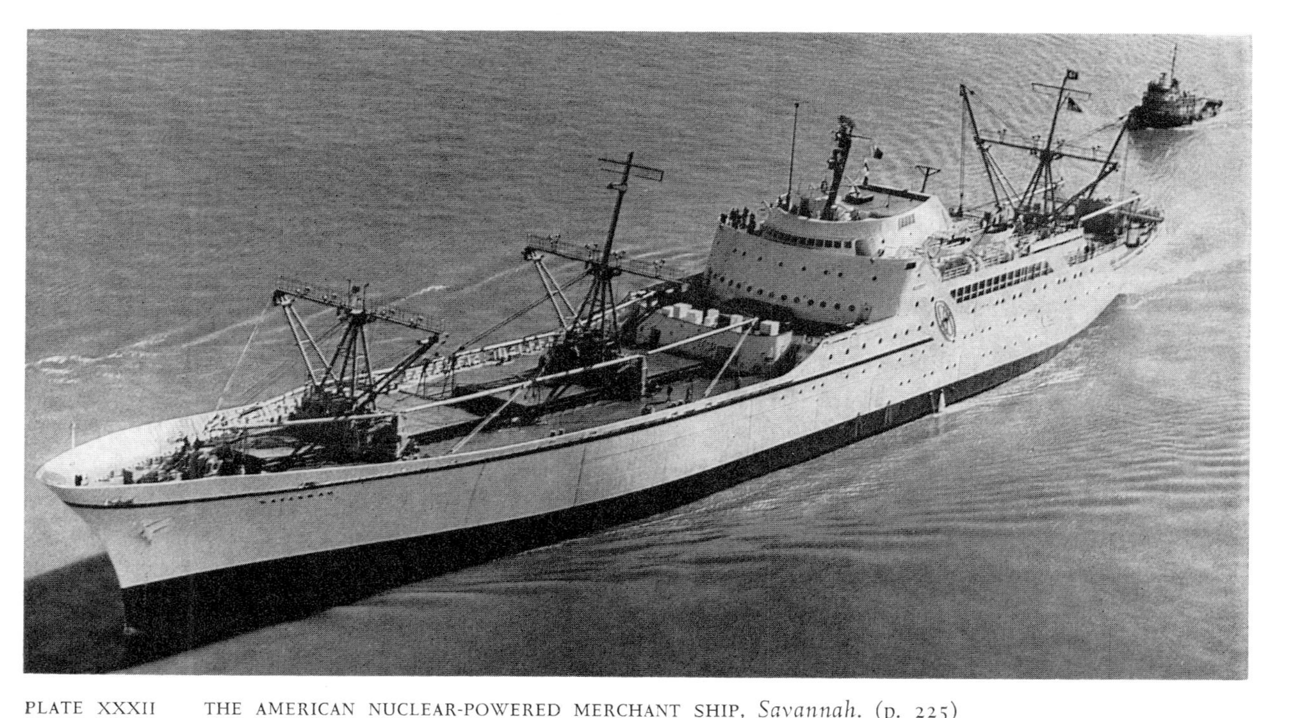

PLATE XXXII THE AMERICAN NUCLEAR-POWERED MERCHANT SHIP, *Savannah*. (p. 225)

PLATE XXXIII A COMPUTER OF THE I.C.T. 1900 SERIES. THE COMPUTER ITSELF IS AT THE REAR RIGHT, AND ALL THE REST IS PERIPHERAL EQUIPMENT FOR FEEDING DATA TO IT OR GETTING RESULTS OUT OF IT. THE WONDER IS THAT SO LITTLE CAN DO SO MUCH. (p. 236)

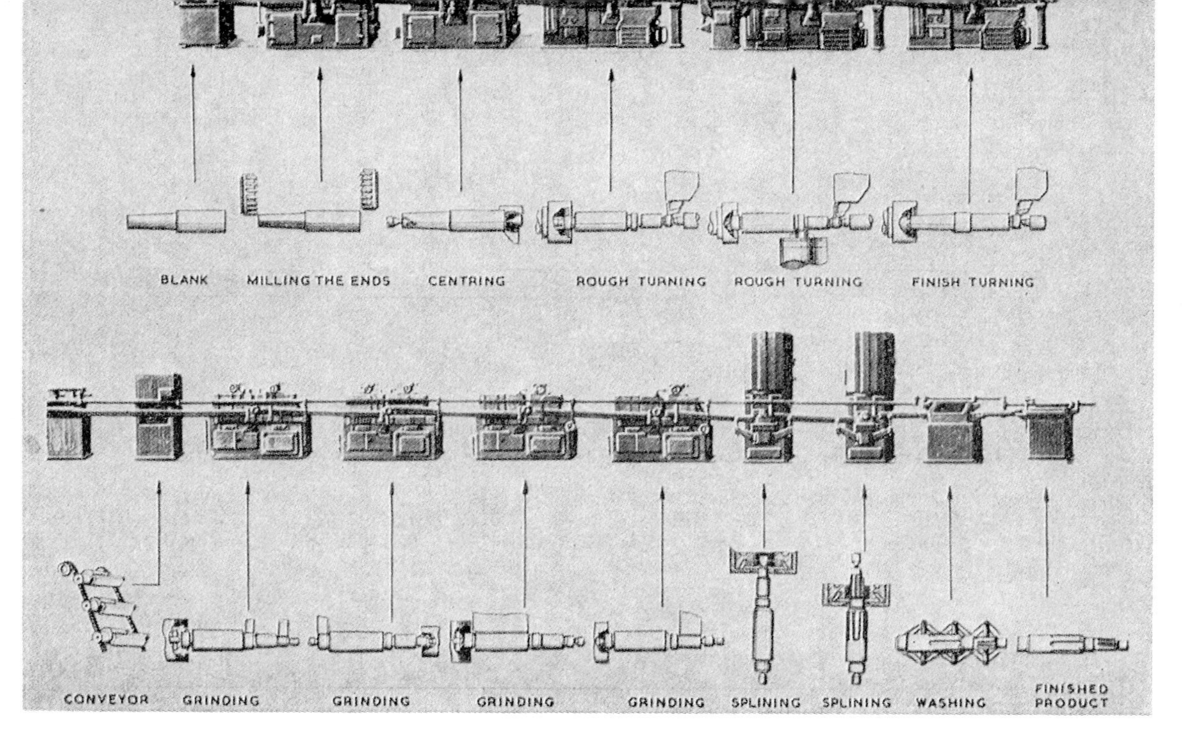

PLATE XXXIV SOVIET AUTOMATIC TRANSFER LINE FOR MAKING SPLINED SHAFTS IN VARIOUS SIZES. (p. 257)

PLATE XXXV EAGLE PROGRAMME-CONTROLLED FLAME-CUTTING MACHINE AT A WALLSEND SHIPYARD. IT WILL WORK SIMULTANEOUSLY ON FOUR PLATES OF 30 FEET BY 10 FEET AND 3 INCHES THICK. (p. 259)

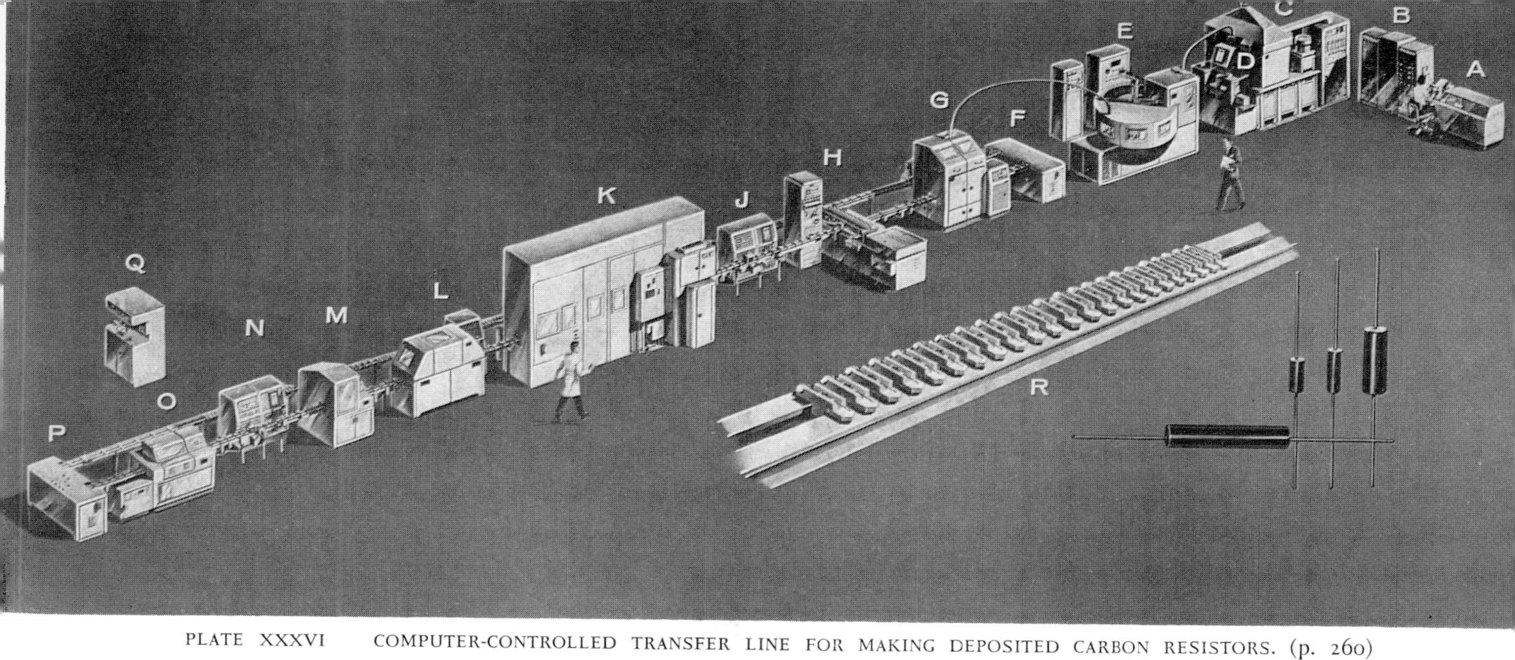

PLATE XXXVI COMPUTER-CONTROLLED TRANSFER LINE FOR MAKING DEPOSITED CARBON RESISTORS. (p. 260)

A *Computer*
B *Output-input control station*
C *Coating station*
D *First inspection station*
E *Terminating station*
F *Conveyor control equipment*
G *Capping station*
H *Helixing station*
J *Second inspection station*
K *Encapsulating station*
L *Leak detector station*
M *Marking station*
N *Third inspection station*
O *Packing Station*
P *Conveyor control equipment*
Q *Cap-lead welding machine*
R *Detail of conveyor line*

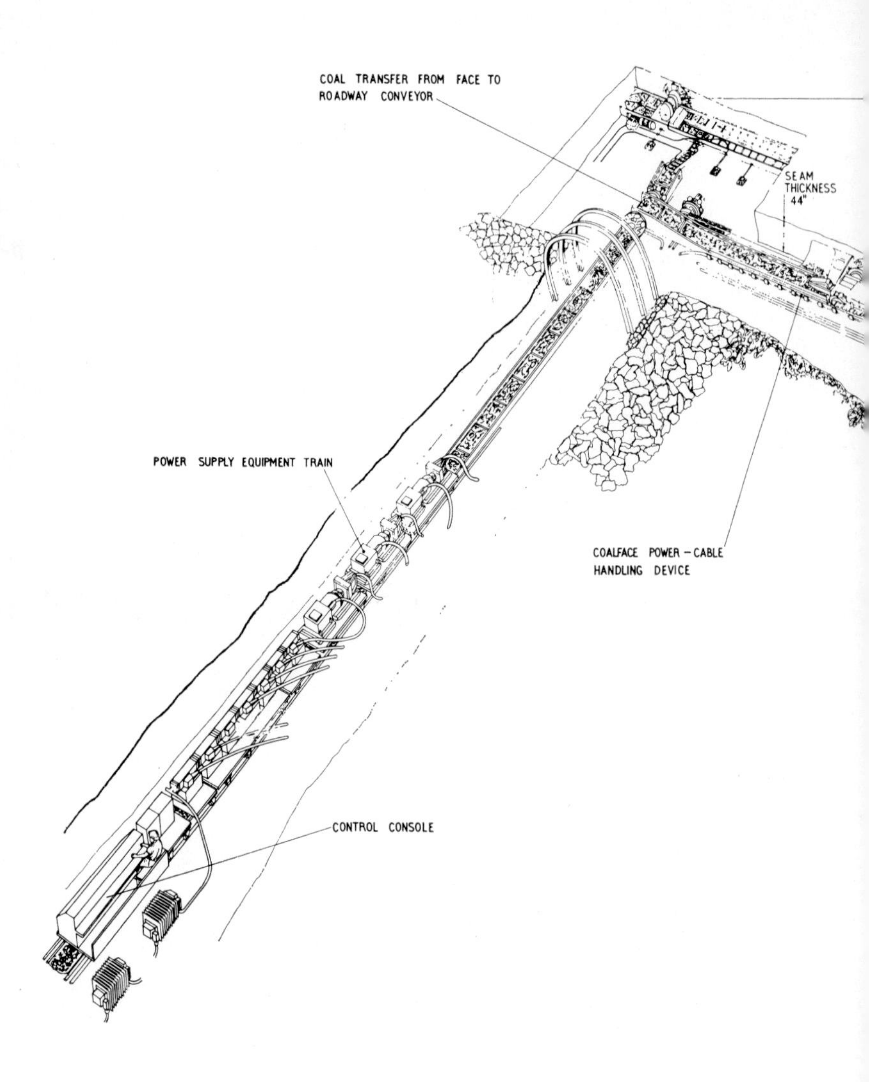

PLATE XXXVII

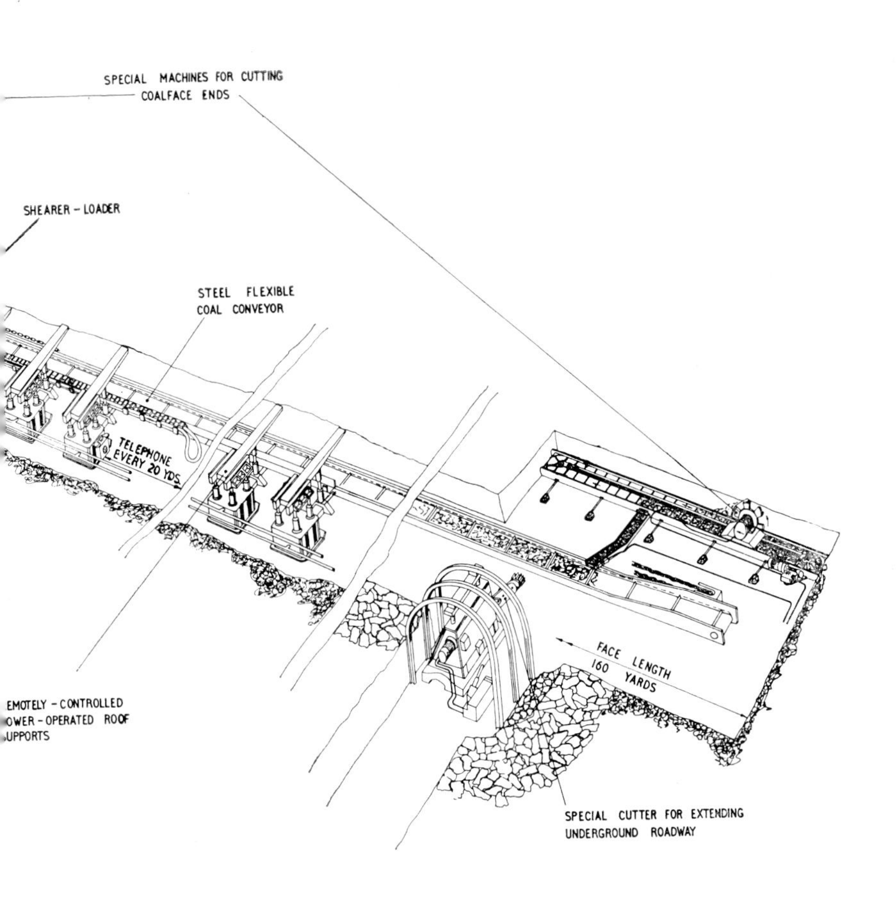

GENERAL LAY-OUT OF A REMOTELY OPERATED LONGWALL FACE AT A BRITISH COAL MINE. (p. 269)

PLATE XXXVIII VIEW ALONG THE REMOTELY OPERATED LONGWALL FACE OF PLATE XXXVII, SHOWING THE SHEARER THAT CUTS THE COAL AND THE HYDRAULIC ROOF SUPPORTS. (p. 269)

PLATE XXXIX SOVIET MACHINE FOR SINKING PIT SHAFTS, SHOWN BEFORE REMOVAL TO THE KARAGANDA COALFIELD, WHERE IT PASSED ITS TESTS. AS IT DIGS, IT LINES THE SHAFT WITH RE-INFORCED CONCRETE. (p. 270)

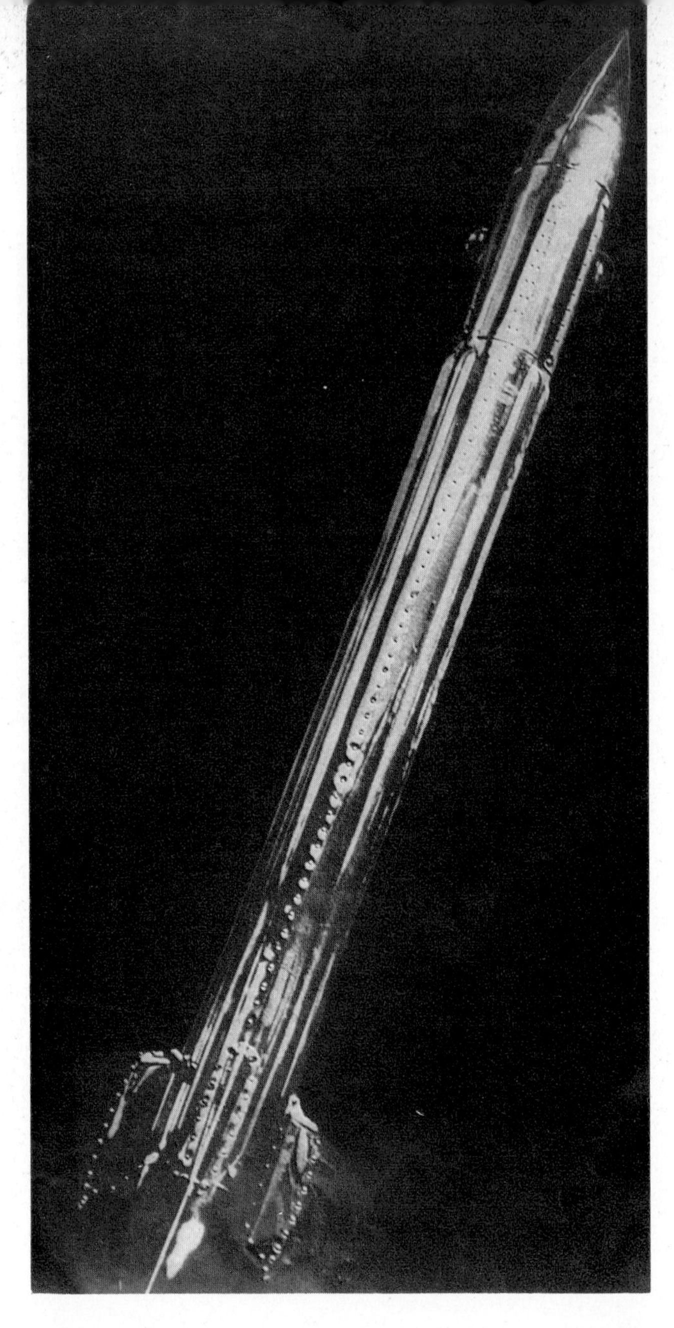

PLATE XL THE FIRST SOVIET LIQUID-FUELLED ROCKET, LAUNCHED IN 1933. (p. 278)

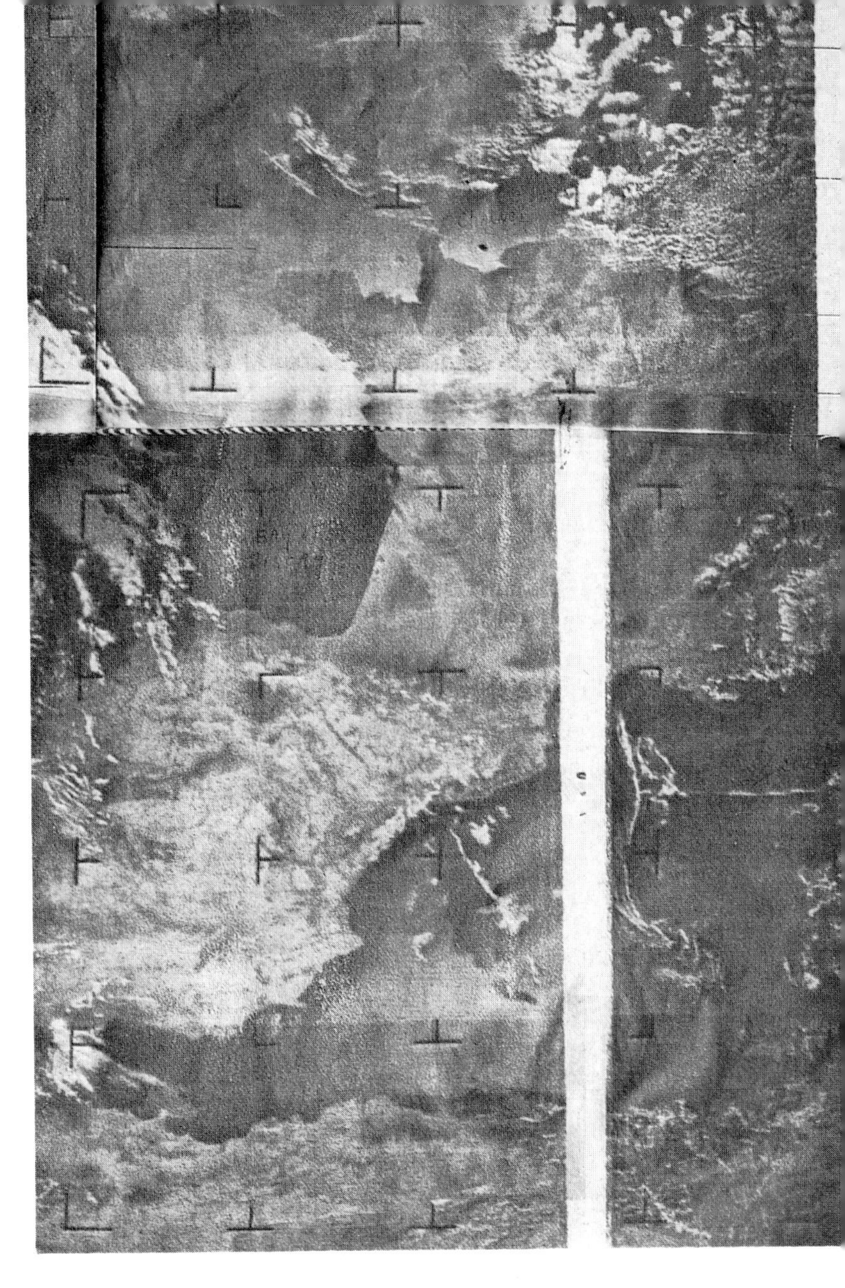

PLATE XLI WESTERN EUROPE AND PART OF ENGLAND, AS PHOTOGRAPHED BY THE *Nimbus* WEATHER SATELLITE. (p. 281)

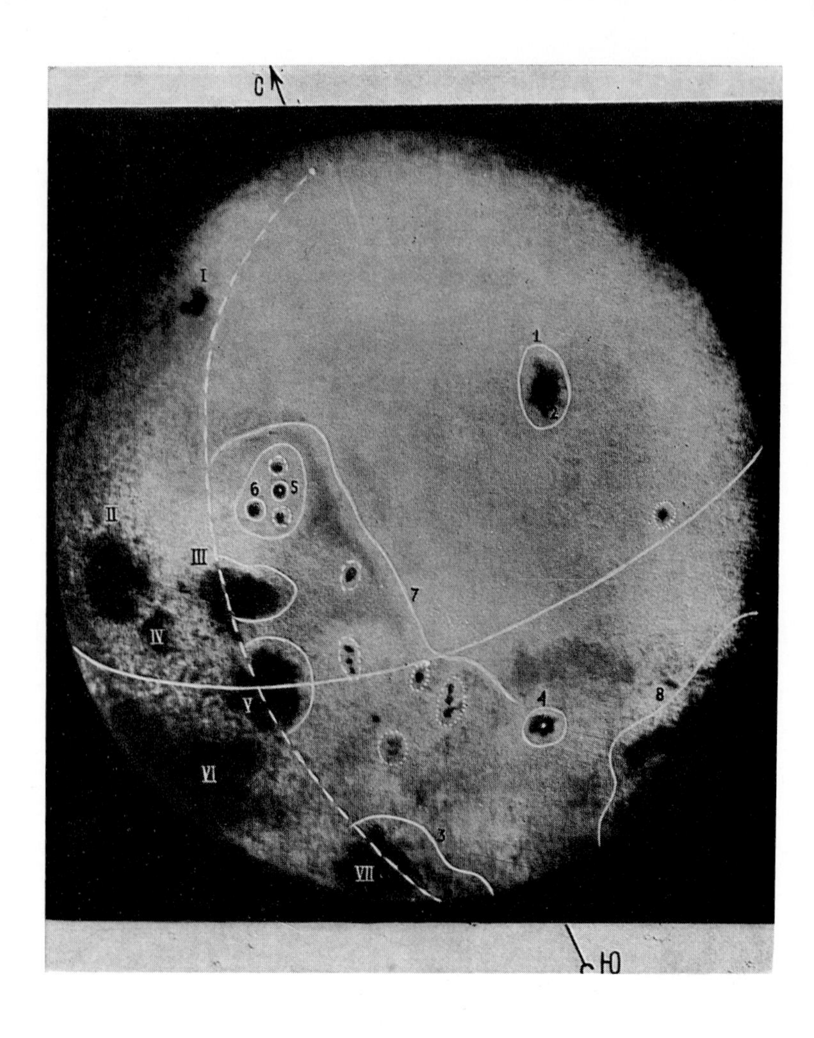

PLATE XLII THE BACK OF THE MOON AS PHOTOGRAPHED BY *Lunik III. Marked features have been named:*
1, Moscow Sea; 2, Astronaut's Bay; 3, Southern Sea; 4, Tsiolkovsky Crater; 5, Lomonosov Crater; 6, Joliot-Curie Crater; 7 Sovietsky mountain range; 8, Sea of Dreams. Features to left of broken line are visible from Earth: I, Humboldt Sea; II, Sea of Crises; III, Marginal Sea; IV, Sea of Waves; V, Smith Sea; VI, Sea of Fertility; VII, Southern Sea. (p. 281)

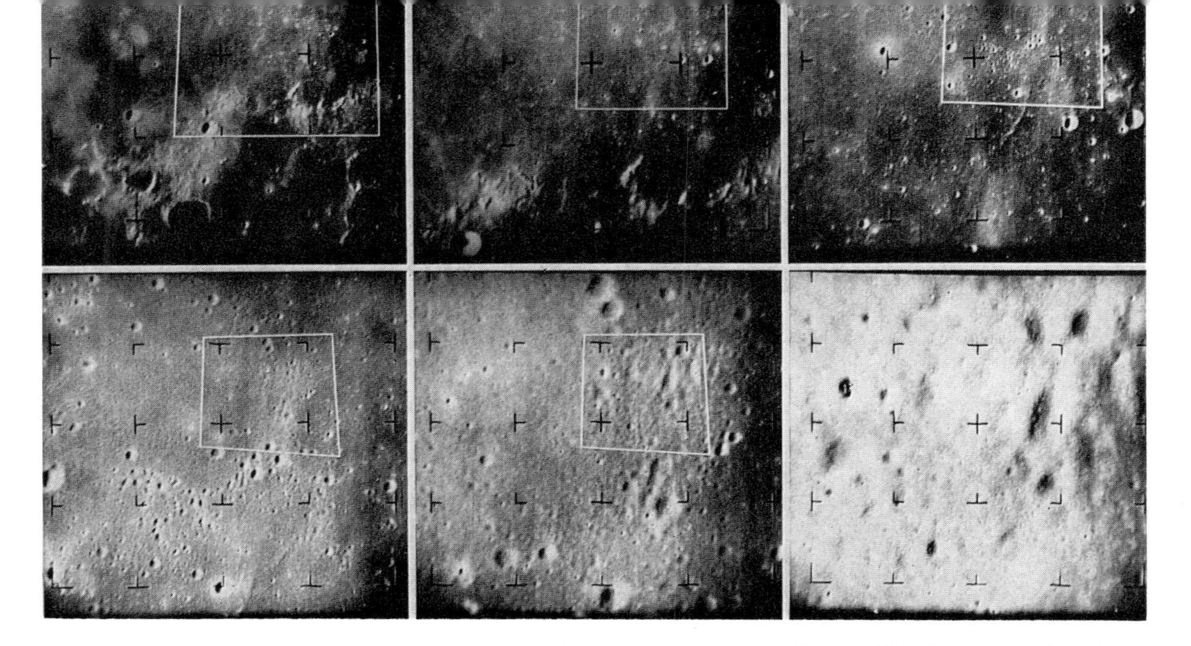

PLATE XLIII SEQUENCE OF PHOTOGRAPHS OF THE MOON'S SURFACE TAKEN BY *Ranger VII, from altitudes of* 480, 285, 85, 34, 12 *and* 3 *miles. White frame in each picture oulines coverage of next.* (p. 282)

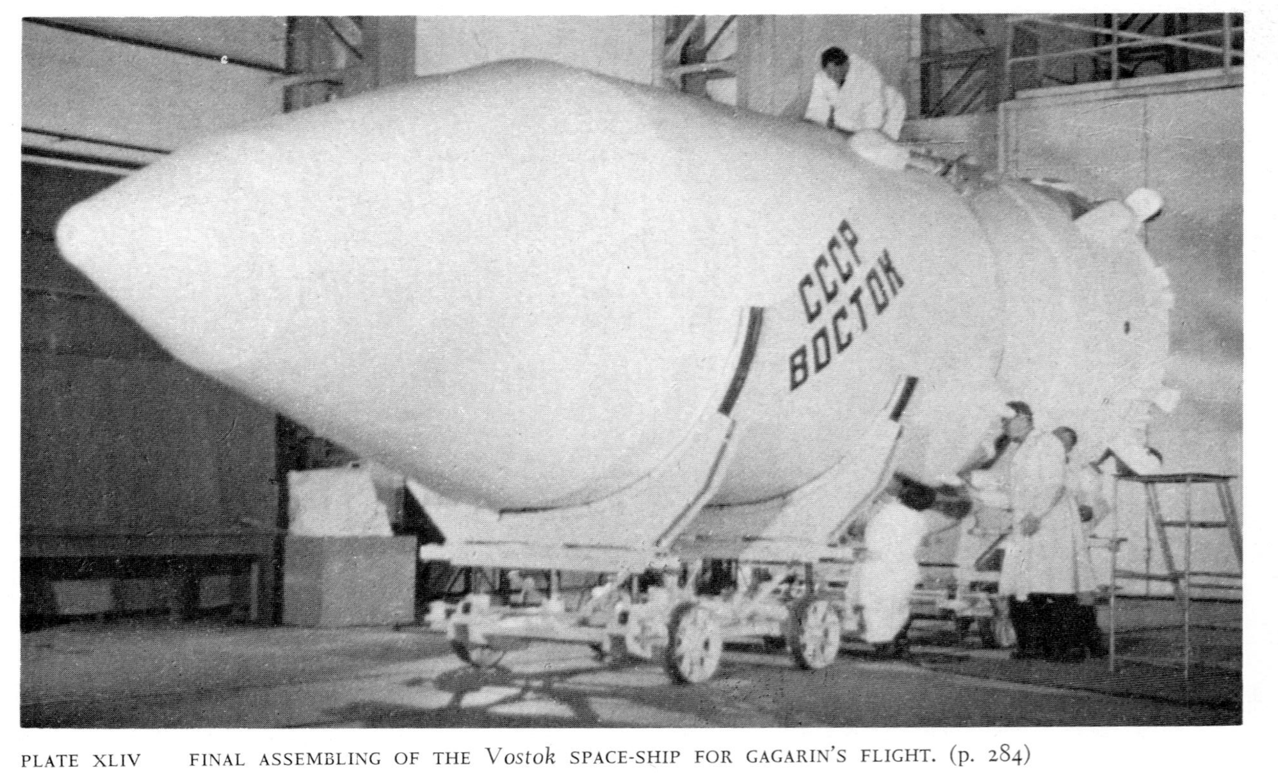

PLATE XLIV FINAL ASSEMBLING OF THE *Vostok* SPACE-SHIP FOR GAGARIN'S FLIGHT. (p. 284)

PLATE XLV AN *Atlas* ROCKET LAUNCHES THE SPACE-SHIP CARRYING JOHN GLENN. HIS CAPSULE IS THE CONICAL PORTION JUST BELOW THE TRELLIS GIRDERS AT THE TOP. (p. 284)

PLATE XLVI (p. 286) A *Gemini* CAPSULE FOR TWO-MAN SPACE-FLIGHTS.

PLATE XLVII FULL-SCALE MODEL OF THE ENGINES OF A *Saturn* ROCKET. (p. 291) BELOW IT IS A MODEL OF R. H. GODDARD'S LIQUID-FUELLED ROCKET OF 1926. (p. 278)

PLATE XLVIII MICRO-MINIATURISED CIRCUITS COMPARED WITH A THUMB-PRINT (p. 309)

INDEX

INDEX